A PRA
TO QUALITY CONTROL

Fourth Edition

A PRACTICAL APPROACH TO QUALITY CONTROL

Rowland Caplen
BSc, CEng, MIEE, MIProdE, MInstP, FIQA

BUSINESS BOOKS

London Melbourne Sydney Auckland Johannesburg

Business Books Ltd
An imprint of the Hutchinson Publishing Group
17-21 Conway Street, London W1P 6JD

Hutchinson Group (Australia) Pty Ltd
30-32 Cremorne Street, Richmond South, Victoria 3121
PO Box 151, Broadway, New South Wales 2007

Hutchinson Group (NZ) Ltd
32-34 View Road, PO Box 40 086, Glenfield, Auckland 10

Hutchinson Group (SA) (Pty) Ltd
PO Box 337, Bergvlei 2012, South Africa

First published 1969
Second impression 1970
Third impression 1971
Fourth impression 1972
Second edition 1972
Second impression 1975
Third impression 1977
Third edition 1978
Fourth edition 1982

Set in IBM Press Roman and Univers

Printed in Great Britain by the Anchor Press Ltd
and bound by Wm Brendon & Son Ltd,
both of Tiptree, Essex

British Library Cataloguing in Publication Data

Caplen, R.H.
    A practical approach to quality control — 4th ed.
    1. Quality control
    I. Title
    658.5'62   TS156

ISBN 0 09 147451 5

CONTENTS

Appendix

INTRODUCTION

In preparing the Fourth Edition of this book, I have taken the opportunity to bring it thoroughly up-to-date. In particular, I have included a chapter on quality circles and have revised the chapters on the design of a quality control system, so that they include further work by myself, which I reported in a paper to the Inspex Conference in Birmingham in 1981. I have rewritten the section on acceptance sampling by variables to take account of the issue of BSS 6002, and made smaller additions to the sections on frequency distribution curves, estimation of process capability, cumulative sum charts and reliability.

The book continues to cover the following:

1   The complete syllabus of the Certificate in Quality Control No. 743 of the City and Guilds of London Institute. Most chapters end with questions taken from past examination papers, with the kind permission of City and Guilds. I have provided answers to the numerical questions at the end of the book.

2   A practical introduction to quality control   The book aims to show how quality control can be applied to any practical situation, and how suitable techniques can be identified and integrated into a useful cost-conscious system. In doing this I have drawn on my experience as a quality manager and as a consultant in industry. For completeness, essential theory has been included.

ROWLAND CAPLEN
April 1982

PART ONE

AN INTRODUCTION
TO QUALITY CONTROL AND
QUALITY COSTS

CHAPTER 1

THE FIVE BASIC STAGES
OF QUALITY CONTROL

1.1 The object of quality control

The word 'quality' means different things to different people. The first car a young man buys appears to him be of superior quality, even though it is several years old and rather the worse for wear. To the company director wanting a new Rolls-Royce, however, that very same car would be merely a load of scrap. For this reason, quality is sometimes defined as 'fitness for purpose'. The second-hand car may be quite satisfactory as a runabout for our young man, but it would be a bad advertisement and insufficiently reliable for the company director. Therefore we have to consider whether the quality in question is satisfactory for the purpose for which it is intended.

Price is important too, because the quality we expect depends on how much we pay for it. When we pay £500 for a second-hand car, we do not expect the same quality as if we were paying £5000 for a brand new one. We shall be satisfied with a car which, in our opinion, is worth the £500 we paid for it.

Thirdly, we shall expect our car to be delivered on time. If the manufacturer promised it in three weeks, we shall not expect to have to wait three months for it. If the delay is because the car was wrongly made in the first place, and had to be corrected before it could be delivered, we shall not have a very high opinion of that manufacturer's quality control.

The above, therefore, sets out what the customer expects, and we can rewrite it from the manufacturer's point of view, as follows.

The object of quality control is to produce a quality that:

1   Satisfies the customer.
2   Is as cheap as possible.
3   Can be achieved in time to meet delivery requirements.

At first sight it is perhaps surprising to find that our object is *not* to produce as high a quality as possible, but merely to satisfy our customer. However, this is all that is required, and indeed it is positively undesirable to produce a higher quality than is necessary, if as a result we have to increase our selling price or delay deliveries.

1.2   Setting about quality control

Having decided our quality objectives, we must now set about achieving them in the simplest, cheapest and most practical way. Each type of production will have its own peculiar quality problems and for each, therefore, we must try to find a simple tailor-made solution. A quality control system which is a winner in one department will be an absolute failure if applied to another department where production techniques are different. Quality control offers us a large number of different quality remedies, and our problem is to select the best ones for the particular production line or job we are considering. Sometimes the methods we choose will have a statistical basis, but very often they will be based on down-to-earth practical ideas. We shall find that statistics for their own sake achieve nothing but confusion, and may even make the people in the department concerned think we are trying to blind them with science.

When we approach a new quality control problem our position is somewhat similar to that of a doctor who is presented with a new patient. First, we must carry out a diagnosis in order to find out exactly what quality ills our 'patient' has, and then we must prescribe an appropriate remedy. In many cases our prescription will be very simple. Its value will not be in its complexity, but in the fact that it is just right for that particular case. We may have a very wide knowledge of quality control, but we shall not apply everything we know, to every department.

The fact that every quality control system is likely to be different in detail from every other might at first sight give the impression that there is no similarity between them at all. Fortunately, this is not so. All quality control systems have basic common features, and we can illustrate this by considering a simple example.

he wall. This indicates that our basic design, or maybe the method of putting in the screws, is wrong. We may decide to modify our design by using longer screws, or we may try to find a better method of inserting them into the wall.

corrective measures will be taken with the object of learning from mistakes, and so avoiding that fault in future. In the factory, our lity control system will provide us with information about our lity shortcomings, and we shall be able to use this to correct our cesses. There is no need to make excessive scrap if we make maximum use of our quality control system.

.8 Using our experience to plan future jobs

Our experience in putting up a shelf will help us with similar jobs in the future. We now know roughly how good a shelf we can make, and if we make another later on, we shall expect to achieve much the same standard again. If we do not, then we shall know that since last time something has changed for the worse, and we shall investigate what it is. We might, for example, find that this lot of wood is not as good as that which we used previously, and we shall take this up with our supplier. In the factory, this is equivalent to watching our weekly scrap percentage, and taking action if it shows a tendency to rise.

Knowing how good a shelf we can make will also help us to judge what other jobs of a similar nature we can tackle. If we can only just manage a shelf, it would clearly be unwise to tackle a kitchen cabinet. We had better buy it. It would be cheaper in the long run than attempting to make it, spoiling the wood, and still having to buy it in the end. In the factory, our quality control system will tell us what our machines, processes, materials and operators are capable of making, and obviously, if we are foolish enough to attempt something that is outside their capabilities, we must expect a high scrap rate, and maybe complete failure.

1.9 Co-ordination

When we put up a shelf at home we have one major advantage over any factory. We do every job ourself, and our customer (our wife) is always there for consultation. Thus, co-ordination between the different functions is perfect. When we design the shelf we know exactly what our 'customer' wants. When we buy the wood we know exactly what will please our 'customer', we also know exactly what sort of wood the 'operator' prefers, and what sort of saw he will use to cut it.

This perfect co-ordination stems from the fact that one man does

1.3 Example of a very simple, yet efficient quality control system

Suppose our wife asks us to put up a shelf in the kitchen. This is a very simple job, and at first sight it does not appear to want any quality control at all, but in fact we shall probably employ a very efficient system. Of course we shall not call it quality control, and we shall probably never even realise that we have used it, but we shall go through exactly the same quality control stages as we should if we were dealing with a complex production line.

We shall almost certainly do the job in the following five basic stages:

1   We shall set the specification. Thus we shall decide how long and wide the shelf is to be, in what sort of wood, and so on.
2   We shall prepare to make it. This will involve collecting together suitable tools, materials, etc.
3   We shall make the shelf, and fix it to the wall.
4   We shall correct any mistakes we have made, and we shall use the experience gained to avoid making the same mistakes in future.
5   Finally, we shall know, by how well we got on making a shelf, whether we are likely to be able to tackle something more difficult, such as a piece of household furniture.

We must now consider these steps in more detail.

1.4 Set the manufacturing specification

We cannot make anything without first deciding what we are going to make, and what it is to be like, i.e. we must settle our manufacturing specification. In the factory, the specification may come to us as a huge pile of instructions, drawings and shop lists, but at home, our specification for a shelf is unlikely to be more than a rough sketch. Indeed, it may be no more than an idea in our head. For example, we might decide to make it 1.00 to 1.15 metres long, by 150 mm wide, to fix it with 100-mm brackets, and to finish it off like Joe Brown's next door.

In quality control language we are setting the quality standard, or the quality of design.

1.5 Prepare to manufacture

Next we must prepare for manufacture, and this is likely to involve us in five substeps, as follows:

1   *We must decide how the shelf is to be made*   Thus, we know what

we intend to finish up with, but we still have to decide our method for getting there. We must decide the order in which we are going to do the various operations, the kind of saw we are going to use, and so on. In factory terms, we shall do some method planning, and indeed if the job was more complicated we might at this stage consciously employ some method study.

2   We must collect together the necessary tools   Probably, we shall already have all the tools we need, but if not we shall have to decide what is required, and purchase it. Thus if the saw we have is not suitable for the job, we shall have to buy or borrow one that is. If it is blunt, we shall have to get it resharpened, and so on. In factory terms, we shall do some equipment planning, with the object of ensuring that all the necessary tools are available, and in good order. No one can make a good job with unsatisfactory tools.

3   We must obtain satisfactory materials   If we have not already got a suitable supply of materials, such as wood, brackets, screws, etc., then we must go out and buy them. When we get to the shop, we shall inspect the wood to see that it is free from knots and other defects, and we shall look to see that the screws are the right size and free from rust. Although we shall not think of it this way, we are in fact getting our own private Purchasing Department to buy satisfactory materials, and we are then carrying out goods inwards inspection on the materials we are offered. Moreover, we are doing this inspection in our supplier's premises, where any unsatisfactory material can be rejected, without it ever having been delivered to us.

4   We must make sure we know how to make and erect the shelf   As a shelf is very simple, we shall probably consider ourselves competent to make one without any further instruction. If not, we may consult Joe Brown next door, since we know that he recently put up a shelf for himself. In factory terms, we are making sure that our operator is adequately trained for the job he has to do.

5   We must plan our inspection and workshop quality control   If the job requires inspection then we must plan for it. Most jobs do, and our shelf is no exception. As our manufacture proceeds we shall require occasional checks to see that the wood is being cut to the right size, etc. We must, therefore, see that we have a suitable rule and square, and if not we must go out and buy what we need.

1.6   Manufacture

At last we can begin the actual manufacture ⊂
things go will depend to a considerable extent
done our quality planning. If our methods, too⌐
training and inspection planning have all been d⊂
probably not have much trouble during manufact

We shall, of course, aim to make our shelf right
certainly do not want to finish it and then discover
and that we have either got to scrap it or tackle the ⊂
putting it right. We shall, therefore, watch what we ar
equivalent to a good operator, well supervised. If the s⊾
wander from our pencil line we shall stop at once and r⊾
shall certainly not saw on regardless, and then at the end
it's scrap, I shall have to start all over again'.

It is good quality control to use inspection to stop scra⌐
made. We must avoid the situation that occurs far too often
where the inspector sits at the end of a production line, insp⊂
made, and throws out the scrap. The inspector's job is to get ⌐
production line and help the operator to avoid the scrap in th⊾
place. This is precisely what we are doing when we watch our s⊾
work, and correct it if it starts to stray, before any damage has ⊾
done. We do, of course, have a great advantage over the factory c⊾
that we play the part of both the operator and the inspector. The ⊾
ordination between 'them' is thus bound to be perfect.

1.7   Correction of quality deficiencies

If, in spite of all our efforts, the shelf does not turn out satisfactorily we shall look for the cause. We shall certainly not press on making lots and lots of shelves, which are all wrong. This, however, is precisely what happens in the factory if no one takes any interest in correcting the causes of scrap. Piece after piece is produced, only to be rejected by the inspector.

The following are some of the troubles we may experience with our shelf:

1   The saw may be bent, indicating that our tooling is unsatisfactory.
2   There may be too many knots in the wood, which means that we are trying to use unsatisfactory materials.
3   Perhaps carpentry is just not in our line at all, which is equivalent to saying we have an unsatisfactory operator.
4   We may find that, however careful we are, the screws do not grip

every job, and is, therefore, bound to know the whole process from beginning to end. As soon as the operations are shared between a number of people this natural co-ordination ceases to exist, and we have to devise a system to replace it. Thus:

1   We shall first have to make sure we know exactly what our customer wants, otherwise, although we may carefully make something which pleases us, we may completely fail to please him. Furthermore, if we send one of our salesmen to find out what our customer wants, we must make sure that, having got this information, he transmits the whole of it to our designers.

2   The designers, in turn, must not only design to satisfy the customer. Their plans must be within the manufacturing capabilities of the factory, and this presupposes that the designers know precisely what these capabilities are. Obviously, the factory must tell the designers exactly what it can and cannot make.

3   The designs will probably take the form of specifications, drawings, shop lists, etc., and these must tell the factory precisely what must be made to satisfy the customer.

4   Within the factory itself, we may have a wide variety of people, who must all be told exactly what part they have to play in the production of the whole contract. For example:
a   The purchasing officer must be told exactly what material to buy.
b   The methods engineer must devise methods which will ensure that the operators make the job in the simplest but most foolproof way. Plant, equipment, tooling, etc., must be provided which are adequate to meet the required quality standard, and this may involve negotiations with the plant engineer.
c   The operators must be told both the method and the quality standard.
d   The inspectors must be equally clear about the quality standard.
e   Stores, etc., must know how to store and handle the materials entrusted to their care, without causing any damage.

Endless co-ordination is thus required, and there are endless possibilities for something to go wrong. No wonder that in a large factory there are so many queries and misunderstandings. One of the most important advantages of quality control is that, if correctly used, it will provide adequate quality co-ordination. Because everyone in the factory is concerned in the task of obtaining satisfactory quality, it is often said that 'quality is everybody's business'.

1.10 A summary of the five stages of quality control

An efficient quality control system for any type of production should, therefore, be based on the five stages which we have just discussed. Indeed, because of its perfect co-ordination, the quality control system used for our shelf was a very efficient one, and we shall find it hard to do as well with any factory application.

If we rewrite the five stages of quality control in quality control terms, they become:

1 Set the quality standard, or quality of design, required by the customer.
2 Plan to achieve the required quality. This will involve:
   a Planning methods.
   b Planning equipment.
   c Obtaining satisfactory materials.
   d Selecting and training operators.
   e Planning inspection and shop floor quality control.
3 Manufacture right first time.
4 Correct any quality deficiencies, i.e. defective work such as scrap, etc.
5 Provide for long-term quality control and planning.

Any factory that can claim to carry out all five stages thoroughly already has a very good quality control system.

1.11 The meaning of control

When we say that we have something 'under control', we mean that we know what we intend to happen, and are confident that we can see that it does. Thus, any control system has certain essential features, as follows:

1 There is a plan (in our case the quality standard).
2 We prepare to carry out that plan.
3 We carry it out, and all the time we compare what is being achieved with our plan.
4 If we begin to deviate from the plan we 'feed back' instructions, so that we return to the plan. (For example, if the saw wanders off the pencil line, we reposition it.)

The essence of any control system is this constant 'feedback' of instructions so as to correct any deviation from plan. Every time the control system detects that something is not going to plan, it sends instructions back up the production line to the point where the deviation is occurring and, immediately on receipt of these instructions, the fault is corrected. For example, the control system may detect that a machine has, or is about to, go out of limit, so it at once instructs the setter to reset it. Clearly, the sooner we detect any fault and correct it the less out-of-limit work we shall make. Hence, people talk about 'reducing the feedback loop'.

CHAPTER 2

THE COST OF QUALITY AND ITS EFFECT UPON THE CUSTOMER

2.1 Cost versus quality

As we saw in Section 1.1, costs are very closely linked with quality. Commercially, a product is worth what our customers are prepared to pay for it. If the quality and delivery are bad then the selling price will be correspondingly low. The days are gone when a producer could add almost any profit margin he liked to his costs of manufacture, etc. There are various reasons for this:

1 Competition is continually increasing.
2 The consumer is tending to become more knowledgeable about the goods he buys, and he has been greatly encouraged in this by organisations such as the Consumers' Association and their publication *Which?*
3 Quality standards demanded by various official bodies, and also by many commercial undertakings. Prominent amongst official regulations are the Ministry of Defence Standards 05-21 upwards.

More and more we find that our selling price has a ceiling and therefore, if our quality costs are higher than they need be, our profit is correspondingly reduced. In practice, quality costs often tend to be of much the same order of magnitude as the profit margin so it follows that, if these costs are excessive, the profit may be largely or even completely lost.

2.2 Analysis of quality costs

There is no precise definition of what is meant by the term 'quality costs'. Since almost everything which we do in a company has something to do with quality, we could say that almost all costs are quality costs. However, in order to clarify quality costs, it is usual to consider them under the three headings of failure, appraisal and prevention.

2.2.1 Failure costs

This heading includes the cost of all products and services which 'fail' to comply with their specifications and drawings. Thus, it includes:

1   *Scrap*, i.e. work which is useless, and must be thrown away.
2   *Rework or corrective operations*, i.e. putting right work which is wrong. In quality control, we use the word 'defective' to denote all work which is not to specification or drawing, etc., regardless of whether or not it can be corrected. Thus, defectives include scrap, rework, corrective operations, etc., from both 1 and 2 above.
3   *Other design and manufacturing costs thereby incurred,* for example:
     a   Loss of production capacity.
     b   Interference with production schedules.
     c   Engineer's time spent in investigating the fault.
     d   Design modifications, etc.
4   *Placating irate customers*   We can never really tell exactly what customer displeasure has cost us, but clearly it can be considerable. There will be the immediate costs, for example:
     a   Sending service engineers to correct the trouble.
     b   Express carriage rates to rush replacement parts to the customer, etc.
     In addition, there will be longer-term costs, for example:
     a   Loss of future orders from that customer.
     b   Loss of orders, because that customer tells other potential customers how inefficient we are.

2.2.2 Appraisal costs

Under appraisal, we include all costs incurred in checking that our quality is right, after the goods are made. If we could be sure that everything was correctly made then we should not need to check it. Thus, primarily, appraisal includes the costs of inspection and test to sort out and eliminate production which at any stage does not comply with its quality specifications.

2.2.3 Prevention costs

This is what we spend to ensure that faulty work is not made in the first place. It is the cost of quality control in its widest sense, and includes, for example:
1 Quality engineering.
2 Inspection, etc., when used to keep production running correctly, as opposed to sorting out bad work after manufacture.
3 Training operators for quality.
4 Methods engineering, etc., to improve quality.
5 Maintenance of machines and equipment to achieve the quality standard demanded.

2.3 The principle of minimum overall cost

We said in Section 1.1 that our objective was to achieve the required quality standard as cheaply as possible. We must, therefore, consider how the above three quality costs contribute to the overall cost.

In Figure 2.1 the horizontal or *x* axis shows the quality of our production, expressed as the percentage of work which is defective. Thus, zero means 'no defective work at all', and the extreme right hand side means that there is a lot of defective work. Vertically, on the *y* axis, we plot cost in pounds sterling, dollars, etc.

First, we draw a line to represent the failure and appraisal costs. As this is the cost of defective work, etc., and the costs of finding it when

Figure 2.1 The relationship between failure, appraisal and prevention costs, and the quality of production

14

made, it will be very roughly a straight line; for instance, if we make twice as much scrap, then the cost of scrap is twice as much.

Next, we draw the cost of prevention. At the extreme right-hand side, where failure and appraisal costs are high, we obviously cannot be spending much on prevention. Therefore, the prevention curve is very near to the axis line. We can now imagine a sequence like this:

1   If the production shop is completely disorganised, making piles of defective work everywhere, then the smallest quality control effort will show a marked improvement.

2   When that shop has got its defectives down to a reasonable value it will have taken most of the obvious quality control remedies, and it will now need a much larger effort to reduce it any further.

3   Suppose, in the extreme case, we were misguided enough to insist that our shop should never make any defective work 'no matter what the cost'. We should spend pounds on better machines, jigs, operators, supervisors, inspectors, etc., all to save a very small percentage of scrap.

Applied to Figure 2.1 this means that as we approach zero defective work the cost of prevention shoots upwards, in most cases to infinity, as shown.

Since we want to work at *minimum overall cost* we now add the curve for failure and appraisal to that for prevention, to get the total cost curve shown. In most practical cases, this curve has a minimum value *just above* zero defective work.

Thus, although as quality engineers we spend so much of our time trying to reduce defective work, there is in fact a 'minimum cost' percentage of defective work below which it is unwise to go.

2.4   'Right first time' or 'zero defects'

In Section 1.10 we said that our philosophy was to be 'right first time', with no scrap or corrective operations. Under the title 'zero defects', our American friends have developed this idea into quite a cult. Everyone is expected to aim for no defective work at all.

How do we reconcile this with Figure 2.1 which shows quite clearly that in most cases minimum overall cost implies that some defective work will be made? The answer is that most production shops work well above the percentage of defectives which would yield minimum overall cost. In these days, when there is so much emphasis on quantity and when incentive schemes tend to be quantity biased, it is all too easy for those on the shop floor to become somewhat indifferent to the amount of defective work made. With a little well-directed effort they can reduce this defective work quite markedly, without any corresponding rise in prevention costs. Therefore, 'right first time' or 'zero defects' are good philosophies, which in practice assist the attainment of minimum overall cost.

2.5 The relation between cost and the quality standard

In Section 2.3 we assumed that we knew the quality standard which our customers required, and that our sole concern was to produce to it at minimum overall cost. In many cases, however, it is our own company designers who actually specify this quality standard in the form of specifications and drawings. Therefore, they must ensure that what they specify is what the customers really want. Thus, we can set up another set of cost curves to show how the quality standard, or quality of design, is related to cost.

Figure 2.2 The relationship between cost and the quality of design

In Figure 2.2 the horizontal or x axis shows the quality of design, and to illustrate what this means, suppose we have to turn up a diameter on a lathe. Then we could, if we wished, set our quality of design as follows:

> 25 ± 0.25 mm = Very low quality of design
> 25 ± 0.10 mm = Low quality of design
> 25 ± 0.05 mm = Medium quality of design
> 25 ± 0.01 mm = High quality of design
> 25 ± 0.000 mm = Impossibly high quality of design

Consider, first, the cost of producing to different quality standards.

If our quality standard is very low, i.e. wide tolerances, anything is good enough, it will still cost us a certain amount to produce, as Y in Figure 2.2, because we must buy materials, pay the operators, etc If we begin to increase the quality standard, the effect on cost is at first very little. The factory can quite easily do a bit better. However, as we go on increasing, there comes a time when the machines and operators, etc., are just not capable of doing any better. Costs rise sharply, and if we insist on trying to exceed the factory capability, they shoot away to infinity.

Now consider the value of the quality to the customer, because this will determine what he is prepared to pay for it, and therefore the selling price. When the quality standard is very low, the customer does not want it; its value to him is near enough zero. As the quality standard rises, the customer becomes interested, and so the price he is prepared to pay rises sharply. However, we approach a point where the customer is completely satisfied, and is not prepared to pay any more for higher quality, which he does not even want. Hence, the curve flattens out.

Now the profit we make is given by:

Profit = (Selling price) − (Costs of production, etc.)

Hence, for maximum profitability, we must work at the quality of design or quality standard for which the difference between curves B and A is greatest. If the designer sets his tolerances unnecessarily tight, the cost of production goes up, and the profit per sale goes down.

Figure 2.2 provides a very useful basis for thought, although in practice it is very difficult to put actual cost figures to it. Indeed, it is not strictly speaking the whole story, because it does not take quantity into consideration. Thus, it could be that it pays to work just below maximum profitability per sale because we thereby undercut a competitor, and our volume of sales, i.e. the number sold, increases so much that our *total* profit is higher, and not lower.

2.6 Customer service

The value of our products to the customer will not be solely determined by their quality at the moment of delivery. The service which our customer gets from them will also be important. Depending on the type of product, it may include

1 Efficient installation and commissioning If we send our engineers to install and commission, then we must ensure that:
a They go at a time convenient to the customer.
b They are polite and considerate.

c   They are as far as possible self-sufficient, and do not have to beg odd materials from the customer.

d   They complete their work, and depart as expeditiously as possible.

2   *Adequate customer training*   As equipment becomes more and more complex. so it becomes increasingly necessary to make sure that the customer is competent to get the best out of it.

a   Instruction manuals must be well written, and in the customer's native language.

b   Where necessary, the customer must be taught to use and maintain the equipment.

3   *Adequate after-sales service*

a   If our customer experiences a breakdown of any sort, then we must carry out repairs quickly and efficiently. Usually, the important thing is to keep the time out of service to a minimum. Thus, two breakdowns which are quickly repaired may be less serious than one which takes a long while to put right.

b   Breakdowns are particularly liable to occur shortly after commissioning, for it is during this time that manufacturing weaknesses often come to light. Reliability engineers call this the early failure period, and such failures as occur at this stage should be corrected as quickly as possible, with no cost and a minimum of inconvenience to the customer. Good quality control will help to reduce the frequency of this type of failure. We shall discuss reliability more fully in Chapter 28.

2.7   Future orders

If our customers are satisfied with our quality, price and delivery, then next time they require our type of product they are likely to order it from us. Hence, as someone rather aptly put it: 'Quality makes sales; sales make jobs.'

2.8   Questions

1   Describe in detail the various items of quality costs with which a quality manager might have to deal, and hence use a diagram to explain how he might set about minimising them.   *(25 marks)*

2a Quality costs are usually divided into:

    (i)   failure

    (ii)   appraisal

    (iii)   prevention.

Explain these terms. *(6 marks)*

2b In a small foundry the cost of each 1 per cent of scrap is approximately £350 per week. At present the scrap level is running at 7 per cent and approximately £200 per week is being spent on prevention costs. It is known that the following relation holds:

    Scrap (%) x Prevention cost = Constant

(i) Draw a graph showing cost vertically and scrap percentage horizontally, and then plot curves for:

Prevention cost	*(5 marks)*
Scrap cost	*(3 marks)*
Total cost	*(2 marks)*

(ii) Deduce the scrap percentage at which the total cost is a minimum. *(2 marks)*

3a A department has established that its quality costs per week follow roughly the relationship below.

    (Scrap percentage) x (Prevention costs, £) = 5000

Each 1 per cent of scrap costs £400 per week, including appraisal costs.

    On one pair of axes plot a curve for EACH of the following

(i) Scrap and appraisal costs *(2 marks)*

(ii) Prevention cost *(5 marks)*

(iii) Total quality costs *(4 marks)*

(iv) Identify the exact percentage of scrap at which the total cost is minimised, and state what this cost is. *(6 marks)*

3b The above calculation suggests that for minimum overall cost, the department should be operated deliberately to make the percentage of scrap at which this occurs. How can this be reconciled with the concept of 'Right First Time'? *(8 marks)*

PART TWO

PREPARING FOR SATISFACTORY QUALITY

CHAPTER 3

THE QUALITY OF DESIGN

3.1 Quality of design and quality of conformance

The quality of any manufactured article can be divided under two main headings:

1 The quality of design The quality of design is the quality specified by the designer, on behalf of the customer. In designing a book, the designer may at one extreme call for expensive leather binding, or at the other, he may only specify a paperback. Thus, a leather-bound book has a higher quality of design than the same book made as a paperback. The leather-bound book also costs more, and so is intended for a higher priced market. In the factory, we frequently refer to the quality of design as the quality standard.

2 The quality of conformance The quality of conformance is the extent to which the factory faithfully complies with the designer's specifications. Thus, a badly made leather-bound edition has a high quality of design, but a low quality of conformance, whereas a well made paperback has a low quality of design, but a high quality of conformance.

3.2 The designer's responsibility for quality

In principle, the customer sets the quality standard. He decides what he wants to buy, and he agrees with the manufacturer the price he is to pay. The customer will probably have quite set ideas about what he expects to get for his money, and the manufacturer's problem, therefore, is to make precisely this and nothing else. In some cases the customer will supply a complete set of manufacturing specifications and drawings, but more often the manufacturer will have to prepare his own.

The job of detailing the quality of design usually falls to the design department, who must prepare a complete set of specifications and drawings which:

1   Will satisfy the customer.
2   Are within the manufacturing capability of the factory.
3   Can be made within the time promised, for the price allowed for manufacture in the contract.

Notice that it is not enough merely to produce a design that will satisfy the customer. The design may be exactly what the customer wants, but if the factory cannot make it then its quality is doubtful from the start. It is also in trouble if manufacture cannot be completed either in time, or for the price allowed, because then there is always a temptation to skimp the quality in order to meet price and delivery. In fairness to the designer, however, we must remember that he is himself a link in the quality chain. If the salesman has already promised the customer an impossibly high quality, an impossibly low price or an impossibly short delivery, there may be little the designer can do to retrieve the situation. Of course, if the order is a valuable one, then it may be possible to justify the purchase of better equipment, which will have the effect of improving the manufacturing capability of the factory. Consider how the designer is expected to know the manufacturing capability of the factory. Unless the factory have told him, he is unlikely to have more than a vague idea. Fortunately, quality control can help with this, and in Section 14.10 we shall consider how to measure the capability of any machine or process, and then this information can be fed back to the designer.

The specifications and drawings produced by the designer should show the quality standard required by the customer, in clear and precise terms. Every dimension should have realistic tolerances, and every other quality should have precise limits of acceptability so that the factory can manufacture strictly to specification and drawing.

3.3 Variables and attributes

The overall quality of design of any product is made up of many individual qualities. Thus, there may be:

Dimensions, e.g. length, diameter, thickness and area.
Physical properties, e.g. weight, volume and strength.

Electrical properties, e.g. resistance, voltage, current.
Appearance, e.g. finish, colour and texture.
Functional qualities, e.g. output, or kilometres per litre.
Effect on senses, e.g. taste, feel, or noise level.
However, whatever qualities are called for, it is always possible to classify each of them as either a variable or an attribute, and this distinction is decided by the method used to observe them.

1   Variables   These include all qualities which are measured in figures. For example:
a   A length which is to be 60 ± 0.05 mm.
b   An angle which is to be 90 ± 0.75 degrees.
c   A voltage which is to be 120 ± 10 V.
d   A furnace temperature which is to be 1000 ± 50°C.
It does not matter what sort of quality it is, or how it is checked. If the results are measured in figures then we are dealing with a variable.

2   Attributes are qualities which are not to be measured in figures. For example:
a   'These components to be painted red.'
b   'All components to be free of burrs.'
c   'This bearing to be well oiled.'
d   'This surface to be scratch free.'
The results of a check for an attribute can usually only be expressed as 'pass' or 'fail', or if you prefer, as 'acceptable' or 'unacceptable'. Thus, in 2a above, we can only report that the article has been painted red, or that it has not. In 2b, our surface is either scratch free, or it is scratched. There may be some argument about what is 'scratch free', but once this has been settled our surface either 'passes' or it 'fails'.

Some qualities can be either variables or attributes, according to the method of test or inspection used. Thus, if we check a diameter with a micrometer, we get the result in figures, say 11.05 mm, and this will be a variable. If, however, we check the same diameter with a go/no-go gauge, we shall only find out whether it passes or fails, and so that same quality becomes an attribute.

3.4   Variables

Variables have some advantages over attributes. Thus, if a drawing calls for a dimension to be 12.5 ± 0.001 mm, we may be horrified by the tightness of the tolerances, but at least we know precisely what we have got to make. Tolerances, therefore, define a variable precisely.

When the designer sets the tolerances, he must be careful to call for the *widest* limits which will be satisfactory. Thus, suppose that a dimension will be quite satisfactory provided that it is held between 12.50 and 13.00 mm. If, to be on the safe side, the designer calls for 12.65 to 12.85 mm, then:

1   The machine will have to be reset more often.
2   Any pieces which are made just outside these limits will be rejected, even though they are in fact satisfactory.

The result is that manufacturing costs rise unnecessarily.

Variables have another advantage over attributes, because they tell us more about the state of the process. Suppose that a dimension is to be kept between 12.50 and 12.70 mm, and that in order to see how it is going we take a sample of five pieces and check them as attributes with a go/no-go gauge. If every piece passes, then we shall assume that production is still satisfactory within its drawing limits, but we shall know nothing more. Suppose, instead that we measure our sample of five with a micrometer, so that we are dealing with variables. The following are some of the results we might get, together with their interpretation:

Five readings in millimetres	*Inference*
12.60	This machine is very consistent, and
12.60	is correctly set in the middle of its
12.60	drawing limits. It requires no im-
12.60	mediate attention
12.60	
12.70	This machine is also very consistent,
12.70	but it is running right on top draw-
12.70	ing limit. If out-of-limit work is to
12.70	be avoided it must be reset
12.70	immediately
12.65	This machine is probably too vari-
12.50	able to work to these limits, and
12.55	although it is correctly set in the
12.70	middle of its drawing limits, it will
12.60	want very careful watching if out-
	of-limit work is to be avoided

Thus, variables give us a lot more information than attributes do and so, in general, are to be preferred whenever it is reasonably practicable to use them. However:

1   Some attributes cannot be expressed in figures.

2   Some variables are much more complicated to observe than the equivalent attribute.

3   Sometimes variables have little or no advantage over attributes.

Therefore, there will always be instances where attributes will be used, and so in Section 3.7 we shall consider how to deal with them.

3.5   Accuracy and precision of measurement

No method of measurement is absolutely accurate and precise. In every case the observed reading is slightly different from the true one. When we make a measurement we assume that our errors of measurement are small compared with the variations which we are trying to observe, but this is not always justified. Thus, if the drawing calls for 19.00 to 19.01 mm, this should obviously not be checked with a micrometer which only measures to the nearest 0.01 mm, because such a micrometer might give us an error of as much as 0.005 mm. In extreme cases, our micrometer would accept work from 18.995 to 19.015 mm, and this would effectively double our drawing tolerances from 0.01 to 0.02 mm. As a rough guide, the errors of measurement should not exceed 10 per cent of the width between the two specification or drawing limits.

There are two basic ways in which a measuring instrument may give an incorrect reading. It may be imprecise due to random errors, and it may be inaccurate due to a consistent bias.

3.5.1   Lack of precision due to random errors

Random errors will cause an instrument to give readings which are round about the correct one, being both higher and lower. When this happens, the imprecision can be reduced by taking a number of readings, and averaging them all together. For example, suppose we have to measure a voltage, whose true value is 100 V. If we take five separate observations of this same voltage, we might get:

99, 100, 102, 101, 98V

If we average these together we get 100 V, which in this case happens to be correct, although this would not necessarily be so. All we can say is that the average is likely to be more precise than the original readings.

3.5.2   Inaccuracy due to a consistent bias

Inaccuracy, or bias, will cause all the readings on the instrument to be a fixed amount, either too high or too low. Common examples are a micrometer or a voltmeter, which has a zero error, so that it always reads say 0.01 mm or 0.1 V respectively, too high. If the magnitude of such inaccuracy or bias is known we can make a correction to our readings, but we cannot offset it by taking several readings and averaging them together. This will only result in our determining the observed reading more precisely, but this will still be equal to the true reading plus or minus the inaccuracy. For example, suppose that because our voltmeter was inaccurate, when we took five readings on a voltage with a true value of 100 V we obtained:

98, 98, 98, 98, 98 V

Averaging our readings give us 98 V, and in no way helps us to remove the inaccuracy. However, if we know from the last time it was calibrated that our voltmeter always reads 2 V low, we can add 2 V on to the 98 V and get the correct reading of 100.

Errors of precision and accuracy usually occur together in the same measuring instrument. Thus, our voltmeter might have read:

97, 98, 100, 99, 96 V

This gives an average of 98 V which is 2 V below the correct value. Notice how averaging helps to remove imprecision, but does not help at all with inaccuracy.

3.6 Routine checking of inspection and test equipment

From the above it follows that all measuring devices should be regularly checked. One convenient way of doing this is by colour coding. Thus, suppose we decide that all measuring instruments shall be checked once per month. When they are checked this month, we put a dab of one colour, say red, on them. Next month when they are checked again, we shall change the dab to another colour, say yellow. If at any time later than this an instrument with a red dab comes to light, we shall know that it has not been checked for that month. We can hang a notice in each shop which says, 'If your instrument does not bear this colour, it has not been checked this month,' and follow it by the colour chosen for this month. If an instrument or gauge is dropped, or otherwise roughly treated, it should always be rechecked before it is used again.

3.7 Attributes

Attributes tend to be difficult to use as quality standards, because they are not easy to define. A variable which has to be 12.5 ± 0.01 mm is quite clear, but a statement like 'This surface must be scratch free', is very vague. Our idea may be quite different from the designer's, and different again from that of the operator or the inspector. We must, therefore, set some sort of standard otherwise every operator and every inspector is left to use his own ideas. Often the best way is to prepare a visual quality standard, i.e. actual examples of the work concerned, showing the *lowest* quality which is just acceptable. Sometimes a visual quality standard is merely a single piece of the work concerned, suitably labelled. However, we may wish to illustrate more than one fault, and we may sometimes need to show bad examples of the fault as well as the 'just acceptable quality'. If the work is not too large, we may decide to mount all these together on a display board, along the lines shown in Figure 3.1.

Section B shows a bad example of each fault, so that both the operator and the inspector understand what the fault is. In soldering, for example, it may be desirable to show a bad instance of a 'dry joint', so that everyone knows exactly what we mean by the term. The notes in section A are used to explain why each fault shown is detrimental to

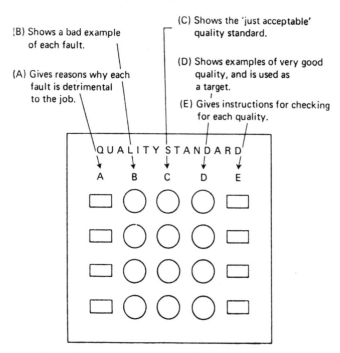

Figure 3.1   An example of a visual quality standard

the final product. It follows by implication that faults which are not illustrated are not particularly important.

Section C shows the quality standard itself, that is, the lowest quality which is just acceptable. Operators and inspectors can then compare what has been made with the standard, and if it is equal to this or better it is acceptable.

Section D shows examples of very good quality. These are not suitable as quality standards, because work of lower quality can be accepted. They may, however, be useful as 'targets'.

Finally section E of the quality standard gives any necessary instructions about the use of the standard.

Each quality standard should be prepared for shop use, and in most cases should be suitable for display. Small components are usually best mounted on a board, or in a glass case. Some sort of dust cover will be necessary if the components are on a board, in order to keep them in reasonable condition.

It is, of course, inevitable that if a standard is used in a workshop, it will deteriorate in time. On the other hand, if the standard is not used there is no point in having it. Sometimes by taking a photograph it is possible to provide secondary standards, and copies can then be given to every operator and every inspector. The operator needs a copy every bit as much as the inspector, because he must make the piece right in the first place.

3.8 Non-visual quality standards

So far we have assumed that our attribute is a visual quality, but this may not be so. Attributes may be recognised by any of the senses. For example:

1 *Hearing* We may have to deal with a permitted noise level as an attribute, although in many cases it can be measured as a variable.

2 *Taste* In the food trade, the final taste of a product is difficult to express as a variable. Furthermore, if we prepare a standard and say that everything we make 'must taste like this', then every time somebody uses the standard we lose a bite! In such cases, the easiest way is often to find someone who can recognise the taste which is required, and get him to do occasional checks, and advise those concerned.

3 *Smell* A similar situation occurs with qualities associated with smell. If the product is sufficiently durable, then we may be able to set up a smell quality standard. Otherwise, we shall have to find someone who can recognise the particular smell required.

4 *Touch* The 'feel' of some materials is difficult to measure, but

in most cases it is possible to set up a suitable quality standard.

Where opinion enters into the assessment of a quality, as in Sections 3.7 and 3.8, then we are said to be dealing with a *subjective quality standard*, often merely referred to as a *subjective standard*.

I have found the following to be a useful guide to the suitability of a subjective standard. It should be possible to instruct the inspectors that, if an item is so near to the 'only just acceptable' quality standard that they cannot be certain whether or not it is acceptable, then it should be *accepted*. If any quality is so critical that this rule is too risky to use, then it is a sure sign that the subjective standard is inadequate for its purpose. It must be redefined, preferably as a variable.

3.9 Critical, major and minor defects

It is often possible for a single piece of production to have more than one fault or defect. Furthermore, one type of defect may be much more serious than another. In such cases it is sometimes convenient to classify the possible defects as follows:

1 *Critical defect*   A critical defect is one that is likely to result in hazardous or unsafe conditions for the people using, maintaining or depending on the product, or one which will cause the failure of a major item, such as a ship. Thus, a defect which would result in the failure of the steering mechanism of a car would be classed as critical.
2 *Major defect*   A major defect is one that, although not critical, will result in failure, or will seriously reduce the utility of the product in which it is incorporated. Thus, a defect which would cause a car engine either to fail or perform badly would be classed as major.
3 *Minor defect*   A minor defect is one that, although undesirable, will not appreciably affect the use of the product concerned. Thus, paint blemishes on a car, if not too extensive, might be classed as minor.

3.10 Modifications to the quality standard

From time to time it will be necessary to modify the quality standard. Thus changes may be requested by the customer, or the designer may wish to improve or correct his design. Either way it is usually the designer who will arrange for the drawings and specifications to be altered. Strict control will then be necessary to make sure that everyone concerned gets a revised copy, when he needs it. The routine might be as follows:

1   Copies of drawings and specifications are kept only in a limited number of suitably placed locations, usually drawing stores.

2   When any drawing is issued or reissued, the prescribed number of copies is sent to each. People who require a copy borrow it from the nearest store, and their name is recorded.

3   Where a reissue is concerned, all copies of the previous issue are recalled and destroyed. It is not satisfactory to let those in possession of the old issue destroy it, because they will not always do so, and then sometime in the future, an obsolete issue will come to light, and work will be made to it before the mistake is discovered.

4   It is usual for the modified drawing to show clearly the alterations which have been made to it, and the date.

5   Sometimes a modified drawing contains an indication of the urgency of the changes, e.g.

    a   *Type 1 modification*   Very urgent. All partially made work to the old drawing is to be scrapped and no more produced until the modified drawing can be used.

    b   *Type 2 modification*   Partially made work which is to the old drawing can be completed, but no more is to be made to it.

    c   *Type 3 modification*   Change to new issue as soon as convenient and economic. For example, when the tooling has to be renewed, or the present stocks of raw material run out.

The factory may wish to request a modification to the quality standard, to make the product easier and cheaper to produce. If the change is to be permanent, arrangements should be made with the designer to have the drawing altered and reissued. Sometimes the request is more temporary. Perhaps the material specified cannot be obtained in time, or the factory wish to use up similar material already in stock. In such cases the factory will request a *production permit,* authorising them to produce to the modified standard. Such permits are issued in advance of production, and are only valid for a limited period, or maybe production quantity. Permanent changes should be covered by a modification to the drawing.

From time to time a batch may be produced outside drawing limits, which although the inspectors will rightly reject, nevertheless could be used. The factory will then ask for a *concession.* This allows them to use the work which has already been made, but they are not permitted to produce any more like it.

When any change in the quality standard is authorised, care must be taken to deal with any repercussions. Thus consequential changes may be necessary to certain components, otherwise the final performance and reliability of the product may be affected.

3.11 Questions

1a Explain the following terms, giving *three* examples of each, and discuss their use as quality standards:

A variable   *(7 marks)*

An attribute   *(7 marks)*

1b Outline the main points to be considered in revising a manufacturing specification.   *(11 marks)*

2 Explain the designer's contribution to quality, both when the initial design is prepared, and subsequently when modifications are required.

(25 marks)

3a What is meant by an attribute in the context of quality control?

(2 marks)

3b State the difficulties often encountered in using attributes as quality standards, and outline practical ways of overcoming them.

(8 marks)

3c When using either attributes or variables as quality standards, explain the usual procedure for dealing with each of the following:

(i)   A batch of work which has been made is not quite to specification, but is thought to be usable.   *(5 marks)*

(ii)   A batch of work if produced under existing conditions will not completely comply with specification, even though it will be usable.   *(5 marks)*

(iii) The material specified is no longer available, but an alternative can be obtained which is believed to be entirely satisfactory.   *(5 marks)*

CHAPTER 4

QUALITY CONTROL OF INCOMING MATERIEL. A BRIEF SURVEY OF THEORY

The word materiel *(with an 'e' in place of the final 'a') has military origins, and denotes the baggage and equipment of an army. In industry it means everything which is supplied to the production lines, and so includes raw materials, components, sub-assemblies and sometimes complete assemblies as well.*

4.1 The case for control of incoming materiel

If bad materiel is used in our production lines, a lot of good work may be done before its shortcomings are discovered. Thus, eventually we not only have to scrap the bad materiel itself, but in addition, lose the good work we have done on it. As this is liable to be costly, we must obviously do our best to ensure that all materiel is satisfactory before it is issued for production.

In principle, of course, if we agree with each supplier precisely what is to be supplied, and if we pay him a fair price for it, then we have a right to expect that we shall receive consistently satisfactory quality. Our problem, however, is to ensure that we do.

If we are a sufficiently large consumer, we may be able to say to our supplier: 'We expect all materiel sent to us to comply with specification, and if you fail very often, we shall stop buying from you'. Provided we are a sufficiently important customer, our supplier is likely to take such a threat very seriously.

However, many companies are not in this strong position. If we can

34

only buy materiel in small quantities, then the threat of losing our custom is unlikely to worry a large supplier. This may be the case if our company is very small. It will also be true of some large companies that specialise in making to individual customer specifications, because they are likely to require a considerable *variety* of materiel, but all in small quantities. Where special materiel is concerned, it often happens that it can only be obtained from one particular supplier. However large our quantities, if the supplier knows we cannot buy elsewhere, the threat to do so is going to be a pretty empty one.

Unless we can ensure that our supplier will not send us any unsatisfactory materiels, we shall need some simple form of control to prevent such materiel from getting into our own production lines. A typical method is to apply goods inwards inspection, but inevitably this will cost money so it is essential that we plan to get maximum results from minimum expenditure.

4.2 The principles of inspection by samples

In principle, our goods inwards inspection will be simple. From each batch of materiel which arrives we take a sample, and check it for the qualities important to us. If the sample is satisfactory, then we infer that the batch is satisfactory, and if the sample is unsatisfactory, we likewise assume that the whole batch is unsatisfactory.

The success or otherwise of such a method will depend on
1   Using a suitable sample size.
2   Checking for the correct qualities.
If the sample is too small, the results we get from it may be completely misleading, whereas if it is too large, it will be unnecessarily expensive to check. Similarly, if we fail to check for all the qualities important for our particular work, we may still accept unsuitable materiel, and if we check for qualities which do not matter, our checks will be unnecessarily expensive.

4.3 Traditional methods of taking samples

It is worth looking briefly at what we might call 'traditional' factory sampling, which is usually based on one of the following:
1   A fixed percentage of the batch, e.g. 5 or 10 per cent.
2   A fixed number of pieces, often ten, a method all too easily degenerating into merely taking a handful from the top of the sack or container.
Unfortunately neither of these is entirely satisfactory.

4.4 Sampling a fixed percentage of the batch

Consider first what happens when we always take 10 per cent of the batch, so that the sample size varies directly with the batch size. Suppose that the batch consists of 100,000 small nuts, so that if we take 10 per cent of the batch, we must inspect a sample of 10,000. Now for most purposes, this is a very large sample indeed. By the time we had checked 1000 of them we should have a very good idea of their quality and, unless they were required for a very critical application, we should not need to check any more.

At the other extreme, suppose that we have a small batch of only fifty pieces. On a 10 per cent basis, we should check a sample of five of them. If we find no defectives, we shall presumably conclude that the batch is 100 per cent good, although obviously this may not be the case. If we find one defective, we are led to believe that the batch is 1 in 5 or 20 per cent defective. As the correct answer may be anywhere from 0 to 20 per cent or even higher, we have not learnt anything worthwhile from our inspection. Thus, a sample of five is too small to give reliable results.

Hence, if we take a percentage of the batch, we shall inevitably find that for small batches our sample is too small, and for large batches it is too large. (In saying this, we are assuming that nothing is known in advance about the quality of the batch, and that this must be determined solely from the inspection results. Sometimes there is good reason for believing that each batch will either be all good, or all bad, a mixture of good and bad being unlikely. Where this is so, a very small sample may be possible.)

4.5 Taking a fixed sample size

Now consider the second traditional method, in which the inspector always takes a fixed number of pieces, usually ten. From Section 4.4 it is clear that for most purposes a sample of ten will be too small. Thus, suppose that we wished to detect the presence of 1 per cent of defectives in our batch. Now 1 per cent means that our batch would contain one defective piece in every 100, so that if we were to take a sample of 100, we should on average only expect to find one defective in it. However, our sample is to be only ten pieces, so our chances of finding any defectives, when the batch contains exactly 1 per cent defectives, are somewhat remote. Indeed, it would be quite easy to miss the presence of as much as 10 per cent, because even then a sample of ten would on average contain only one defective, and we would be quite likely to draw a sample which contained no defectives at all.

4.6 The risks of being wrong with samples

We can develop this argument further by working out exactly what a sample of ten would do, and at the same time show how to calculate how other samples would behave. Although the method is the same, the actual calculation gets more involved as the sample size increases, so it is best to start with a small sample even though such a small sample is of little practical value. We shall need to assume a correspondingly high percentage of defectives to give our small sample a chance to work, so let us assume that we are checking a batch which really contains 20 per cent of defectives.

When we draw a sample from a batch, we always hope that the sample will contain the same percentage of defectives as does the batch. Thus, we hope that our sample of ten will contain two defective pieces, and eight good. Because of the 'luck of the draw', however, we shall certainly not get this every time. Even though we mix our batch well, we shall find varying numbers of defectives in our samples.

Suppose that from our batch which really contains 20 per cent defective pieces, we take 100 successive samples of ten pieces each. We note the number of defectives in each sample we draw, then return it to the batch, and mix well before we take the next sample. Our results could be plotted as a graph, as shown in Figure 4.1. The horizontal (or x) axis shows the number of defectives which may be found in each sample, and the vertical (or y) axis shows the frequency with which each

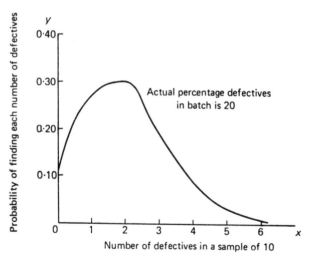

Figure 4.1 The probabilities of finding each number of defectives in a sample of ten

number of defectives was in fact found. Thus, in our example, eleven of the 100 samples of ten contained no defectives at all, so above zero defectives on our graph we plot a point at 11/100, i.e. at 0.11. For mathematical reasons, we usually express probabilities as a fraction of 1 rather than as a percentage, so we actually plot 0.11 instead of 11 per cent.

As we should expect, our graph shows us that a sample is more likely to contain two defectives than any other number but notice, nevertheless, that this probability is only 0.30. Thus, the chances are only about one in three that we shall get the 'right' answer! Indeed one defective, with a probability of 0.27, will turn up nearly as often, and three, four or even five defectives will appear from time to time.

4.7 The meaning of probability

The system of expressing probabilities means that a probability of 1.0 indicates certainty, because it denotes that something will happen 100 times out of 100. At the other end of the scale, a probability of 0 means impossibility, because it denotes that something will happen 0 times out of 100. Thus:

> The probability that the sun will rise tomorrow = 1.0
> The probability that I shall ever be queen of Great Britain = 0

If we toss a penny, the chances are one in two that it will come down heads, and one in two that it will come down tails. Therefore:

> The probability of a head = 0.5
> The probability of a tail = 0.5
> The probability of either a head or a tail = 1.0

4.8 The addition and multiplication of probabilities

There are two simple rules concerning probabilities, which we shall want to use:

1 The addition rule   Suppose that due to containers breaking in transit, we are faced with a batch of mixed pieces, containing:
>   50 per cent bolts,
>   30 per cent nuts, and
>   20 per cent washers.
If we now take a sample of one piece:

The probability it is a bolt		= 0.5
The probability it is a bolt *or* a nut	= 0.5 + 0.3	= 0.8
The probability it is a bolt *or* a washer	= 0.5 + 0.2	= 0.7
The probability it is a bolt, nut *or* washer	= 0.5 + 0.3 + 0.2	= 1.0

This is a general rule where only one thing can happen at a time, e.g. our sample cannot be both a bolt and a nut at the same time — it must be one or the other. If we denote the things that can happen by A, B, C, D, etc., then the probability that say either A, C or D will occur is the *sum* of the individual probabilities of A, C and D.

2 *The multiplication rule* Suppose that a large batch is 20 per cent defective and we decide to take a sample of two. Therefore:

The probability the first is defective	= 0.2
The probability the second is defective	= 0.2
The probability they are *both* defective	0.2 × 0.2 = 0.04

Thus, where it is possible for two or more things to occur *together*, the probability they will do so is the *product* of their individual probabilities.

4.9 Calculation of the probability of each number of defectives in a sample, using the binomial distribution

The curve shown in Figure 4.1 was not in fact obtained by taking a large number of samples of ten from a batch containing exactly 20 per cent defectives; it was calculated as follows. Our example batch contains exactly 20 per cent defectives and 80 per cent good. Suppose we draw a sample of just one piece from it. Then:

The probability it is defective is 20 in 100	= 0.2
The probability it is good is 80 in 100	= 0.8
The probability it is either defective or good	= 1.0

It is useful to apply the addition rule here. In this simple case, it is obvious that our sample must be either good or defective, and that therefore the probability of one or the other must be 1.0. In more complicated problems, however, there may be a considerable number of possibilities to consider. It is then useful to check that they add up to 1.0 since, if they total less, it indicates that some possibilities have been overlooked. (If they total more than 1.0, of course, it indicates a mistake in the calculation.)

Next suppose we draw a sample of two pieces from our batch. There are now four possible combinations, as follows:

The probability of 1 defective followed by 1 defective
$$= 0.2 \times 0.2 = 0.04$$
The probability of 1 defective followed by 1 good
$$= 0.2 \times 0.8 = 0.16$$
The probability of 1 good followed by 1 defective
$$= 0.8 \times 0.2 = 0.16$$
The probability of 1 good followed by 1 good $\quad = 0.8 \times 0.8 = 0.64$
Total (to check that all possibilities have been considered) $\quad = 1.00$

In the above calculation, we assumed that our batch contained exactly 20 per cent defectives. In order to work out the general case, we now assume that the batch contains a fraction p of defectives, and q good. Then, for a sample of two pieces:

The probability of 1 defective followed by 1 defective $\quad = p^2$
The probability of 1 defective followed by 1 good $\quad = pq$
The probability of 1 good followed by 1 defective $\quad = qp$
The probability of 1 good followed by 1 good $\quad = q^2$
Check total $= (p^2 + 2pq + q^2) = (p + q)^2$

If we repeat this calculation for any other sample size, which we denote by n, we shall find that the check total always reduces to $(p + q)^n$. This is the basic expression for the binomial theorem, and in order to calculate the data for Figure 4.1, we have to expand $(p + q)^{10}$ as follows:

$$(p + q)^{10} = p^{10} + 10p^9 q + 45p^8 q^2 + 120p^7 q^3 + 210p^6 q^4 + 252p^5 q^5$$
$$+ 210p^4 q^6 + 120p^3 q^7 + 45p^2 q^8 + 10pq^9 + q^{10}$$

If we now want to know the probability of getting say 2 defectives and 8 good in our sample of 10, we must work out the term containing p^2 and q^8, i.e.

$$45p^2 q^8 = 45(0.2)^2 (0.8)^8 = 0.30$$

The expanded terms of the binomial theorem are known to statisticians as the *binomial distribution,* and we can calculate the probability that a sample will contain any chosen number of defectives denoted by r, by using the general term of this distribution, which is:

$$\frac{n!}{r! \, (n - r)!} p^r q^{(n-r)} \tag{4.1}$$

The exclamation mark stands for *factorial* and it means that the number concerned is multiplied by the next number lower, and the next again, and so on right down to 1. For example, factorial $5 = 5! = 5 \times 4 \times 3 \times$

$2 \times 1 = 120$. In the above example, we had:

Sample size	$= n = 10$
Fraction defective in the batch	$= p = 0.2$
Fraction good in the batch	$= q = 0.8$

We wished to know the probability of finding $r = 2$ defective pieces in the sample, and this is given by

$$\frac{10!}{2! \, (10 - 2)!} \, (0.2)^2 (0.8)^8 = 0.30 \text{ as above.}$$

4.10 The Poisson distribution

The expansion of $(p + q)^n$ becomes cumbersome if n is large, and therefore it is usual to introduce an approximation. Instead of using the binomial distribution, we use the Poisson distribution. The change makes little difference so long as q is much larger than p, which is usually the case. The general term for the Poisson distribution is:

Probability of r defectives in a sample of n is

$$\frac{(np)^r}{r! \, \exp (np)} \tag{4.2}$$

Exp(np) means exponential of (np), and we get its value from mathematical or statistical tables. The term (np) is often referred to as the expected number of defectives and is denoted by m. Thus if we take sample of 200 from a batch which is 5 per cent defective, we should expect 5 per cent or 10 of our sample to be defective. Thus

$$m = np = 200 \times 0.05 = 10$$

If we then want to know the probability that the actual number of defectives found will be, say, 8, we use Eq. (4.2), i.e.

Probability of $r = 8$ defectives in the sample
$= 10^8/8! \, \exp(10) = 0.1126$

In practice it is not often necessary to use the Poisson distribution for sampling, because convenient sampling tables have been prepared, which we shall discuss in Section 5.7. Even where special sampling plans have to be worked out, we can use tables which give the values of both the binomial and the Poisson distributions, so it is unusual in practice to have to evaluate either Eq. (4.1) or (4.2). See for example *Statistical Tables for Science, Engineering, Management and Business Studies*, by J. Murdoch and J. A. Barnes, published by Macmillan.

4.11 The risks of being wrong when inspecting with samples

When we use a sample in order to judge the quality of a batch we take a risk that we may wrongly accept or reject it, merely because the sample happens to be better or worse than the batch. We can reduce this risk by taking a larger sample, but we cannot eliminate it unless we do a 100 per cent inspection. Even 100 per cent inspection is seldom completely reliable because inspectors tend to get bored, and then they make mistakes.

From this it follows that if our production line is such that we cannot risk even one defective piece being fed into it, then effective 100 per cent inspection is the only answer. However much of a batch we may have inspected without finding a single defective, we can never say with certainty that the remainder of the batch is also completely free of defectives. We may be able to say that it is probably free, but we cannot say that it is certainly so.

4.12 Question

1a Samples of n components are drawn at random from a large batch which contains a fraction p that is defective and q that is satisfactory. Show by considering the possible selections that when $n = 2$ and $n = 3$, respectively, the probability of getting any particular combination of defective and satisfactory components is given by the appropriate term of a binomial distribution. *(13 marks)*

1b A large batch is known to be 2 per cent defective. Using tables or otherwise, deduce

- *(i)*   The probability that a random sample of 10 will contain 1 or more defectives.
- *(ii)* The probability the same sample of 10 will contain exactly 1 defective.
- *(iii)* The sample size which must be drawn if the probability of 2 or more defectives is to be approximately 90 per cent.

(12 marks)

CHAPTER 5

THE OPERATING CHARACTERISTIC

5.1 The construction of the operating characteristic

In Section 4.6, we only considered the case in which our sample of ten was taken from a batch containing exactly 20 per cent defectives. Obviously, if we inspected a batch containing, say, 40 per cent defectives, the chances are that we should get more defectives in each sample than Figure 4.1. Therefore, the figure in fact shows only one of a whole family of curves, all of which can be deduced from $(p + q)^{10}$ by inserting appropriate values for p and q. Because this family of curves gets relatively complicated, we usually prefer to plot what is called an operating characteristic, or sometimes a power curve.

Each operating characteristic is associated with a particular sampling plan, and a sampling plan tells us:

1 The sample size (n), which is to be drawn.
2 The maximum number of defectives (c), which are allowed, if the batch is to be accepted.

Suppose we work out the operating characteristic for a sampling plan where $n = 10$ and $c = 2$. This means that the sample size is to be ten, and if zero, one, or two defectives are found in the sample, the batch will be accepted, and if three or more are found, it will be rejected.

We first calculate the probabilities of finding zero, one or two defectives in samples of ten drawn from batches which actually contain a range of percentage defective, say 10, 20, 30 and 40 per cent. We shall of course utilise the expression $(p + q)^{10}$, and we then get the following results:

Number of defectives found in a sample of ten	Probability of finding that number of defectives in a sample of ten, taken from a batch which actually contains the percentage of defectives given at the head of each column			
	10%	20%	30%	40%
0	0.35	0.11	0.03	0.006
1	0.39	0.27	0.12	0.04
2	0.19	0.30	0.23	0.12
	—	—	—	—
Total probability of 0, 1 or 2 defectives	0.93	0.68	0.38	0.166

Since with our sampling plan the batch is to be accepted if zero, one or two defectives are found in the sample, we total each column above to find the overall probability that the batch will be accepted. Next, using the bottom total line of figures, we plot a curve showing the probability that a batch will be accepted against the actual percentage

the probability that the pop will be accepted with 20% of defectives when 2 or less samples out of 10 were defective is 0.7

Figure 5.1 The operating characteristic for a sampling plan in which the sample size is ten. The batch may be accepted if the sample contains no more than two defectives

44

of defectives which it contains. This is shown in Figure 5.1 and it is called an operating characteristic.

5.2   The properties of the operating characteristic

Any one operating characteristic relates to a particular sampling plan. Thus, our example in Figure 5.1 relates to a plan in which the sample size is ten, and up to two defectives are allowed for the batch to be accepted. Now the operating characteristic tells us the probability that the sampling plan concerned will accept a batch containing any particular percentage of defectives we may care to offer it. In practice, of course, we have a batch containing an unknown percentage of defective and we have to choose a sampling plan which will:

1   Accept what we consider to be a satisfactory batch, and
2   Reject what we consider to be an unsatisfactory batch.

We can divide any operating characteristic into roughly three sections as shown in Figure 5.2.

5.2.1   The zones of acceptance and rejection

Within the zone of acceptance, nearly all batches will be accepted, and within the zone of rejection, they will nearly all be rejected. Therefore, we must choose our operating characteristic so that its zone of accep-

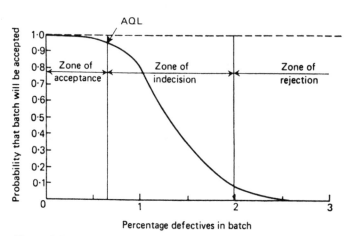

Figure 5.2   An operating characteristic, divided into the zones of acceptance, indecision and rejection

45

tance accepts what we consider to be a satisfactory batch, and its zone of rejection rejects what we consider to be an unsatisfactory batch.

5.2.2 Zone of indecision

Between the zones of acceptance and rejection, there is the zone of indecision. It is a region where we cannot be very certain whether any particular batch will be accepted or rejected. Indeed, roughly in the middle, there is a percentage of defectives for which the probability of acceptance is 0.5. As a batch must be either accepted or rejected, its probability of rejection is, therefore, $1.0 - 0.5 = 0.5$. Thus, the batch is just as likely to be accepted as it is to be rejected! Clearly, this point does not help us to sort satisfactory batches from those which are unsatisfactory.

Unless we are prepared to do 100 per cent inspection we cannot eliminate the zone of indecision. We can, however, reduce its width by taking a larger sample, but this will increase our inspection costs and so may or may not be justified. Fortunately, the zone of indecision is not nearly such a practical disadvantage as we might at first suppose. A batch in this zone is worse than what we have considered an acceptable batch, and better than what we have considered unacceptable. Its quality is thus borderline, and in most practical cases it will not matter much whether we finally decide to accept or reject it.

5.3 Specifying an operating characteristic

An operating characteristic is fully specified if any two points on it are fixed. By this we mean that if we specify any two points on our graph through which we want our operating characteristic to pass, there will only be one such characteristic which will do this. We cannot then add a third point through which it must also pass. It may happen to pass through the third point, but we cannot make it. Various ways of setting these two points are in use, and these give rise to many of the different sampling inspection tables which are published. Nearly all of them are derived from the same basic theory leading to the establishment of the operating characteristic, and the following are some of the methods in use.

5.3.1 Lot tolerance percentage defective (LTPD)

In this method we select the percentage of defectives in a batch, at and above which we wish to be almost certain it will be rejected. This is called the *Lot Tolerance Percentage Defective* or LTPD, and in the example in Figure 5.3 it has a value of 3 per cent. There is of course a small risk that a batch containing the LTPD will be accepted, merely because an untypically good sample happens to be drawn. We as the consumer will then feed into our production lines, a batch we intended to reject. This is therefore called the *consumer's risk*, and as a definition, it is the probability that a batch containing *exactly* the LTPD will be accepted. It is usual to set the consumer's risk at 0.1, so that the probability of rejection is $1.0 - 0.1 = 0.9$.

The second point on the operating characteristic is chosen by setting the percentage of defectives which we are prepared to accept. The idea is that this should be the normal percentage, which our producer's process makes, when it is correctly adjusted and in control. It is therefore called the *process average*, and in Figure 5.3 it has a value of 1 per cent. Again there will be a small risk that a batch containing the process average will be rejected, and returned unfairly to the producer. This is called the *producer's risk*, and it is the probability that a batch containing exactly the process average percentage of defectives, will be rejected. Like the consumer's risk, the producer's risk is usually set at 0.1.

Readers who wish to use this method should consult *Sampling Inspection Tables* by H. F. Dodge and H. G. Romig, published by John Wiley.

Figure 5.3 Lot tolerance percentage defective

47

5.3.2 Acceptable quality level (AQL)

In the example in Figure 5.2 a batch is very likely to be accepted if it contains 0.65 per cent defectives or less. This point on the operating characteristic is, therefore, called the *Acceptable Quality Level* or AQL. The probability of a batch containing exactly the AQL percentage of defectives being accepted is often set at 0.95, but other values near this are also used. The producer's risk is thus approximately 0.05.

The AQL system has been adopted by both the United States and British Governments, and this has had the effect of making the use of AQL very common in both countries. Both Governments have issued specifications giving AQL sampling inspection tables. In the United States this is Military Standard 105D. In Great Britain it was originally Defence Specification DEF-131A, with an explanatory booklet called Defence Guide 7A, but these have since been replaced by BSS 6001 and BSS 6000, respectively.

There has recently been increased interest in the LTPD method of specifying an operating characteristic. The considerations are roughly as follows. When the AQL is specified, the uncertainties of the zone of indecision are beyond it at higher percentages of defectives. If the operating characteristic is not sufficiently steep, then batches containing considerably more than the AQL percentage of defectives have an appreciable chance of being accepted, to the disadvantage of the consumer. With the LTPD method the position is reversed. The zone of indecision is below the LTPD and any attempt to use too flat an operating characteristic will result in additional batches with lower percentages of defectives being rejected, to the disadvantage of the producer. Hence with the sellers' market of recent years, it is not surprising that AQL has been dominant. A change to a buyer's market however, might result in consumers reverting to LTPD.

5.4 Properties of the acceptable quality level

The AQL is defined as the maximum percentage of defectives which, for the purposes of sampling inspection, can be considered satisfactory as a process average. It is thus the 'only just acceptable' quality because, in principle, any increase in the percentage of defectives above the AQL value should tend to cause the batch to be rejected. Thus, in Figure 5.2, the AQL is 0.65 per cent defective. This is intended to mean that whereas 0.65 per cent defective will be accepted, over 0.65 per cent will tend to cause the batch to be rejected. To reject it with certainty, however, it would be necessary for the operating characteristic to fall vertically to zero, immediately 0.65 per cent defective was exceeded. This is not possible unless we do 100 per cent inspection.

If we increase the sample size the operating characteristic will become steeper, and if we decrease it it will become flatter. Thus BSS 6001 to which we referred in Section 5.3.2 provides for three general inspection levels, as well as four special levels. The general inspection levels are referred to as *normal inspection, reduced inspection* and *tightened inspection.* They are illustrated in Figure 5.4. The idea is that normal

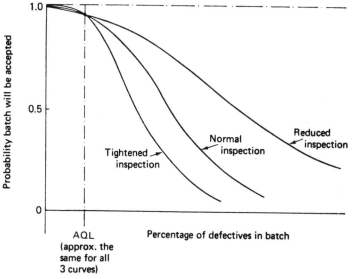

Figure 5.4 Levels of inspection

inspection should be used in general cases. Tightened inspection requires a larger sample size than normal inspection, but in return we get a much steeper operating characteristic, which is more efficient in rejecting batches containing a percentage of defects just above the AQL. Conversely reduced inspection requires the smallest of the three sample sizes, but batches must contain a percentage of defects well above the AQL before there is any real risk of them being rejected.

5.5 Deducing the operating characteristic from the sampling plan

Starting from the sampling plan, we can construct the operating characteristic as follows. Suppose the plan is:

49

| Sample size | $= n = 100$ |
| Allowed number defective | $= c = 1$ |

1   In column (1) below, set out a convenient range of values of p, the fraction of defectives in incoming batches. As a rough guide the value of p where it equals c/n will occur at about the centre of the range. Thus for our example, $p = c/n = 1/100 = 0.01$ or 1 per cent defective, will be around the middle value chosen. The choice is not critical, because extra values can easily be added later, or surplus ones discarded.

2   In column (2) we put the expected or average number of defectives m, which will be found in the sample. We obviously hope that the sample will contain the same fraction defective p as does the batch. Thus for the first line of the table we have, $m = np = 100 \times 0.002 = 0.2$.

3   We now use a table of cumulative Poisson probabilities which, when we enter the value of m, will tell us the probability of r or more defectives. We want to know the probability of 1 or less defectives, so we set $r = (c + 1) = 2$. Inserting $r = 2$ and the values of m in column (2), gives us the probability of 2 or more defectives as column (3).

4   We subtract column (3) from 1.0 to get the probability of less than 2 defectives, i.e. 0 or 1.

5   To draw the operating characteristics we plot column (4) vertically, against $100p$ (so that we have percentages) from column (1).

(1)	(2)	(3)	(4)
p	$mn = np$	Probability of 2 or more defectives	Probability of 0 or 1 defective
0.002	0.2	0.0175	0.9825
0.004	0.4	0.0616	0.9384
0.008	0.8	0.1912	0.8088
0.010	1.0	0.2642	0.7358
0.015	1.5	0.4422	0.5578
0.020	2.0	0.5940	0.4060
0.030	3.0	0.8009	0.1991
0.040	4.0	0.9084	0.0916

5.6 The relation between batch size and sample size

Throughout our discussion of sample size and the number of defectives to be allowed, we have made no mention of the size of the batch. So long as the batch is large, it does not have any appreciable effect on the sample size to be drawn from it. A sample of a certain size gives us a certain amount of information, and we do not have to enquire whether it came from a batch of 50,000 or 100,000.

Batch size only becomes important when it is small enough for its constitution to be appreciably changed by drawing the sample from it. In our example in Section 4.9, we had a batch which contained exactly 20 per cent defectives and we, therefore, assumed that every time we drew a sample of one our chance of getting a defective was 0.2. To take an extreme case, suppose that our batch consisted of only five pieces, so that four were good and one was defective. Further, suppose that we draw samples one at a time:

For the 1st sample, the probability of a defective is 1 in 5 = 0.2

If the defective in the batch is not drawn then:

For the 2nd sample, the probability of a defective is 1 in 4 = 0.25

If the defective is still not drawn each time, then we get successively:

For the 3rd sample, the probability of a defective is 1 in 3 = 0.33
For the 4th sample, the probability of a defective is 1 in 2 = 0.5
For the 5th sample, the probability of a defective is 1 in 1 = 1.0

Obviously if a batch of five has only one defective, and if this defective is not among the first four drawn, it absolutely must be drawn fifth, because there is then only one piece left. Thus, notice that as the sampling proceeds, the probability that a defective will be drawn progressively increases (unless, of course, it has already been drawn, in which case the probability of a defective is zero). This means that for small batches there is less chance of missing defectives than with large batches. Thus, it is possible to make some reduction in the sample size when the batch is small, but the reduction is nothing like proportional to the reduction in batch size. Sampling inspection is thus more efficient when the batch is large, in the sense that a smaller percentage of the batch has to be inspected.

5.7 AQL sampling inspection tables

BSS 6001 provides a complete range of AQL sampling inspection tables. It is in the nature of a reference book, and in most cases will be too complicated to be given to the shop floor inspector. We shall, therefore, need to extract from it a suitable range of sampling plans for everyday use, and an example of how this can be done is given in the Appendix, Table 1. Unless the reader has some special requirements, it will probably suit his ordinary needs as it is.

The following points about Table 1 are of interest.

1   Any required AQL can be selected at will, and we shall consider the best way to do this in Chapter 6.

2   Provision is made for batch sizes up to over 500,000. In general, it is undesirable to sample larger batches than this, as a single batch. The economic consequences if a batch should be wrongly either accepted or rejected are usually too great and, unless the items in it are very small, it will probably be difficult to get the whole batch together at one time so that a representative sample can be taken. Further, it is very unlikely that such a large batch consists of a single production run. It is almost certainly a mixture of several production runs, and if it is practicable, these should be separated. Each production run can then be sampled as a batch in its own right.

3   We use Table 1 as follows. Suppose that we wish to inspect a batch of 1000 items, at an AQL of 1 per cent. The table tells us to take a representative sample of 80, and check it for the qualities which are important to our application. If we find up to and including two defectives in the sample we can accept the batch, and if we find three or more we must reject it.

4   Table 1 is arranged so that the steepness of the operating characteristics increases as the batch size increases. This reduces the risk of a wrong decision on a large batch, where such a mistake might be costly.

5.8   Double sampling plans

Although Table 1 will probably satisfy our immediate needs, BSS 6001 does nevertheless include a number of more advanced plans which we must explain. So far we have only discussed *single sampling plans.* This means that we always get a decision about our batch from a single sample. Thus, in our example in Section 5.7, we said that for a batch of 1000 items to be inspected at 1 per cent AQL we must take a sample of 80, and accept the batch if not more than 2 defectives were found.

In a *double sampling plan,* there are two sample sizes, and two allowed numbers of defectives. Thus, the following is an example of a double sampling plan:

First sample = 80   Accept number = 1   Reject number = 4
Second sample = 80   Accept number = 4   Reject number = 5

This means, take a sample of 80 and inspect them. If the number of defectives found does not exceed 1, accept the batch on the first sample. If the number of defectives is 4 or more, reject the batch on the first sample. If the number of defectives is more than 1, but less than 4, i.e. if it is 2 or 3, take a second sample of 80 and inspect. If the number of defectives from *both samples together* does not exceed 4, accept the batch. If it is 5 or more, reject it.

Double sampling plans have the advantage that when a batch is either very good or very bad it is accepted or rejected on the first sample, which is normally smaller than the corresponding sample for a single plan. If batches continually go to the second sample before a decision is reached there is little advantage. The saving in inspection has, in any case, to be offset against the disadvantages of a more complicated sampling plan.

5.9 Multiple sampling plans

The principle of double sampling can be extended to *multiple sampling plans*. Thus it is possible to have any desired number of stages, and the multiple plans given in BSS 6001 have seven, as the following example shows.

	Sample size	Cumulative sample size	Accept number	Reject number
1st sample	50	50	*	4
2nd sample	50	100	1	5
3rd sample	50	150	2	6
4th sample	50	200	3	7
5th sample	50	250	5	8
6th sample	50	300	7	9
7th sample	50	350	9	10

The above means:
1   Inspect a random sample of 50.
2   If 4 or more defectives are found, reject batch.
3   If there are less than 4 defectives, inspect another sample of 50. (* indicates that not enough pieces have yet been tested to be able to accept the batch, even if there are no defectives at all.)
4   If 5 or more defectives are found in both samples together, reject the batch.

5   If 0 or 1 are found, accept it.
6   If they are between 1 and 5, i.e. 2, 3 or 4, inspect a third sample of 50.
7   Repeat steps 3 to 6, using the accept and reject numbers given, as often as is necessary to reach a decision, each time count *all* the defectives found so far.
8   A decision must be reached by the 7th sample at the latest, because up to 9 defectives then accepts the batch, and 10 or more reject it.

5.10   Sequential sampling plans

If we continue to increase the number of stages in a multiple sampling plan, the sample size at each stage becomes progressively smaller, and ultimately reduces to a sample of one. This is then called a *sequential sampling plan*.

In practice we take items from the batch one at a time. We inspect each, and then before inspecting the next, we check to see whether we have got enough information to decide the fate of the batch. BSS 6001 offers a very simple method of doing this. With each plan it gives two numbers, which it calls the *handicap (H)* and the *penalty (b)*. After inspecting each item, we work out the *score,* given by:

Score = $(H +$ No. of acceptable items found$) -$
$(b \times$ No. of defective items found$)$

We accept the batch if the score reaches twice the handicap, and reject it if the score falls to zero or less.

Clearly it is possible for a very borderline batch to continue indefinitely without reaching a decision. A maximum sample size is therefore given with each plan, and if this is reached, the corresponding multiple plan is consulted to get a decision.

Sequential sampling plans have the advantage that they reach a decision after the inspection of a smaller total number of items than is possible with the other plans. They are therefore attractive where the cost of inspection is high, and especially if the item under test is destroyed. They are however much more complicated to use than the corresponding single or double sampling plans.

5.11   Average outgoing quality limit (AOQL)

This is a special technique which only applies if batches which are rejected by sampling inspection, are then submitted to 100 per cent inspection, to sort the acceptable items from the defectives. Thus batches which are passed to the next operation will consist of a mixture of:

1 Those which have been accepted, but which may never-the-less contain a small percentage of defectives, i.e. up to the AQL or a little more.
2 Batches which were rejected and submitted to 100 per cent inspection. Since all their defectives have been removed, they now return as 100 per cent good items.

Figures 5.5 and 5.6 illustrate how this routine will operate.

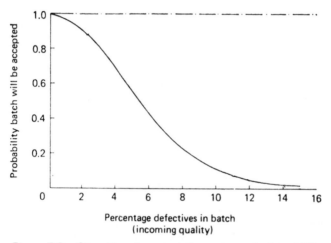

Figure 5.5 Operating characteristic used to calculate AOQ curve in Figure 5.6

1 If the incoming batches contain zero defectives, they will all be accepted, and the outgoing quality from sampling inspection will be 100 per cent good.
2 If the incoming batches all contain say 1.5 per cent of defectives, the operating characteristic tells us that 95 per cent of them will be accepted, and 5 per cent will be rejected and then submitted to 100 per cent inspection. Our *average outgoing quality* (AOQ) expressed as percentage defectives, will therefore be:

$$AOQ = \frac{(0.95 \times 1.5)}{(0.95) + (0.05 \times 0.985)} = 1.4\%$$

3 If we continue this calculation for other values of defectives in incoming batches, we get

Defectives in batch, %	AOQ %
1.5	1.4
2.5	2.2
4.0	2.8
5.0	2.8
7.5	2.0
10.0	1.3
15.0	0.4

Notice that at the start of the above table, the AOQ increases, as the percentage of defectives in incoming batches increases, but that after a while it reaches a peak, and then begins to fall again. This is because as the operating characteristic drops, an ever-increasing proportion of batches will be rejected, submitted to 100 per cent inspection, and so return as 100 per cent good. This peak percentage of defectives in outgoing batches is called the *Average Outgoing Quality Limit* or AOQL. Figure 5.6 shows that for our example, the AOQL has a value of approximately 2.9 per cent, and that it occurs for an incoming quality of approximately 4.7 per cent defectives.

Figure 5.6   Average outgoing quality limit

Notice that we are discussing the *average* outgoing quality limit. Odd batches containing more than the AOQL percentage of defectives will, if submitted, sometimes be accepted. All that the scheme says is that the average will not exceed this.

5.12   Acceptance sampling by variables

All the sampling plans which we have so far discussed are concerned with attributes, since even where a piece is actually measured in figures, we have only taken note of whether it passed or failed. It is however possible to do acceptance sampling using variables. To appreciate how it is done requires a little more quality control theory than we have so far discussed, and consideration of it has therefore been postponed until Section 13.19.

5.13 Questions

1a A consignment consisting of 3500 resistors, 1500 capacitors and 10,000 transistors has accidentally got thoroughly mixed. A sample of 2 is drawn at random. What are the probabilities of *each* of the following:

    (i)   both are resistors

    (ii)   one is a capacitor and one is a transistor

    (iii) both are transistors or both are capacitors

    (iv) neither is a resistor?   *(8 marks)*

1b A consignment is to be checked by taking a sample of 350 and accepting the whole provided that not more than 2 defectives are found. Draw the operating characteristic for this plan.   *(13 marks)*

1c Insert the following on the operating characteristic in (1b):

    Acceptable Quality Level (AQL)

    Lot Tolerance Percentage Defective (LTPD)

    Producer's risk

    Consumer's risk   *(4 marks)*

2a Sketch a typical operating characteristic for a single sampling plan.   *(5 marks)*

Mark the positions of the following:

    (i)   Acceptable Quality Level (AQL)

    (ii)   Lot Tolerance Percentage Defective (LTPD)

    (iii) Consumer's risk

    (iv) Producer's risk   *(8 marks)*

2b The following alternative sampling plans are being considered with a view to checking the quality of a large batch:

    Plan X   Sample size $= n = 100$ Acceptance number $= c = 2$

    Plan Y   Sample size $= n = 175$ Acceptance number $= c = 3$

For each plan calculate (using tables or otherwise):

    (i)   The producer's risk for an AQL $= 0.8\%$ *(4 marks)*

(ii) The consumer's risk for an LTPD = 4.0% *(4 marks)*

State, giving a reason for your answer, which of the two plans you would consider preferable if you were

    (iii) The producer
    (iv) The consumer *(4 marks)*

3a Using tables or otherwise, plot 2 operating characteristics on the same axis, one for *each* of the following sampling plans:

    Plan 1   Sample size $(n_1) = 10$ Allowed number defective (c_1) = 0

    Plan 2   Sample size $(n_2) = 110$ Allowed number defective (c_2) = 2

    (10 marks)

3b Mark the position of the Acceptable Quality Level (AQL) at a producer's risk of 0.10. Since both plans have almost the same value of AQL, what considerations might determine which would be used in a particular case? *(5 marks)*

3c Explain the inspection routine with which an Average Outgoing Quality Limit (AOQL) might be used, and hence explain the meaning of the term. Sketch a typical curve showing the relation between incoming quality and average outgoing quality, and mark the position of the AOQL. [The candidate is not expected to relate this curve to the values given in parts *(a)* and *(b)* of the question.] *(10 marks)*

CHAPTER 6

SETTING UP FOR THE INSPECTION OF MATERIEL

6.1 Specifications for materiel

When we buy a batch of materiel or components we naturally hope that the quality will be exactly what we require, and this presupposes that the supplier knows exactly what we want, and is able and willing to supply it. Clearly, however, our supplier will not know what we want unless we have told him, and this is where our buying specification is important. It does not need to be complicated, but it must specify precisely what we need, and this means that we must set out the various individual qualities, in terms of variables and attributes, as we discussed in Sections 3.3-3.9. Thus, our specification must give tolerance limits for all variables and, if there is any doubt, it must also give the method of measurement. Similarly, all attributes must be clearly set and agreed, so that the supplier knows in practical terms what we want.

Nowadays there are many universally agreed quality standards, prominent among which are those of the British Standards Institution. In some cases, these standards are internationally recognised. Where such standards are appropriate, it will invariably pay to use them since:

1   We shall avoid the expense of drawing up our own specification.
2   An appropriate manufacturer will regard our order as 'standard' rather than 'special', and the price he charges us should reflect this.

6.2 Selecting the most suitable AQL for a particular application

The best AQL in any particular case will be the one that incurs the lowest overall cost, when everything has been taken into consideration. In practice, however, we never know exactly what all the relevant costs are, and so we have to compromise between what is theoretically correct and what is practically possible. Thus, we shall now consider a method of choosing an AQL which has been developed by the author and which has been found to work well in practice. It is not absolutely exact, and any attempt to make it so would certainly render it impracticable, possibly still without achieving ultimate precision. However, the reader can easily alter it to suit his own particular needs.

We must explain the method in detail although in practice a suitable AQL can be chosen by consulting Table 2 (see Appendix). There are three main costs involved in the selection of an AQL for checking a particular batch of materiel:

1   The cost of doing an acceptance inspection.
2   The cost, or value, of the batch to be inspected.
3   The cost incurred if any unsatisfactory items in the batch get fed through to our production lines.

6.3 Estimating the cost of incoming inspection itself

Once we have decided what checks have to be applied to each piece, there is usually no difficulty in estimating how long these checks will take. Thus, each item checked might take one minute of the inspector's time, and our Accounts Department would tell us what this minute would cost, including overheads. Hence we can easily find the cost of checking one piece in the batch and, if the test is destructive, we must add to this the cost or value of the materiel destroyed. Suppose, for example, that it costs 6p to check each piece in the batch, and that the materiel concerned arrives in batches of 200 pieces. If we consult Table 1 of the Appendix we can read off the sample size for every value of the AQL for a batch size of 200. Now the cost of inspecting the whole sample will be equal to the cost of inspecting one piece multiplied by the number of pieces in the sample. Thus, in our example, for an AQL of say 1 per cent, the cost of inspecting the sample for one batch would be the sample size of 50, multiplied by the cost of inspecting one piece (6p), making 300p in all. This is shown plotted in Figure 6.1, where it is marked 'Inspection cost'.

6.4 The value of the materiel to be inspected

If we keep a batch which contains a proportion of defective pieces then we usually have to pay for them, whereas if we return the whole batch to the supplier as unsatisfactory, we do not. Hence, the actual purchase value of each piece in the batch must, in principle anyway, be considered when deciding which AQL to choose. If the cost of a piece is low, as is often the case, its value may not be sufficient to affect our final choice.

6.5 Reducing the cost of production scrap and rework resulting from the use of defective materiel

As explained in Section 4.11, when we use samples to inspect batches we accept the fact that, if defective pieces are present, some will get through in the batches which are good enough, as a whole, to pass inspection. These defective pieces will thus be fed to our production lines. How much trouble they will cause will depend partly on how far they can get before they are detected. There are three broad possibilities:

1   The defective pieces may be such that they are quite unusable, and so are bound to be thrown out by the operator. For example, washers which have no central hole are quite unusable and so we do not have to

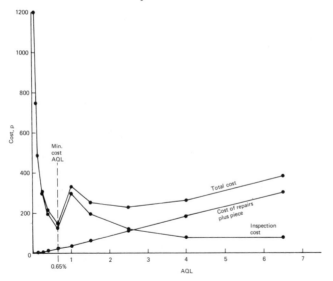

Figure 6.1   Graph showing derivation of the AQL that will achieve minimum overall cost for the example in the text.

worry about the consequences of them being used. No production effort of our own will be lost, and the nuisance value will in most cases be small.

2　The defective pieces may be usable, but the fault such that it is pretty sure to be discovered during subsequent test or inspection before the product leaves our factory. Thus, when a faulty piece is discovered it will be necessary to correct the fault or, if this is not possible, to scrap the whole piece or assembly. In a simple case, it may involve no more than removing a component from an assembly and replacing it with a good one, but in a more serious instance, it may be necessary to scrap not only the defective piece itself but also a lot of good work which we have done on it.

3　The worst case of all is when the fault is such that the piece is not only likely to be used, but its fault is unlikely to be discovered by any of the tests which we apply before the finished product leaves the factory. Thus, any faulty pieces which get fed to our production line are likely to be used, and the finished product containing them sold to our customers. Sooner or later they will fail, and we shall have a dissatisfied customer on our hands.

Fortunately, it is often possible to reduce the damage caused by defective pieces by suitable planning of the method of production. For example, suppose that we make a fairly intricate sub-assembly which we sell to a customer, who incorporates it in a large piece of equipment. Further suppose that it is important that the base of our sub-assembly does not exceed a certain size, because if it does it will not fit into the customer's equipment. Thus, if a sub-assembly is put together with an oversized base, it will have to be completely dismantled and rebuilt with a correct base. If the sub-assembly has already been sent to the customer, we shall incur the customer's displeasure as well. At first sight, we might think that it would be necessary to do very strict 100 per cent inspection on bases when they arrive from the supplier. Clearly, we must at all costs prevent them from being used on our sub-assembly production line. In fact, however, this strict and costly 100 per cent inspection is unlikely to be necessary. If we provide the sub-assembly operator with a jig which is so designed that it will *not accept* an oversized base, then we can be quite sure that, whatever size our supplier sends us, no oversized base can ever be used by that operator. In this way we can save ourselves the cost of 100 per cent inspection, and be certain that we have protected our own production line at the same time. It is well worth spending a little time to consider what can be done to ensure that any defective pieces which happen to get into our production line are thrown out again, at the earliest possible moment.

6.6 Estimating the cost of scrap and rework incurred through feeding defective materiels into our own production lines

It is usually not too difficult to estimate the cost incurred if one defective piece is fed into our production lines. We merely find out how far it is likely to get before its faults are discovered, and then estimate how much it will cost to correct the damage it has done. Thus, we estimate how long it will take to get the defective piece out of whatever product we are making, and replace it with a good piece. To this we must add the cost of any work or other materiels which are also lost. We may have done a lot of good work on the faulty piece, or the faulty piece may be inseparably attached, e.g. welded, to one or more good components, all of which must be scrapped with the faulty piece. When we convert the repair time to money, we must allow for any overhead expenses attached to the operator who does the repairs.

We can thus estimate the cost involved if one faulty piece is fed into our production lines. Next, we need to know how many such faulty pieces will in fact be fed in, in order to calculate the total repair cost involved. This is more difficult, because it depends not only on the value of the AQL that we choose for our incoming sampling inspection, but also on what proportion of defective pieces the batches of materiel contain when they arrive from our supplier. Obviously, if our supplier never sent us any defective pieces, it would not matter at what AQL we inspected, nor indeed whether we did any incoming inspection at all. We should never get any defectives fed through to our production lines. However, in practice, we never know in advance what percentage of defectives our incoming batches of materiel are going to contain. Indeed, if we did, we should not need to do incoming inspection to find out! Of course, if the materiel is one which we have inspected before, we can get some idea of what to expect by consulting the inspection records. Very often, however, there is nothing to tell us what to expect, and a long investigation would not be justified.

Perhaps the easiest approach is to assume a suitable average level of defectives which batches passing incoming inspection are likely to contain. We do not have to worry about batches which fail incoming inspection, because they will not be fed into our production lines. Thus, all the very bad batches will be kept out and those which get through will be either of good quality or, if borderline, good enough to have passed inspection. The lower we set out AQL the more batches we shall keep out and the higher we set it the more we shall let through. Therefore, if we assume that our supplier will send us all sorts of batches, from very good to very bad, then the average percentage of defectives in batches which pass inspection will be related to the value of AQL at which we inspect. If our suppliers are, in general, good, then the average level of defectives in batches which pass inspection will be much lower than the value of AQL at which we are inspecting. For example, if we were to inspect at 1 per cent AQL, on batches which were, in general, very good, we might find that the average level of defectives in batches which passed is only, say, 0.1 per cent.

So far we have considered the materiel, labour and overhead cost incurred when a defective piece is fed into our production lines, but we have said nothing about its nuisance value, although this may be quite appreciable. When a faulty piece is discovered there will be production delays while it is rectified. This, in turn, may lead to late deliveries and so to customer irritation. We may have to set a machine up a second time to make replacements for work we have had to scrap and, if this happens often, factory morale will suffer. All in all, therefore, the true cost of allowing defective materiel to get into our production lines is likely to be appreciably more than the direct replacement cost. We can make some allowance for this by assuming, when we set an AQL, that the average percentage of defectives in batches which have passed incoming inspection is greater than it really is. Thus, in calculating Table 2 of the Appendix it has been assumed that the average percentage of defectives in batches which have passed inspection is equal to the value of AQL used.

We, therefore, assume that every time a defective piece is used in our production the cost incurred is equal to the cost of repairs plus the cost of the piece itself, and that the proportion of such pieces getting into our production lines is equal to the AQL at which we carry out our inspection of incoming materiel. Suppose in the example which we started in Section 6.3 that each piece in the batch costs 10p and that repairs when a defective piece is used cost 15p. Thus, every time we buy and use a defective piece, it costs us 25p. Now the batch size is 200, and we propose that if the AQL is 1 per cent to assume that 1 per cent of the pieces in batches which pass incoming inspection will be defective. However, in order to pass a batch, the inspector must check the prescribed sample and in the process remove any defective pieces in it. For an AQL of 1 per cent, the sample size is 50. Hence, after incoming inspection, only $200 - 50 = 150$ of the batch would contain the assumed 1 per cent defectives.

Therefore, the average loss incurred per batch through using the defectives we have assumed in batches which pass inspection at 1 per cent AQL is

$$(1.00/100) \times 150 \times 25 = 37.5p$$

As the cost is directly proportional to the AQL used, apart from the correction for the sample size inspected, the curve shown in Section 6.3 for 'Cost of repair plus piece' is nearly a straight line.

6.7 Calculating the minimum overall cost

In Figure 6·1 we have now only to add the ordinates of the two lower curves together, in order to obtain the total cost of incoming inspection, the piece itself and subsequent repairs per batch. In our example, the minimum cost occurs at an AQL of 0·65 per cent, and so this will be the best AQL in this particular case.

We can work out this same example in figures as follows:

Number of pieces in batch	= N	= 200
Cost of inspecting one piece	= i	= 6p
Cost of one piece	= a	= 10p
Cost of repairs and retest if 1 defective piece is		
is used for production	= r	= 15p
Therefore, cost of repairs plus piece	= r + a	= 25p

A Available AQLs, %	B Sample size (n)	C Cost of inspection	D Number not inspected	E Cost of repairs, etc.	F Total cost = (C + E)
All	200	1200	0	0	1200
0·065	200	1200	0	0	1200
0·10	125	750	75	1·9	751·9
0·15	80	480	120	4·5	484·5
0·25	50	300	150	9·4	309·4
0·40	32	192	168	16·8	208·8
0·65	20	120	180	29·2	149·2*
1·00	50	300	150	37·5	337·5
1.5	32	192	168	63·0	255·0
2·5	20	120	180	112·5	232·5
4·0	13	78	187	187·0	265·0
6·5	13	78	187	303·9	381·9

The derivation of each of the above columns is as follows:

A   *Available AQLs*   Set out all the AQLs given in the top row of Table 1. Start with 'All', because in some cases 100 per cent inspection will work out cheapest.

B   *Sample size*   From Table 1, copy the sample size corresponding to each AQL for the batch size concerned.

C   *Cost of inspection*   Multiply each sample size in column B by the cost of inspecting one piece.

D   *Number not inspected*   Subtract each sample size from the batch size.

E   *Cost of repairs, etc.*   For each line work out

(Column A/100) x (Column D) x $(r + a)$

F   *Total cost*   Add column C to column E.

For this particular example, the minimum cost occurs in column E at 0·65 per cent, and is marked with an asterisk.

6.8   Table 2 for choosing the most economic AQL

As we probably buy a considerable variety of materiel, we shall in principle need a large number of calculations to find the best AQL in each case. To avoid the work which this would involve, Table 2 has been prepared, and this does all the calculation for us.

Thus, in practice, only the following steps are required, in order to choose a suitable AQL:

1   We decide how each piece in the batch is to be inspected, and what for our purpose is to be considered an acceptable piece, and what unacceptable. (See Section 7.3 for further details.)

2   We estimate, as accurately as is reasonably practicable, how much it costs to inspect one piece in the batch (= i). Often, this consists only of the inspector's time plus overheads, but there may also be some materiel used. If the test is destructive, we must include the cost of the piece itself. There may also be an allowance per piece for setting up the test equipment, etc.

3   We estimate what it costs if a faulty piece passes through incoming inspection and is fed into our production lines (= r). We add the cost of one piece (a) to the cost of repair (r), to allow for the money wasted in buying a faulty piece.

4   We divide the cost of repair plus the piece itself, as calculated in (3) above, by the cost of inspecting one piece, as (2) above

$(r + a)/i$

5   We use the ratio so obtained, together with the batch size, to consult Table 2. This gives us the best AQL without further calculation.
a   If our batch sizes vary it is safest, though not necessarily cheapest, to take roughly the largest batch size which normally occurs.
b   'All' in Table 2 indicates that 100 per cent inspection should be employed. Where 100 per cent inspection is called for this should not be regarded as a 'failure of sampling inspection' but rather as a special case in which the best sample size equals the batch size.

If inspection is fairly cheap, and the cost incurred if one single defective piece gets into our production lines is large, then it may well be cheapest to inspect every piece, in order not to risk one defective getting through.

6 The AQL which we have calculated will be the most economic from our point of view. If we set our AQL higher than this then our overall costs will rise, due to increased troubles on our production lines; if we set it lower than this, our overall costs will rise, due to increased incoming inspection costs. It does not necessarily follow, however, that the AQL so chosen also represents the percentage of defectives which we expect to find in a batch of that type of materiel.

a Table 2 may quote an AQL of say 2.5 per cent, but this does not necessarily mean that we expect to find 2.5 per cent of defectives in batches which we receive, but merely that it will not pay us to inspect more closely. If for any reason, for example nuisance value or because it will have a bad effect on morale, an AQL of 2.5 per cent is quite unacceptable, then we must substitute a lower value.

b At the other extreme, Table 2 may quote an AQL of 0.065 per cent. Now if batches are regularly to contain less than 0.065 per cent defectives, they have got to be more or less perfect all the time. For any particular job, it may not be reasonable to expect the manufacturer to make perfect batches all the time, even if that AQL is the most economic from an inspection-cum-repair point of view. If this is the case, we must increase our AQL from the most economic value up to the minimum value at which our manufacturer can reasonably be expected to work.

c Sometimes the requirements of (a) and (b) above will clash. The lowest AQL which our manufacturer will accept is higher than the maximum which our production lines can accept. This means that that manufacturer cannot supply materiel which is good enough for our type of production. Either we must modify our production methods so that we can accept lower standards, or we must find a manufacturer who can supply better materiel. In the meantime, assuming that production must go on, we must either accept the available quality, or every batch which fails incoming inspection at the AQL we have chosen must be subjected to 100 per cent inspection, so as to ensure that regardless of the quality which we are sent only satisfactory batches are passed on to production.

CHAPTER 7

A PRACTICAL ROUTINE FOR THE INSPECTION OF INCOMING MATERIEL

7.1 The importance of a simple, but well defined, incoming inspection routine

Chapters 4, 5 and 6 have been devoted to deciding the best sampling plan for a particular application. Thus, we can now select the best sample size, and state how many defective pieces should be allowed in that sample before the whole batch is rejected. Setting the sampling plan is only half the problem, however. It is just as important to have an efficient practical routine for the inspection of incoming materiel. In particular, we must ensure that the checks which are applied to each type of materiel are appropriate, bearing in mind the use that our production lines are going to make of it. We must also see that simple records are kept, so that suppliers who consistently send unsatisfactory materiel can be discontinued.

7.2 The incoming inspection record card

A typical incoming inspection record card is shown in Figure 7.1. One of these is used for each type of materiel, i.e. for each part number, and where one materiel is supplied by more than one supplier it is usually best to have separate cards for each supplier as well.

1   At the top of the card, there is space for the part number, the name of the part and the name of the supplier.

Part no. or code no.	INCOMING INSPECTION RECORD	Cost
B 7461/1		55p.

Name of part	Supplier
RETAINING ROD	SUPER ROD CO.

Sampling scheme A.Q.L. = 0.65%	Division ENGINE

Test specification	Fault code
CHECK WITH RULE THAT OVERALL LENGTH = 40 ± 1 mm	A
" " MICROMETER, LARGE DIAMETER = 12.5 ± 0.08 mm	B
" " " , SMALL " = 6.50 ± 0.05 mm	C

Date	G.R.N. no. or works O.N.	No. in batch	No. insp.	No. faulty	% faulty	A	B	C	D	E	F	G	H	Misc.	Pass	Fail	Insp's initials	Return to supplier	100% insp.	Rectify	Senior insp's initials
9 Sep	1241	500	80	1	1.2	1	-	-							✓		Jω				
17 "	1296	950	80	0	0	-	-	-							✓		LA				
30 "	1352	2,100	125	0	0	-	-	-							✓		LA				
2 Oct	1401	700	80	4	5	4	-	-								x	Jω	✓			RGC
15 "	1488	2,500	125	0	0	-	-	-							✓		Jω				
21 "	1564	2,500	125	1	0.8	1	-	-							✓		PSJ				
1 Nov	1621	1,500	125	3	2.4	3	-	-								x	PSJ	✓			RGC
9 "	1653	1,700	20	20	100	-	20	-			WRONG TYPE SENT					x	Jω	✓			RGC
17 "	1767	5,000	200	0	0	-	-	-							✓		LA				
23 "	1791	5,000	200	0	0	-	-	-							✓		LA				
4 Dec	1854	5,000	200	3	1.5	3	-	-							✓		Jω				
20 "	1923	3,500	200	0	0	-	-	-							✓		LA				
1 Jan	1969	2,500	125	0	0	-	-	-							✓		LA				
14 "	2043	2,500	125	4	3.2	4	-	-								x	PSJ	✓			RGC
4 Feb	2112	2,000	125	3	2.4	3										x	Jω		✓		RGC

Figure 7.1   Example of an incoming inspection record card

2   In the top right-hand corner, we put the price that we have to pay
for one piece. It is useful, when we are deciding what action to take
about doubtful materiel, to know the amount of money with which
we are dealing.

3   Below the name of the part, we put the AQL at which inspection is
to be carried out. We shall have chosen this as discussed in Section 6.8.

4   Next comes the test specification. It is important that the checks to
be applied should be listed by someone who is familiar with the use
which will be made of the materiel in question. Otherwise it will be
inevitable that our incoming inspectors will sometimes waste time
checking things which do not matter, and at other times omit to check
something which is vitally important. In addition to the checks themselves, the inspector should also be told the method of measurement
and, where gauges are to be used, he should be told the gauge number.
For electrical tests, appropriate information about meter ranges and
consumption should be included.

We give each check a fault code, and these consist of successive
letters of the alphabet (A, B, C, etc.). This will enable us to identify the
various checks in the fault analysis, further down the incoming inspection record card.

5   The lower half of the card and the back are used for a simple record
of the results on successive batches. The column headed 'GRN or Works
Order No.', is used to identify the batch. Thus, we can use the number
of the goods received note (GRN), if there is one, or we can use our own
works order number, or we can supply a batch number.

In addition to showing the number of pieces inspected and the
number faulty or defective, the card also indicates the type of fault.
Thus, an entry of 2 under fault A would indicate that 2 pieces failed on
check A of the test specification. This information is valuable if we have
trouble with the quality of a materiel. We can then look to see what its
most common faults are.

7.3   Setting up the incoming inspection routine

Before we can operate the incoming inspection routine, given in the
next section, it must be set up by a responsible person who is familiar
with the requirements of our production lines. For example, this person
might be a production engineer or a senior inspector. The steps are as
follows:

1   He prepares a separate incoming inspection record card for every different materiel which we buy. Where we buy one materiel from more than one supplier, he prepares a separate card for each supplier. It helps to colour the top left-hand corner of such cards, say red, to indicate to the incoming materiel inspector that there is more than one supplier, and so reduce the risk that he will enter his results on the wrong card.

2   He decides how each piece is to be inspected, and what is to be considered an acceptable piece, and what unacceptable. This is where his knowledge of the job is so valuable. Usually, not all qualities are equally important, and he must decide which are sufficiently significant to justify the cost of checking them. Since incoming inspection is not a creative operation in its own right, its value will depend upon the extent to which it keeps out defective pieces which would result in costly production repairs. He must consider each check individually and ask himself, 'Will the cost of applying this check be less than the subsequent cost of production repairs if we do not apply it?' Unless the answer is yes, he should omit the check. In particular, he must examine complicated and expensive tests very carefully before he includes them.

3   He must make sure that the inspector will know what quality standard is required, in clear practical terms. All variables must have tolerances, and attributes must have visual or other quality standards, as appropriate. Unless this is done, we may well find that one inspector will accept what another will reject. Further information is given in Sections 3.7 and 3.8. Where the quality standard, or a specification, has been agreed with the supplier this agreement must obviously be the basis for incoming materiels inspection.

4   He next uses Table 2 to choose a suitable AQL, and he enters this on the card in the box provided, immediately underneath the name of the part. It is possible to have two AQLs for checking the same piece. Thus, a very important quality, which would cause a lot of trouble if it went wrong, might be inspected at a very low AQL such as 0.065 per cent, while several ordinary qualities might be checked at a higher AQL such as 1.0 per cent. He must consider the complication of having two AQLs, and decide whether it is worth the saving in inspection achieved. He must remember that the inspector is bound to take the larger sample from the batch and, having done so, the choice is merely between checking the whole sample for all the qualities involved or remembering that after the smaller sample has been checked certain tests can be omitted. Often the complication of two AQLs is not justified by the small saving in inspection achieved.

71

7.4 Operating the incoming inspection routine

The following is a suggestion for the routine to be operated by the incoming materiel inspector, but we can adapt it to take account of our own particular needs.

1   When a batch of materiel arrives from the supplier, the inspector takes from the file the incoming inspection record card corresponding to that part number and that supplier.

2   The card tells him the AQL at which he is to check, and he consults Table 1 to convert this into the sample size, and the number of defectives allowed.

3   He takes the prescribed sample, and carries out the prescribed checks.

4   He enters the results of his checks on the next line of the card.

5   If the batch passes inspection, it goes on to the materiel stores, and the card goes back into the file.

6   If the batch fails inspection, both it and the incoming inspection record card are put aside for the attention of the senior inspector.

7   Periodically, say once per day, the senior inspector examines the batches that have failed inspection. He first satisfies himself that the checks have been correctly carried out. (In the example card shown in Figure 7.1 we can see that every time 'L.A.' gets a batch no defectives are found in the sample. Now we know that some batches do contain defectives because J.W. and P.S.T. find them from time to time, and their results are being accepted by the senior inspector. Therefore, it is clear that inspector L.A. needs further help and instruction, etc., in the way checks are to be carried out.)

8   Next the senior inspector must decide the fate of the batch and, in making this decision, he may need to consult his colleagues, for instance the production engineer, progress controller, foreman, etc. Ideally, if a batch fails inspection, it should be returned to the supplier complete. There are two reasons for this:

a   It puts pressure on the supplier to improve his quality.

b   It helps the supplier to understand what has gone worng, and so improve his own quality control.

Sometimes, however, the pressure of industrial life makes it very difficult to return a batch. If our own production lines are desperately in need of the materiel in question, it may be very unwise to send back the whole batch, good as well as bad, to the supplier. In such cases, the senior inspector may decide on one of the following courses of action:

a   To carry out 100 per cent inspection, in order to sort the good pieces in the batch from the bad ones. The good pieces can then be used for production, and only the bad pieces returned to the supplier.

b   In some cases, the shortcomings of the defective pieces may be such that it is a practical proposition to rectify them, so that the whole batch can be used for production.

Whether the senior inspector decides to return an unsatisfactory batch or not, it is important that a suitable letter of complaint should be sent to the supplier concerned giving full details of the faults found.

7.5   Making full use of the information collected

After the routine described in Sections 7.1 to 7.4 has been in operation for some time, a lot of useful information will have been collected on the incoming inspection record cards. We should make full use of this as follows:

1   We can work out the average percentage of defectives that each supplier sends us, and we can see whether over a period he gets better or worse. An improvement might indicate that our in incoming inspection is having a good effect on him. A marked deterioration would obviously have to be investigated.

2   We can compare the types of fault sent us by each supplier. Where two suppliers send the same materiel it often happens that, although they both send roughly the same percentage of defectives, they each have their own 'favourite' faults.

7.6   Vendor rating

So far, we have assumed that each of our suppliers will continue to send us batches which contain a proportion of defective pieces and that, overall, we shall be justified in assuming that the average percentage of defective pieces, in batches which pass incoming inspection, will be equal to the AQL. This is not necessarily true. Our purchasing department will no doubt do their best to buy materiels from consistently reliable suppliers. Where they succeed, we may well find that such materiel is almost always good and seldom contains any defective pieces at all. In such cases, it may well be a waste of time and money to carry out full incoming inspection as we have discussed, and vendor rating may be useful.

Vendor rating, also called supplier grading, takes many forms. In principle, we match the amount of incoming inspection which we do to our supplier's performance. This must be done to suit our own particular requirements, but the following is a guide.

BSS 6001, discussed in Section 5.4 provides for:

a Normal inspection.

b Tightened inspection.

c Reduced inspection.

We put all our suppliers into one of these grades, for each materiel they supply. The suggested routine is as follows:

1 Each supplier/materiel begins on normal inspection. If, at any time, 2 out of 5 successive batches are rejected, that supplier is demoted to tightened inspection. Then when 5 successive acceptable batches have been received, he can be returned to normal inspection. If after 10 successive batches he is still on tightened inspection, we suspend inspection and investigate.

2 Where quality is usually satisfactory, and we only need a warning if it suddenly deteriorates, we can use reduced inspection. In BSS 6001 there is a gap between the accept number c and the reject number d in the reduced inspection tables. This is to be interpreted as follows.

No. of defectives found	Action
Less than or equal to c	Accept and continue on reduced inspection.
Between c and d	Accept but revert to normal inspection.
d or more	Reject and revert to normal inspection.

So far promotion and relegation has been based entirely on quality. Many companies, however, add additional weightings to take account of price and delivery as well. A typical method is as follows.

Starting with a maximum rating of 100 points, we divide these between quality, price and delivery, according to the importance which we attach to each. For example:

Maximum points awarded for quality	= 40
Maximum points awarded for price	= 35
Maximum points awarded for delivery	= 25
Total maximum	100

Suppose now that we have to assess the following supplier:

(a)   90 per cent of his batches are accepted on sampling inspection.
(b)   His price is £70 per batch, although the cheapest we could buy elsewhere is £60 per batch.
(c)   80 per cent of his deliveries are on time.

We calculate like this:

Quality rating $= 40 \times \dfrac{90}{100}$ $= 36$

Price rating $= 35 \times \dfrac{60}{70}$ $= 30$

Delivery rating $= 25 \times \dfrac{80}{100}$ $= 20$

Overall rating for that supplier and that materiel $=$ 86 out of 100

Purchasers frequently visit the manufacturing premises of a new supplier, before placing an order with him. Their object is to check whether the supplier's quality control system is likely to be able to ensure that the required quality is consistently achieved. If it is, then it may be possible to reduce or even dispense with incoming materiel inspection, and replace it with an occasional sample check, just to confirm that all is going well. This latter is usually called a *quality audit*.

7.7   Taking samples from a batch

Every sample which we take must be representative of the batch, because we are going to judge the quality of the batch by the quality of the sample. To get a representative sample, we usually try to take it at random. Now, in principle, a random sample is one in which every piece in the batch has an equal chance of being selected for the sample. Pieces at the bottom of the batch have just as much chance of being chosen as those on the top. It is possible to achieve this in practice. For example, we could number each piece in the batch and then, using random numbers, could decide, in a truly random and unbiased way, which pieces were to be chosen for the sample. Clearly, however, this would take impossibly long to do for every batch of materiel which we received. We must, therefore, modify what is theoretically desirable to what is reasonable and practical. Some care and experience are necessary in doing this, and the following points will help:

1   Never take the whole sample from one part of the batch.

2   Make sure that the sample does not come entirely from the top layers of the batch. The bottom must be represented as well as the top, and one side as much as the other.

3   If a consignment consists of more than one package, then from each package we take a sample which is roughly proportional to its size. It helps to keep the sub-sample from each package separate. We never know whether a consignment received from an outside supplier is really all one production run or whether it is a mixture of two or more. If we find that of five sub-samples taken two are good and three are bad, we have an immediate indication that we have a consignment consisting of two manufacturing runs. If this is confirmed by further inspection, then only the three bad packages need to be rejected. However, the sub-sample is unlikely to be large enough to reject a package without further inspection. To make a decision on a single package, we must treat it as a batch in its own right and take the full prescribed sample from it.

4   From the above, it follows that we should never mix two small consignments together to make one large one for economy in sampling, unless we know that both consignments are from the same production run.

5   We must beware of sampling bias if we have a batch in which some pieces are obviously defective. For example, suppose that finish is important, and we receive a batch in which some pieces are obviously blemished. It will be very difficult to sample this fairly. Every time a piece is drawn, there is inevitably a decision to be made: 'Shall I take a good or a bad one?' It may help not to look at the moment of taking such a sample.

6   Where something is known about the past history of the batch, a stratified sample may be useful. For example, if we know that the machine making the batch went wrong sometime during the run, we shall expect the box containing that batch to be bad at the top, and good at the bottom. If we can find the point of changeover, then we can separate the bad from the good without doing 100 per cent inspection. Thus, to get a stratified sample, we break the batch into sections, each of which is as homogeneous as possible within itself, although each differs in quality from the other sections. We then sample each section in proportion to its size. Depending on our results, we may keep the

batch permanently in sections, if they differ sufficiently from each other, or we may reunite them. A stratified sample tends to be more representative of the whole batch than a truly random sample.

7.8 Questions

1   Explain what is involved in organising a system of goods inwards inspection, and indicate the advantages that would be expected to result from it. *(25 marks)*

2a   Outline the contribution to quality which can be made by a purchasing department. *(6 marks)*

2b   List the main points which should be borne in mind in preparing a specification for the purchase of incoming raw materiels and/or components. *(11 marks)*

2c   What is meant by vendor rating? *(8 marks)*

3   *(In the following question, candidates were permitted to make any necessary assumptions, provided they were clearly stated.)*

(a)   A manufacturing company buys considerable quantities of a particular resistor from one supplier. Inwards goods inspection records over a period show that 95 per cent of consignments were acceptable, the remainder being returned complete to the supplier. Of his deliveries 80 per cent arrived on time and the rest were late. The price paid was £25 per batch of 250, although they could have been bought elsewhere for as little as £20 per batch. Suggest a suitable vendor rating scheme for this product, and hence work out a rating for this vendor. *(12 marks)*

(b)   When the resistors are received, inspection costs 3p per resistor, but if a defective resistor is used in the factory, its subsequent removal and replacement by a good resistor costs 35p. The inspection tables used by the company require the following number to be inspected for each Acceptable Quality Level (AQL) for a batch size of 250:

AQL, %	0.065	0.10	0.15	0.25	0.40	0.65	1.0	1.5	2.5
Sample size	200	125	80	50	32	20	50	31	20

Use economic considerations to deduce a suitable AQL. *(13 marks)*

CHAPTER 8

METHODS, EQUIPMENT
AND INSPECTION

8.1 Defining the method

We must now set the method by which the job is to be done, and decide the plant and equipment which will be required. If all of our production can be correctly made using satisfactory materiel, then clearly the whole of it will be good. Conversely, it must follow that, if some or all of our production is unsatisfactory, then either the materiel or the method and equipment or the way in which it is used are incorrect in some way. If, as is usually the case, some production is good and some bad, there must be a variation in one of these and we must ask ourselves, 'If we can make some of our production good, why cannot we make it all good?'

Part of the answer lies in having a consistent method for each article we make. If we leave each operator to decide his own method, we are bound to get variations in quality from one to another. Therefore, we must decide upon the correct method, and see that every operator knows what it is and adheres to it.

8.2 Assistance from method study

Method study aims to achieve the required quality and quantity in the easiest, cheapest and quickest way. Thus, at the start of a project, the methods engineer must find out precisely what quality standard his method is required to produce. He must then devise his method to achieve that quality, as well as the required quantity, in the easiest possible way. It must be such that it is as easy as possible for the operator to do the job correctly, and as difficult as possible for him to do it incorrectly. The ideal method from the quality point of view is one that cannot be done incorrectly.

One trap that the methods engineer must avoid is that of assuming that method study consists only of reducing the amount of work in an operation. This is important, of course, but if he ignores the quality requirements then the final method is unlikely to be satisfactory. He may end up with what he thinks is a very good method, e.g. 'I have cut the work by 50 per cent', only to find that he has, at the same time, cut out one or more movements which are vital if the required quality is to be achieved. Hence, although the rate of production goes up, the scrap rate goes up with it.

It is advantageous for both the methods engineer and the quality engineer to be consulted at the design stage. The restrictions each must face, and the contribution each can make, can then be economically integrated together. The methods engineer may be able to point out that a particular quality standard would be very difficult and expensive to achieve and, therefore, propose a cheaper method producing a slightly lower quality standard. Similarly, the quality engineer may be able to make suggestions to ensure that the required quality standard is achieved as easily as possible by all concerned. Meanwhile, the designer can look after the customer's point of view, and contribute design suggestions.

8.3   Examples of how good methods can improve quality

A good example of a method which improves quality is to be found in the home. When we decide to put on the portable electric fire, we have a little assembly job to do. There are three wires on the fire, line, neutral and earth, and these must be correctly connected to the line, neutral and earth wires of the electricity supply. Failure to assemble correctly may not only result in the fire not working, but is also liable to be dangerous. Therefore, the assembly must be done correctly and, if we did not know otherwise, we might conclude that such an operation would always require at least 100 per cent inspection. In fact, however, this is not necessary because the wires of the fire are connected to a three-pin plug, and those of the supply to a corresponding socket, and the plug and socket will only go together one way – the correct way. No inspection is necessary.

In the radial drill section of a machine shop, rejects were incurred because the operators sometimes confused drills of similar size, and so drilled a wrong-sized hole. The solution to this problem was not to dress down the operators, who were doing their best already, but to provide a very simple drill holder. Each time a job was set up the correct drills were put into the holder in the right order. The operator had only to take the drills in the sequence offered to avoid mistakes. Provision was also made at the same time to tell operators whether holes were the correct depth. The result was that errors in hole size and depth reduced considerably.

There is a wide scope for simple jigs and fixtures which will assist the operator to do the job correctly, and so make it less likely that he will do it incorrectly. Such jigs and fixtures are not confined to production lines. They can often be used to improve methods of inspection. Method study is indeed a most valuable ally of quality control.

8.4 Quality control can assist methods

We have talked about the ways in which method study can assist quality, but equally quality control can assist methods. Any quality control investigation will draw attention to the places where methods could be improved, as well as to those where quality requires attention.

Any working quality system tends to accumulate a lot of useful information. Quality control charts, inspection records, etc., will show where difficulties in production have been experienced, and what types of scrap and rework have been made as a result. Often, a change in method is the best way to improve the situation. Thus, the Pareto curve which we shall consider in Section 16.7 may well be the starting point of a method study project, as much as one in quality control.

8.5 Making the method self-proving

In the same way that we try to plan each individual operation, so that it cannot be done incorrectly, we can often link operations together so that they check each other. An example of this occurred on an assembly which had two fuses of different electrical values. They were of the same mechanical design, however, so each fuse would fit perfectly into the position intended for the other. Originally, one operator put in both fuses and from time to time became confused, so that she either put in two fuses of the same value, instead of one of each, or she put one of each but the wrong way round. A good permanent solution to this problem would be to modify the design of one fuse holder, so that the fuses were no longer interchangeable. In this particular case, however, this was not acceptable to the customer, and the solution adopted was to separate on the assembly line the insertion of the two fuses. One operator at one stage of the assembly put in one fuse, and another operator, later in the assembly, put in the other. With this arrangement, the first operator only handled one yalue of fuse which she put into only one position in the assembly. It was unlikely that she would accidentally put a fuse into the wrong position, because this would be inconsistent with her normal routine. Similarly, the other operator inserted her fuse into the only empty position. If the first operator had done her job correctly, the second could not possibly make a mistake. If by any chance the first operator had put her fuse in the wrong place, the second operator would be sure to notice it, and correct it before inserting her own fuse.

8.6 The effect of speed of working on quality

Speed of working is not necessarily the enemy of quality. It depends upon the type of production, the method used and the individual operator. It often happens that an operator who produces a lot of work also provides consistently good quality. This usually means that he is achieving his good output not by rushing, but because he has devised and practised a good method which yields both quality and quantity, combined with a reasonable working pace. Everyone concerned with the setting of piece work rates will have met the operator who can apparently make the rate look silly, by devising an improved method by which he can achieve a very high output. Often, the improvements involved are only details, and unless the original method has been very accurately recorded, it may be difficult to prove that a change has taken place. Such improved methods may work to the benefit of quality, as well as of quantity.

If a method is to be subjected to any form of piece work incentive, it must be possible for the operator to strive for good earnings, without his quality dropping below the acceptable level. Intricate operations which can be easily short cut, to the detriment of quality, are not usually suitable for piece work, although it may be possible to make them satisfactory by appropriate changes to the method.

8.7 A comparison between quality control and method study

Quality control and method study have more in common than is often realised. They collectively strive to produce the required quality and quantity as cheaply as possible, and at the time required. Even the way a project is tackled is much the same in each case. Thus, compare the following six steps for carrying out a quality control project with the corresponding steps for a method study project.

Quality control	Method study
1. Select the project.	1. Select the project.
2. Ascertain the quality standard, the quantities involved, and record the existing method of quality control.	2. Ascertain the quality standard, the quantities involved, and record the existing method of production.
3. Analyse the information collected.	3. Analyse the information collected.
4. Develop the improved quality control system.	4. Develop the improved method.
5. Explain the new system to those concerned, and install it.	5. Explain the new method to those concerned, and install it.
6. Maintain the new quality control system.	6. Maintain the improved method.

8.8 The necessity for satisfactory equipment

No one can be expected to turn out a good job with unsatisfactory equipment, e.g. tools, machines and jigs. This does not mean that every operator must have equipment of the highest quality, but it does mean that the equipment provided must be adequate to produce the quality demanded. Every typist in the company does not need the most expensive, brand new electric typewriter, because the quality of typing she is expected to produce will not always justify it. The secretary of the managing director will need a first-class machine, because the quality of the work which she produces must be first class. The girl who types records in the stores, however, will not be expected to achieve such a high quality. So long as the records are legible and can be typed quickly that is probably all that matters. A typewriter of quite modest quality may be adequate for the job.

Thus, in order to decide what sort of equipment will be satisfactory for a particular job, we need to know:
1   The quality standard which is demanded, as discussed in Chapter 3.
2   The quality of output which any prospective machine or other equipment is capable of achieving.
Fortunately, quality control will itself provide us with this latter information. Thus, the information collected on our quality control charts can often be analysed to tell us the capability of the machines, etc., concerned. If not, we may have to do a special observational run, as described in Section 14.10, in order to get this information.

8.9 The role of the inspector

Many production departments employ inspectors, and as we obviously want to make best use of them we must ask ourselves what their true function is. It is sometimes said that they alone are responsible for quality, but a little consideration will show that this is not strictly correct. It is not the inspector who puts the quality into the product. This comes from a combination of the quality of the original design, the method and equipment used, the materiel, and the skill and care of the operator. If the job is then wrong, no amount of inspection will put it right.

This does not mean that the inspector cannot have any influence on the quality produced. If the rule is that nothing can leave the department until the inspector has passed it, then the production people will be forced to make everything to pass inspection. This, however, is an indirect rather than direct method of controlling quality. The control of quality remains in the hands of the production staff, and the inspector must influence them in order to improve it.

A major snag to control by rejection of defective work is that it shuts the stable door after the horse has gone. Too often with this system the inspector appears in the role of 'chief thrower-out of scrap', whose job is to do his best to find something wrong with work which production men and women have sweated to make. No wonder the inspector is sometimes unpopular.

Fortunately, with quality control, the inspector's role is not to throw the scrap out but to assist the production staff, and the operator in particular, to make everything right first time. If he can achieve this there is nothing to throw out, and only in so far as he is unable to attain what is after all an ideal will he have to resort to sorting good from bad.

8.10 The purpose of the quality schedule

By inspection we usually mean that, at certain stages in the course of production, we compare what has been made with what should have been made. Our standard of reference may be the specification, drawing or a visual quality standard. If the quality concerned is an attribute, we shall only be able to state that it is or is not acceptable. If it is a variable, observed in figures, however, we shall also know how near or far from each limit that quality is.

The checks we decide to make must be appropriate to the job, and made with suitable measuring instruments. We do not want our inspector to waste time checking things that do not matter, or to miss out an important check. Things which are unlikely to go wrong need little checking, and those which are difficult to hold within limits will need a considerable amount of attention.

The inspectors must agree among themselves what the checks are to be, but they are not the only people involved. The production engineer or method planner must plan his method so that it is compatible with the checks which are to be applied. If a dimension is important enough to be watched closely by the inspector, it must also be carefully considered when the method is drawn up. The operator needs to know what the checks are. His job is to make everything right first time which, in practical terms, means to pass inspection. If he knows what qualities will be checked, he can watch them carefully during the production run. If he does not know, he may go to a lot of trouble to make what he considers a good article, only to find that the inspector applies an unexpected check which fails it.

Unless the operation is a very simple one, it will be necessary to prepare a quality schedule which lists all the checks which must be applied, together with the method by which they are to be measured or observed. In many cases, the quality schedule can conveniently form part of the planning route card or, alternatively, it may be carried on the quality control chart. Because so many people use it, the title quality schedule is preferable to that of inspection schedule.

8.11 The preparation and use of the quality schedule

The quality schedule should contain all the additional information about quality which the operator, his supervisor, the production engineer or the inspector require. Like the incoming inspection record in Section 7.3 it must be prepared by someone who is familiar with all the quality requirements of the job. This may be a senior inspector or a planning engineer. While the method is being planned, it is often convenient to plan the quality control as well. At that time, the drawings will already be out, and the tolerances and other limits well in mind.

Whoever prepares it will have to see that there is no doubt about the quality standard. He will want to know the method of manufacture, because this will affect the intensity of inspection required.

The following is typical of the information which the quality schedule may contain:

1   Any information that will help to interpret the quality called for by the drawing, specification, etc.
2   A list of all the checks that the inspector is expected to apply. These will include:
    a   Each variable, converted where necessary into the actual units in which the inspector will measure. Tolerances must be

given if they are not already shown on the drawing or specification.

b   Each attribute, with a reference to the quality standard required.

c   The method of measurement, such as micrometer, etc., and where appropriate the gauge number.

d   How many pieces are to be checked, and how often.

e   The accuracy of measurement, as discussed in Section 3.5.

3   Any information which will be required in order to draw up the quality control chart.

4   Attention can be drawn to any quality which is particularly important or which, for any reason, needs careful watching.

5   It is important to make sure that every time a drawing or specification is revised, the quality schedule is updated as well.

8.12   Initial or first-off inspection

Initial or first-off inspection is a well known and valuable aid to quality control. Whenever and wherever a production run is started, it will be prudent to check the first piece, assembly, etc., before the main run commences. Even in process work, where the first piece cannot be checked as such, it will be desirable to check the set-up itself, for example the positioning of jigs, fixtures and moulds, the temperature used and the materials which have been issued, etc.

We can detect many faults by checking the first-off, and so prevent the whole batch from being wrong. The following are some examples:

1   We can check whether the machine or other equipment is correctly set up.

2   We can discover whether the operator has fully understood his instructions.

3   In many cases, we shall be able to detect the use of incorrect materials.

4   We may well notice any discrepancies between the drawing, the planning route card, and the quality schedule. They can then be investigated before hardly any damage has been done.

A first-off inspection is almost always worth doing, but sometimes it is more useful than at others. This will depend partly on the value of the work being produced, and partly on how far a correct first-off ensures a correct run. The more expensive the work being made, and the more it costs to put it right if it is incorrectly made, so the more it will pay us to make sure that the run starts off correctly. Sometimes a correct first-off almost ensures that the rest of the run will be correct. For example, in printing, if the type is correctly set in the first place, at least the spelling cannot be wrong during the rest of the run.

8.13   The purpose of patrol inspection

First-off inspection ensures that the job starts correctly, and the object of patrol inspection is to help the operator to make the whole run correctly. From time to time the patrol inspector will visit the machine or operator concerned and take a sample of the latest work made. He will check this to the quality schedule, and tell the operator whether it is all right or not. If the quality is wrong on any point, then this must be corrected as quickly as possible. Ideally, the machine or process should be adjusted just before it goes out of limit, so that no out-of-limit work is produced. Usually, however, this is only possible if it is practicable to measure in figures. If attributes are used, then little or no warning is given until the work is actually out-of-limit. Obviously, if something does go wrong, the sooner it is discovered and corrected the less out-of-limit work will be made. If an operator goes wrong, it is much kinder to tell him quickly, so that he can correct himself before he has made a lot of out-of-limit work. The operator should be encouraged to regard the inspector as a friend, who assists him in the task of keeping defective work to a minimum.

8.14   The use of patrol inspection

If we are to get maximum value from our patrol inspectors, we shall need a fairly set routine for them to operate, and the following is a typical example:

1   After each inspection has been made and found satisfactory, all work produced so far is cleared from the machine or operator into a container holding the whole day's production.

2   All work which is made from then to the time of the next inspection is kept in a smaller container on or near the machine, etc.

3   When the next patrol inspection is carried out:

    a   If the sample passes on all checks, the work on the machine is added to the day's production.

    b   If it fails on one or more checks, then the quality must have gone wrong since the last check was made, and so all the out-of-limit work produced will be already isolated from the bulk of the production in the smaller container holding that period's run. Therefore:

        (i)   The machine or operator is immediately stopped, so

that no more out-of-limit work is produced.

(ii)   The inspector takes possession of the last period's work, and carries out 100 per cent inspection on it, to sort the good work from the bad.

(iii) The machine is reset, and the equivalent of a first-off inspection, at least on the qualities which were out of limit, is done before production recommences.

4   The frequency with which patrol inspections should be made is discussed fully in Sections 13.9-13.13, and the number of pieces to be checked in Section 13.8.

8.15   Taking and assessing samples on patrol inspection

The primary task of a patrol inspector is to help keep production running correctly and therefore, whatever the sample size, it should always include the last or almost the last piece made because this gives the latest news of the machine's condition. It will tell the inspector and operator whether the machine is still running correctly.

In judging a sample, the inspector must ask himself not so much, 'Is this piece satisfactory?' but rather, 'Is this machine all right for another period's run?' For example, if the machine has reached top drawing limit, the work itself may be just all right. However, if that machine is allowed to run for another period, it would certainly go out of limit and defective work would be made. Therefore, the machine must be reset immediately.

8.16   The last-off

At the end of the run, the last piece made should be checked to see whether the tools, etc., are still in satisfactory condition. If they need regrinding or any other attention before they will be fit for another run, this must be arranged *before* they are returned to store. Otherwise, next time those tools are required there will be a delay while they are reground and, if the job is urgent, there will be a temptation to make do with them as they are.

The last-off check can usually be combined with the last patrol inspection. It is usually desirable to do a patrol inspection at the end of a run, in order to check on work made since the last routine inspection.

8.17　Final test and inspection

The term 'final test and inspection' is usually used to denote any inspection done after manufacture has been completed, with the object of making sure that the goods concerned are satisfactory to send to the customer, or maybe to another department for the next operation. Thus, the foundry may carry out a final inspection to ensure that their castings are all right to send to the machine shop, and the machine shop may, in turn, perform a final inspection to be certain that machined castings are all right to go to the assembly department, and so on.

　　Now, throughout manufacture, we try to make everything right first time. If we can be sure of doing this, then the resulting batch will be 100 per cent good and no final inspection will be necessary. The fact that final inspection is sometimes necessary indicates that we have been unable to guarantee 100 per cent good work. There is a risk that in spite of all our efforts, some of the work may be defective. Therefore, in considering whether final inspection is necessary, we first ask ourselves if it is possible to arrange production so that every batch is bound to be satisfactory, and final inspection unnecessary.

　　If final inspection must be carried out, then the problem is very similar to that of the inspection of incoming materiel, which we discussed in Chapters 4, 5, 6 and 7. Indeed, we can consider that the final inspector is, in effect, carrying out incoming acceptance inspection on behalf of the customer or the department which is about to receive the goods. Final inspection should, therefore, be regarded as a check that our production quality control is working satisfactorily, and not as the quality control system itself.

　　In principle, the economic considerations which we discussed in Chapter 6 still apply. The cost of any final inspection which we make, plus the cost of the trouble we shall give our customer or the next department if we let defective work get through to them, must in total be a minimum. Final inspection is often done on a 100 per cent basis, but there is no rule about this. In suitable cases, sampling inspection using an AQL can be employed.

8.18　Questions

1a　What is meant by the statement that 'The customer is the final inspector'?　　　　　　　　　　　　　　　*(4 marks)*

1b　Hence, what is the role of the inspection department?　*(21 marks)*

CHAPTER 9

QUALITY AND THE OPERATOR

9.1 Be fair to the operator

The operator is a most important factor in achieving satisfactory quality. If he is not interested, then we shall be lucky if we have much success, however good in principle our quality control system is. In the first place, we must be quite fair to our operator, for unless he knows he will get a square deal he is unlikely to be very co-operative. It is no good giving him a badly planned method, poor materiel and unsatisfactory tools, and then expecting him to produce a first-class job. The care with which we have done our initial quality planning will be reflected in the quality that the operator is able to produce, and, therefore, we must be careful not to assume that, because something has gone wrong at the manufacturing stage, it is necessarily the operator's fault.

As Figure 9.1 illustrates, every operator is entitled to:
1   A satisfactory method, as discussed in Chapter 8.
2   Satisfactory tools, machines and other equipment, as considered in Section 8.8.
3   Satisfactory materiels, as discussed in Chapters 4, 5, 6 and 7.
4   Satisfactory instructions concerning:
   a   The method he is to use.
   b   The quality standard he is required to achieve, and the inspection which will be applied to help him achieve it.

The operator then does the job, and if patrol or other inspection is used, it must be impartial and to reasonable quality standards. As far as possible, such inspection should be done in full view of the operator

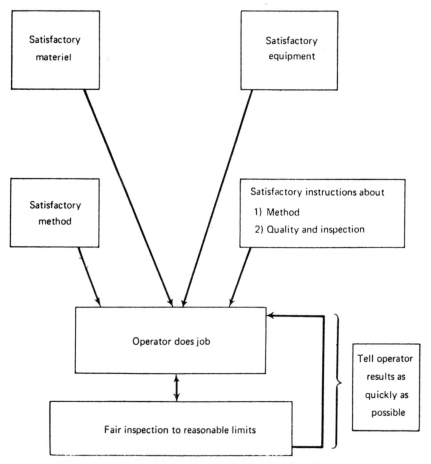

Figure 9.1 Giving the operator a fair chance to do the job correctly

but, if this is not practicable, then the operator must be told the results as quickly as possible afterwards. This will not only help to keep the operator's interest, but it will also assist him in keeping his quality right.

The word 'satisfactory' above must be interpreted in terms of the final quality required. For example, a poor consignment of wood, which is quite satisfactory for making packing cases, would be quite unsatisfactory for making high-class furniture. A lathe that is quite satisfactory when working to drawing limits of ± 0.12 mm, may be completely use-less when attempting limits of ± 0.012 mm. Thus, the operator must be given reasonable materiel, tools, equipment and instructions for the quality standard he is expected to produce.

9.2   The selection and training of operators

If we employ untrainable or untrained people we cannot reasonably expect to get satisfactory quality. Thus, in a factory, both the Personnel Department and the Training Department, by the selection and training of suitable operators, make a valuable contribution to the control of the ultimate quality.

We must try to select people who are not only capable of doing the job but are interested in doing it well. We must check what training they have already had and, if this is insufficient, provide whatever is still required.

Because an operator has been engaged as a 'skilled' man, we must not assume that he knows everything that a skilled man should know. When an operator fault produces scrap, it is easy to fall into the trap of saying, 'He's a skilled man; he should know better than that.' Maybe he should, but if in fact he does not then he will have to be told, otherwise he will go on making the same mistake. Our quality control system will soon tell us if an operator consistently makes the same mistake, and then we must provide suitable help and instruction to cure him of it.

We must also remember that by a 'skilled' man, we usually mean a man who is skilled in one particular trade. For example, a skilled foundryman should be generally skilled in the art of foundry work. However, in our foundry, we may make a special range of castings which require a special running system or a particular method of pouring the molten metal. Obviously, we cannot expect even a skilled foundry-man to know this, and so he will have to be taught it. This principle applies, of course, to both skilled and unskilled men. If the job is at all special, men will need instruction in doing it. Indeed, there can be very few cases where a man can be safely put on a new job without any instruction at all. Thus, every time he puts a different man on a particu-lar job, the supervisor must normally give him a period of detailed in-struction. This will include:

1   How to do the job.
2   Key points, which must be especially kept in mind (see Section 9.3).
3   The quality standard required.
4   Care of the tools and equipment, etc.

It is prudent to train men in advance of actual requirements. If two operators are required for a given job, we shall be wise to have a third man trained ready so that he can take over at short notice if either of the two regular men are ill. The spare man can be employed on other work until he is required.

It is of great assistance to prepare a simple training schedule for each department, similar to that shown in Figure 9.2. Notice how clearly the training schedule shows that only one man, P. Roberts, can undertake the three jobs concerned with the controls and the contacts. Another man will have to be trained for these jobs as quickly as possible otherwise, if P. Roberts is away, there will be no one available who knows how to do them. On the left-hand side we put the names of

	Degrease (sub-assemblies)	Assemble (OP. 1)	Assemble (OP. 2)	Fit control circuit	Fit special control T.P.6	Adjust contacts		
R. Brown	3.4.69 R.H.	6.7.75 M.C.	2.1.73 R.H.					
J. Smith	5.5.71 R.H.							
P. Roberts	14.1.72 R.H.	4.12.74 R.H.	20.7.73 R.H.	13.1.75 M.C.	3.3.75 M.C.	16.5.81 M.C.		
S. Jones		14.4.73 R.H.						
K. Good		21.8.74 R.H.						
F. Long			1.11.74 R.H.					
P. Large	16.2.81 M.C.							

Figure 9.2   Example of a training schedule

all the men and women in our department, and along the top we list all the jobs which have to be done. When a man is trained for a job, we write the date and the initials of the supervisor who did the training in the rectangle opposite that man's name, and under the name of the job in question.

It is then easy to see at a glance whether enough men have been trained for each job, and if not, to carry out the necessary training before an emergency arises. When an operator is ill, it is a simple matter to consult the training schedule to see who has already been taught to take his place. Even if the regular supervisor is himself away, another can immediately tell from the schedule who has been trained, and so select a competent operator to take over the job. The insertion of the date of training in the schedule permits refresher courses to be given if a long time elapses after the original date of training, during which time the man has not been called upon to do the job. The training schedule can be displayed in the regular supervisor's office.

9.3 Key points

In any work there are some points which must be especially kept in mind if the operator is to do a good job. These are usually called 'key points', and it is obviously necessary for the operator to understand them fully, and to observe them.

It is often convenient to divide the key points into two groups, as follows:

1   Standard key points which apply to every job the operator does.
2   Special key points, which apply only to one particular job, or maybe a limited group of jobs.

If the operator always does the same job, or is on very long runs, then he only requires the standard key points. In the more general case, however, although he may do only one class of work he will do a variety of jobs or part numbers within that class. He will, therefore, need standard key points to cover the general class of work, and special key points for each particular job or part number. Suppose, for example, that our operator is a painter. He will need standard key points about brush sizes, and how to apply the paint to his general class of work. He will also need special key points to tell him what colour paint to put on each individual job, and whether any areas are to be left unpainted.

As standard key points are always required, it is often convenient to summarise them on a card which can be permanently displayed at each place of work. Such a card needs protection, for example with glass or Perspex, otherwise it soon becomes very dirty and, even if it can still be read, it then looks unimportant and so does not have the right psychological effect. The letters printed on the standard key-point card need to be large enough to be read while the operator is doing his work. If he has to deliberately stop and consult it, he may not bother. An example is shown in Figure 9.3. When the operator is first put on a job, we must explain the standard key points to him and make sure that he understands them.

Special key points change with each different type of work, and so must be fed to him as a matter of routine every time he receives a new job. He must not be expected to remember the special key points of a job from the last time he did it.

```
┌─────────────────────────────────────────────────────────┐
│                                                         │
│                    KEY-POINT CARD                       │
│              Machine moulding in the foundry            │
│                                                         │
│                                                         │
│    At the start of every run.                           │
│                                                         │
│            (1). Check that pattern plate is undamaged.  │
│                                                         │
│            (2). Check jolt and draw action of machine.  │
│                                                         │
│    When making every mould.                             │
│                                                         │
│            (1). Clean pattern table, before mounting    │
│                 plate.                                  │
│                                                         │
│            (2). Blow pattern clean.                     │
│                                                         │
│            (3). Check box is undamaged, and edges flat. │
│                                                         │
│            (4). Check box is flat on pattern plate.     │
│                                                         │
│            (5). Drive home securing wedges.             │
│                                                         │
│            (6). Cover pattern with grade 3 facing sand. │
│                                                         │
│            (7). Jolt and ram, to compact sand beneath   │
│                 box bars.                               │
│                                                         │
│            (8). Check scraper edge flat.                │
│                                                         │
│            (9). Draw and check mould undamaged.         │
│                                                         │
│                                                         │
└─────────────────────────────────────────────────────────┘
```

Figure 9.3   Example of a standard key-point card

A common yet effective method of dealing with special key points is to use the ordinary planning route card, or maybe the job ticket. This is usually issued with every job, and it tells the operator the method he is to use, and possibly how many he has to make. A quality schedule should be added, so that the operator knows precisely what final quality is expected and what inspection will be applied. The preparation of a quality schedule is described in Sections 8.10 and 8.11. A planning route card is frequently used in conjunction with machine shop work, but its equivalent can usefully be extended to many types of work.

9.4 How does the operator know if he is going wrong?

We have so far:
1   Chosen and trained our operator.
2   Made sure that he understands the standard and special key points which apply to each job which he does.
3   Given him a quality schedule, and ensured that he knows what quality standard is required.

The above, together with our planning of methods, materiel and equipment, should ensure that our operator has every chance of starting off each job correctly. We shall probably use a first-off check to make sure that this does in fact happen, and then we shall be faced with the problem of seeing that the whole batch or production run is correctly made. Primarily, this is a matter of making sure that the operator knows as quickly as possible when anything goes wrong, and that he then corrects himself, or maybe informs someone such as the setter or his supervisor.

We must, therefore, ask ourselves how the operator will know if anything goes wrong. In Figure 9.4, purely in order to make this argument

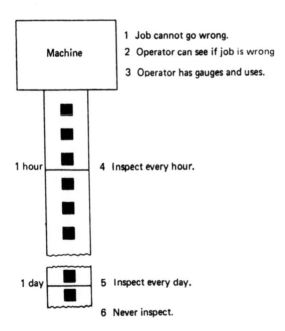

Figure 9.4   The ways in which an operator may know or be told when the quality goes wrong

95

clear, imagine that the work made by our operator travels on a very long conveyor belt down the shop. We now list, in order of preference, the possibilities which may be open to us in ensuring that the operator knows as quickly as possible when the quality of his work goes wrong.

1   The ideal case is where the method is so designed that the operator cannot go wrong. Thus an assembly may be arranged so that it will only go together the correct way.

2   Next best is the situation where the operator can see, feel, hear, taste or smell at once if anything goes wrong, and so correct himself. If our operator is painting pillar boxes, and finds that he has been issued with green instead of red paint, he will know at once that this is wrong, and stop.

3   Next in sequence is the case where the operator is given gauges, or other checking equipment, and taught how to use them. This method is only inferior to (2) above, because the operator will not know that something has gone wrong until he makes his check, and this may be only done with, say, every fifth piece.

4   Patrol inspection comes only fourth in the list. In this case, an inspector checks the operator's work at regular intervals, and tells him *immediately* whether it is satisfactory or not. The operator can then quickly correct anything which is wrong and, when nothing is wrong, have the satisfaction of knowing that his job is still all right. If this method is used:
a   See that the checks are done on a regular basis; not so regular that the operator can guess which piece will be checked, but sufficiently regular that if the check is 'once per hour', it does not degenerate into 'once per day'.
b   As far as is practicable see that the inspector does his checks in full view of the operator. It is not enough to ensure that the checks are correctly done; the operator must be satisfied that this is so. Try to interest him in the tests, and get him to realise that the inspector is there to help him make good work, not to catch him out after he has done something wrong.

5   Moving now into situations which cannot be considered entirely satisfactory, we have the case where the operator is not told the results of inspection on his work until the next day. This situation is most likely to arise on processes where long time cycles, or maybe several operations, must be completed before inspection can be carried out. The risk is very real that a whole days's production may be wrongly

made before the fault is discovered. Chapter 21, therefore, considers ways of reducing this risk.

6   Finally, we have the case where the operator is never told whether his work is right or wrong. Do not assume that this state of affairs cannot exist. It can easily establish itself if not guarded against, even though it may not be an intended part of the routine. For example, the operator may always leave an unacceptable burr on his work, and the inspector may obligingly remove it when he inspects, without saying anything about it to the operator or his supervisor.

If the operator goes wrong, he will make defective work until he is told or finds out for himself. The longer he takes to find out, the more defective work he will make. If, therefore, we can ensure that he finds out at once, he need hardly make any defective work at all.

Thus, any method which waits for the inspector to discover that the operator has gone out of limit will be, other things being equal, inferior to getting the operator to control himself. If the inspector checks every hour, it is possible for the operator to be out of limit for almost an hour before this fact is discovered. On average, every time he goes out of limit, he will make half an hour's defective work before the fault is discovered.

We must, therefore, work down the list given above, and choose the very first method which is practicable, i.e. (1) in preference to (2), (2) in preference to (3), and so on. Possibilities (5) and (6) are added for completeness, but should not be regarded as in any way satisfactory choices.

9.5   Helping the operator, and being helped by him

Try to establish an atmosphere of mutual trust and co-operation between the operators and their supervisors. We have already agreed that, when an operator is given a job to do, he has a right to expect satisfactory materiel methods and equipment, to be told what quality standards are required and, if inspection is necessary, for this to be carried our fairly and the results fed back to him as quickly as possible. We must encourage our operators to report to their supervisor immediately one of these features is unsatisfactory. Operators are often shy about doing this, because they regard it as 'complaining'. Unless they do, however, the supervisor may be completely unaware of their difficulties, and therefore do nothing about them. When such a difficulty is raised, make sure that action is taken as quickly as possible or, if action is impossible, explain this to the operator concerned. Do not let him think you have not bothered about the point he has raised.

9.6   Interesting the operator in quality

An operator is unlikely to produce his best quality unless we interest him in doing so. The following points will help to build up the right atmosphere in a department:

1   See that the operator clearly understands the use to which the work he is doing will be put, and that he realises the trouble and cost that will be incurred if his work is wrong. Particularly in the early stages of manufacture, it is possible for an operator to make the same component for years, without ever knowing its precise use or importance in the final assembly. Similarly, he may not realise the cost which the company incurs every time one is scrapped.

2   Where appropriate, use quality control charts as described in Chapters 11, 12, 13, 14 and 15, in order to show the operator how well he is doing. It is not uncommon to find that an operator does not really know how good or bad his work is. This is especially so if, for practical reasons, inspection cannot be carried out either by him, or in front of him. Many operators depend entirely on the feedback of inspection results to tell them how things are going, and this feedback is unlikely to be really effective unless the operator has his results recorded on a quality control chart or its equivalent.

3   Plan the work so that each operator gets what he considers an interesting share of it. If a job is broken down into very small work elements, each operator may have to repeat his element several thousand times a day, and he may find this so monotonous that he loses interest in his quality. Thus, a balance has to be struck between what seems to be the best method, purely from the point of view of getting maximum output, and the method which will achieve the best quality. Of course, some operators do not mind monotony, especially if they have someone to talk to while they work, and such people do a very useful job.

4   Operator control, which is discussed in Sections 9.7, 9.8 and 9.9 below, helps considerably in interesting an operator in his work.

9.7   Operator control

When an operator checks his own work, as was described in (2) and (3) of Section 9.4, this is called 'operator control', and it can be most effective way of reducing the amount of defective work. It must, however, be very carefully planned and introduced, and the following points must be emphasised:

1   Checks which we expect the operator to do must be both simple and quick. They must be simple, because we cannot expect the operator to suddenly become a skilled inspector, and they must be quick because otherwise production will be appreciably held up while the operator performs his checks.

2   A particularly attractive application is that of a machine operator who is able to check one piece while his machine is working on the next. In this case, no production time is lost at all, and we are able to make use of time when the operator would otherwise be idle.

3   We must be absolutely fair to the operator. If he is on piece work, any inspection we expect him to do must be taken into account when the rate is set. If, of course, we are using idle time during the machine cycle the time allowed is unlikely to be affected.

4   If gauges or other checking equipment are to be employed, then the operator must be taught how to use them and what checks he is to make. For this reason, operator control tends to work better on long-run production than on short runs.

5   Operator control must be carefully explained to the operators concerned. They must want to work it. If the operators suspect that we are not being fair with them, or are trying to use them to put the inspector out of work, then they will not be likely to co-operate, and operator control will be a failure. Even if they only *think* that they are being unjustly treated they will not co-operate, in spite of the fact that we may be trying to be absolutely fair. Therefore careful explanation is essential.

9.8   A typical operator control routine

As with all quality control, it is essential to design the operator control routine to suit the type of production concerned. The following, therefore, is typical of the sort of routine which can be used, but we should not be afraid to modify it to suit our individual requirements:

1   Each time the operator is told to set up for a different production

run, he receives a planning route card or method card (see Section 8.10) for that job. This tells him all the key points which will require attention, and it includes a quality schedule showing what inspection is necessary.

2   The operator or setter sets up the job to pass the required inspection and, when he is satisfied, he submits his first-off to the inspector. It usually pays to have an independent check to make sure that the job starts off correctly for, if it is wrong at the start, the whole batch is obviously likely to be wrong.

3   When the inspector checks the first-off he does so to the quality schedule, and therefore no 'surprises' are sprung on the operator. Unless he has overlooked something, the first-off should pass and, if it does, then the operator is given the go ahead to commence production. If something is wrong, this must be corrected and another first-off submitted.

4   The operator then carries on with production, checking in accordance with his quality schedule. This may call for every piece to be checked or it may, for example, only call for checks, say, on every fifth piece. If the checks are quick and cheap and the cost incurred every time a piece is wrong is high, then we shall call for every piece to be checked. On the other hand, if the checks are relatively expensive, if they take so long that they appreciably hold up production or if the cost incurred when a piece is scrapped is low, then we shall call for checks at relatively infrequent intervals. The frequency of inspection is more fully discussed in Sections 13.9, 13.10, 13.11, 13.12 and 13.13.

5   So long as the work he is making is satisfactory, the operator carries on producing. If a piece fails his inspection, he puts it aside from the good ones, and considers how it happened. If he simply 'made a mistake' he corrects himself, and carries on producing. If the fault is caused by the machine then, depending on the instructions which we have given him, he may either reset it, or call the setter or supervisor. If the materiel is at fault, he will probably have to raise it with his supervisor, to whom he will certainly go if he is in any doubt about the reason for his pieces failing inspection.

6   When the operator is not inspecting every piece, he will not be certain, when he finds a faulty piece, whether that is the first wrong one he has made or not. He will, therefore, have to check all those which have been made since his last routine check, and remove those which are faulty.

7   Thus, regardless of the frequency of inspection, the operator finishes up with a set of good pieces, plus maybe a few faulty pieces, which have been kept separate. There is thus no need for the inspector to do full inspection which would have been necessary if operator control had not been used.

8   However, from time to time, the inspector will carry out a quality audit, in order to check that operator control is working satisfactorily. This will probably be a sample check, which may be made during a long run or at the end of a short run. Full 100 per cent inspection will only be carried out if the quality audit gives unsatisfactory results.

9   Operator control can be most successful, but it requires mutual confidence and trust between ourselves and our operator. If we cannot trust him, we certainly will not be able to work operator control successfully. However, it is only fair to trust him in the first place. If he does not do his inspection properly, or tries to slip faulty pieces through in the good ones, the quality audit will soon catch him out.

9.9   Operator control and piece work

If our operator is on piece work, the time he will be expected to spend on inspection must be counted when assessing his rate. In addition to this, however, he must be allowed some sort of payment for any faulty pieces he declares. On ordinary piece work, the operator is usually only allowed to count for payment the good pieces that he makes. Faulty pieces are not included. If we try this with operator control, we shall in effect be saying to our operator, 'Here are the gauges; you are to carry out the checks you have been told to, and put the faulty ones aside, so that we do not have to pay you for them.'

Faced with an offer like that, no operator is likely to carry out his checks conscientiously. The temptation to try to slip any bad ones in with the good, and hope that the inspector will not find them, will be too great.

There are several methods of getting round this difficulty, but they all depend on making some sort of payment for defective work which the operator declares. The most common method is to pay the operator in full for the defective work which he declares, up to some limit such as 2 per cent. A limit is obviously necessary, as otherwise it would be possible for the operator to work all day making everything completely wrong and then, at the end of the day, to declare it all to be scrap and claim full payment for it! The limit should be set so that any reasonably careful operator can work inside it, declare such scrap as he makes and get paid for it. Once an operator has exceeded his limit, there is no incentive whatever for him to declare any additional scrap. The limit is only intended to affect the careless worker.

Another method is to make the payment for faulty work less than that for good work. For example, the operator might be offered full payment for good work, half payment for faulty work which is declared, and no payment for faulty work which is not declared, and is found subsequently by the inspector. In this case, the operator has an incentive to make good work if he can, because at the best, he only gets paid half for faulty work. On the other hand, if he accidentally makes a mistake he has an incentive to declare it, because he then gets paid half instead of nothing. If these methods of payment are used, they must only be applied to faulty pieces which are due to operator errors. Machine, materiel and other scrap, which is outside the control of the operator, must be paid in full if declared.

9.10 The role of the inspector when operator control is used

We might think that the use of operator control was detrimental to the status of the inspector, but this is not so at all. The inspector is relieved of simple, quick, repetitive checks, and can concentrate on the more difficult inspection tasks which the operator cannot be expected to do. The operator is self-contained and, within clearly determined limits, can get on with the job unhindered. Hence, the operator and the inspector are usually on better terms with each other, and the inspector's status in the factory increases.

The Inspection Department still have the following responsibilites:

1   They must teach the operators to use the inspection equipment, e.g. gauges, which is issued to them.

2   They must continue to carry out difficult and time-consuming checks. As we said in (1) of Section 9.7, we cannot expect the operator to be a skilled inspector able to undertake complicated tests. We equally cannot expect him to make lengthy checks, because these would hold up production unduly. Checks which cannot be made at the workplace itself are similarly usually ruled out.

3   Inspectors must check all the inspection equipment which is used to ensure that its accuracy is satisfactory. Gauges, etc., used by the operator should be as accurate as those used by the inspector. The guages used by the operator should not be set to a tighter limit than those used by the inspector. One of the important jobs of operator

control is to encourage mutual trust and confidence between the operator, the inspector and the supervisor. This may be shattered if the operator finds out that he is not trusted to work to the same limits as the inspector.

4   The inspectors must carry out quality audit checks, in order to ensure that operator control is running smoothly.

9.11   Work structuring, job enrichment and job enlargement

A number of attempts have been made to make industrial work more interesting, using terms such as *work structuring, job enrichment* and *job enlargement*. Although various companies have used the technique in a variety of forms, most of them are broadly as follows.

An operator is given a reasonable section of the work to do, and is made responsible for both manufacture and ensuring that its quality is correct. Thus he or she might be given say a complete heater to build, test and pack. It would carry their identity marks, and so would be easily traced back if it later proved to be wrong. According to the type of work, etc., some form of quality audit might be imposed. This technique is thus a development of operator control, in which operator control of method has been included.

Sometimes the operators work in small groups. They will be made responsible for say the assembly of a television chassis, or a recognisable part of a car but will be allowed to share the work amongst themselves as they please. They may elect to build the whole thing complete individually, or they may share it in a more normal way, but change jobs from time to time to avoid monotony. The type of work may of course impose some restraints.

9.12   The craftsmanship theory

According to the *craftsmanship theory,* all people have an inherent desire to take a pride in their work. Suitably encouraged they will work well, check their work, and make suggestions for improving quality. They will understand that they have a personal responsibility to make work correctly in the first place, and that no amount of inspection can correct it later. Thus, throughout this chapter, we have been discussing the craftsmanship theory.

9.13 The indifference theory

This theory propounds that operators are not interested in their work, and that the most effective way to increase output is by the extensive use of piecework and similar incentive schemes. To ensure the necessary quality, we must use inspectors and penalties for poor work. Operators treated in this way are unlikely to make suggestions, and indeed their relations with management will probably be poor.

Throughout this book we have rejected the indifference theory. No doubt operators do exist who have no intention of co-operating in the general quality effort, and as a last resort, tougher measures may have to be applied. Certainly however, everyone should be assumed to be co-operative, until he has proved the contrary.

9.14 Questions

1 Discuss the measures which can be taken to encourage and, as far as possible, ensure that an operator produces satisfactory quality.

(25 marks)

2a Compare the contribution to quality made by the operator, with that made by the shop floor inspector. *(10 marks)*

2b Discuss the techniques and conditions under which it is possible for the operator to become his own inspector.

(15 marks)

3a Discuss the meaning of
(i) the craftsmanship theory
(ii) the indifference theory *(10 marks)*

3b What precautions and preparations should be used in order to introduce operator control to a department? *(15 marks)*

CHAPTER 10

QUALITY CIRCLES

10.1 The origin of quality circles

In the UK industrial organisation is usually based on a suitably updated version of the ideas of F.W. Taylor (1856-1915). Thus we can nearly always identify top management who decide overall policy, middle management who execute it, i.e. the executives, and specialists such as quality engineers who provide advice in their own field. All this results in detailed instructions which the work force are expected to carry out, and at one time more or less blind obedience was demanded. Although this is no longer true, no great mental contribution is usually expected from operators.

Industrial organisation in the USA has tended to be similar, and after Japan capitulated in 1945, it too adopted American ideas, even though its problems were rather different. Before the war Japan had a reputation for being able to copy any Western idea, but always produced a version which, whilst cheaper, was very inferior in quality. Somehow this image needed to be changed, but by the end of the 1950s little progress had been made. No doubt Japanese quality had improved, but not nearly enough to erase her bad image. Her exports generally were very low and car exports were almost non-existant.

Over a long period during both the 1940s and 1950s Professor Ishikawa, amongst others, studied the situation and concluded that much of the trouble originated from the gulf between management and shop floor, i.e. from what is often referred to as the 'them and us' attitude. Operators were frequently well aware of the cause of quality problems and, with modern standards of education, often knew how to cure them. The trouble was that they were not usually asked. The solution, he concluded, was to introduce quality circles. The first of these began around 1962, and were so successful that today Japan is reputed to have over 1,000,000 circles, involving some 10,000,000 workers. The reputation for quality and reliability which Japan now enjoys, seem to stem largely from its use of quality circles.

10.2 Definition

A quality circle is a group of employees doing similar work, under one supervisor, who meet voluntarily for say an hour each week, to discuss their quality problems, recommend solutions and, with management approval, implement them.

10.3 The principle of quality circles

Most companies have an organisational structure based on the family tree. Everyone reports to a superior who is one status level higher than himself, and all but the lowest rank control subordinates who are one status level lower. Quality circles are built into this structure, as shown in Figure 10.1.

A circle consists of a team leader plus 5 to 10 members, all doing similar work. The majority of circles operate at shop floor or office floor level. Typically the foreman is the team leader, and most or all of the circle members are his subordinates. The circle will have a maximum of, say, 10 members, even though the foreman may have more people under him. People who do not report to the foreman will only be invited when they can contribute something, and then only for a limited period. Thus the quality engineer, production engineer, safety officer, etc., will not have a permanent seat, since their presence would be liable to inhibit discussion amongst shop floor members. When needed they will be co-opted just for the advice they can give on some particular problem, and will then disappear from the circle again. Since members must be interested in the work of the circle, it is essential for them to be volunteers rather than conscripts.

Typically a circle meets once a week, for an hour or an hour and a half, to consider quality problems in their own area. Mostly they will tackle down-to-earth practical problems; the sort they understand only too well. They will make suggestions for solving them, which the circle leader will record. Later the best ideas will be selected, and integrated into a set of proposals. The circle members will explain these to management, and assist in implementing them.

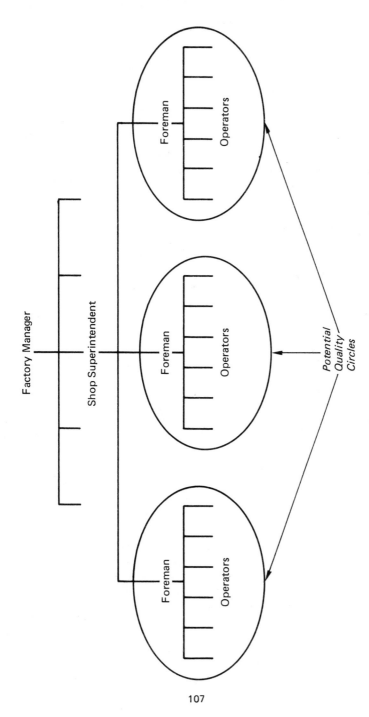

Figure 10.1 Part of a typical family tree showing potential quality circles

Terminology varies a bit from one company to another. We have used the usual term quality circles, but they are also called QC circles, and quality groups.

10.4   Making a start

Since quality circles are essentially voluntary, they cannot be started simply by the managing director issuing a directive that they will henceforth be formed throughout the company. Indeed, the first step is usually to persuade the top management that quality circles would be beneficial. To this end the quality manager will probably have to prepare and give some sort of presentation, talk, etc., specifically for them. Lip service approval is not enough; top management must be seen to be actively interested in quality problems, and ways of overcoming them.

Once approval has been obtained, planning of the whole quality circle organisation can begin. Obviously this will be done to suit the type of work and organisation concerned, but usually there is a *steering committee* and a *co-ordinator*, in addition to the circles themselves.

10.5   The steering committee

The steering committee looks after the overall planning, development and continuity of the circles. It must not be so large that it is slow and cumbersome, yet all sections of the company should be represented, and members should be drawn from all status levels from top management to trade union representatives. Typically it meets once a month, and its primary job is to provide overall surveillance. It effectively brings the circles into the general company organisation, and provides links from the top right down to shop floor level. It will decide overall circle policy. Thus from its knowledge of where interest, need, etc., are, it will decide which sections of the company should be next to be brought into the circle structure.

The steering committee will also provide support and back-up wherever required. Many circles' proposals will probably be cheap and easy to implement, but occasionally considerable expenditure, expertise, reorganisation, etc., may be involved. Cost and other experts will then have to work out the proposals in detail, so that the steering committee can consider them. Once the latter is convinced that the proposition will be beneficial and viable, it must use its influence to obtain top management approval. Since the steering committee always includes senior management representatives, it will be in a much better position to do this than the quality circle which first thought up the idea.

10.6   The co-ordinator

The co-ordinator is the link man between the steering committee and
the quality circles. He must report to a senior member of management,
often the managing director himself, and he must be a member of the
steering committee. The steering committee will determine overall
policy and provide the necessary back-up, but as they only meet periodically, it is the co-ordinator who must provide day-to-day continuity. He
is in continuous and direct contact with the circles. Initially he will be
instrumental in setting them up, and later he will provide day-to-day
help, advice, encouragement, co-ordination, etc. In a large company
where circles prosper, he will eventually require a small staff to assist
him.

The Americans use the term 'facilitator' for what in the UK is usually
called the co-ordinator.

10.6.1   Selection of the co-ordinator

The co-ordinator has a key role and it is essential to ensure that the
right person is chosen in the first place. He/she must be:

1   Acceptable to other employees   People must be prepared to trust
and respect him. Someone with a reputation for being sly or crafty will
be of no use, even if that reputation is undeserved.

2   Enthusiastic and energetic   If the co-ordinator is not himself
convinced about the value of quality circles, he is not going to persuade
anyone else that they are worthwhile. A lot of detailed work will be
required, and he must be prepared to work hard and painstakingly.

3   Not easily discouraged   Some people who are not convinced about
the value of quality circles may tell him so bluntly. For example, there
may be a shop steward who retorts: 'The moment you set foot in my
shop, I shall lead the men out through the factory gate'. There will
inevitably be some set-backs, although hopefully they will be small,
and everything must be done to minimise them. Again there will be
peaks when the demands of several circles at once will tend to over-
whelm him. The man or woman chosen must be able to withstand all
these pressures without going to pieces.

4   Suitably experienced and skilled   The co-ordinator must be familiar
with his company's organisation, and with how its administrative
system works. Frequently he is going to need to get something done,

e.g. a new jig may be requested by a circle, and he must know his company's routine for doing this. In particular, he must not upset someone by inadvertently taking action within their sphere of control, without consulting them.

He will need enough technical knowledge to talk sensibly to almost anyone, but he must not pretend to understand the technical basis of every process in the factory. He merely asks the advice of the people in the department concerned. Obviously he needs to be familiar with the most commonly used quality control techniques, but again he can consult the quality engineers as necessary. He must be able to talk to circle members and explain to them the techniques they require to use. It will probably be helpful to send him on one of the courses which are offered for quality circle co-ordinators.

10.6.2   Work of the co-ordinator

The co-ordinator is responsible for the introduction of quality circles and for their efficient day-to-day operation. He is the link man who unites the circles one to another, and links the circles collectively to the management, the latter being formally through the steering committee, and less formally through contact with the departmental managers.

The requirements of industry change constantly. New products are introduced, old ones disappear, quantities increase and decrease. To cope with these, new departments are created and old ones are merged or discontinued. The structure of quality circles must be continually modified to match. Hence the servicing of existing circles will soon become an important part of a co-ordinator's work.

The status of a co-ordinator is a curious one. As the number of circles grows, he will gather a lot of responsibilities, and because he reports to someone high up, he will tend to be regarded highly. Nevertheless because he works largely by persuasion, he will have little direct authority. If as a last resort someone has to be 'instructed' to do something, he will ask that person's own supervisor to do it. He will not instruct that person himself.

10.7   Launching quality circles

The quality manager may decide to launch the first few circles himself, since this will give him a clear and first-hand understanding of the problems involved. Almost immediately, however, a co-ordinator must be chosen and trained.

Next, two or three potential circle leaders must be chosen with care. The following are guidelines:

1   Choose an area of the company which has obvious practical quality problems, i.e. problems which shop floor experience will probably be able to solve. Initially avoid problems which are technically complicated.

2   Earmark potential leaders who are likely to be interested and co-operative.

3   A single circle will probably find it difficult to exist by itself, yet if too many circles are started at the same time, the co-ordinator may be unable to cope. Hence start with about three circles, but try to get them in related areas, e.g. two machine shop circles and an assembly circle, all concerned with the same product. Thus the assembly circle will be able to refer problems concerned with components back to the machine shop circles, and *vice versa*.

4   The foremen invited to become circle leaders must be keen to accept. This is particularly important for the first few circles.

In parallel with the above, an adequate amount of publicity from management will be required, and this needs careful co-ordination. Areas where circles are to be started need to be fully informed in advance. However, it is bad for a department to receive a lot of publicity and then no action for a long time. Hence the publicity should be timed to just precede the actual formation of circles.

The circle leaders must be trained. Do not rush this. People who have not studied for some while need time to adjust to it again. One to one and a half hours a week is enough, and it must be in company's time. According to their background, they may need help in running a small meeting, putting ideas across, dealing with a dissenter, etc. Certainly they will need help with quality circle techniques, although these should be kept as simple as possible. The following are typical of those which circles commonly find useful:

The quality standard (Sections 3.3 to 3.8).

Pareto analysis and measles charts (Sections 16.7 and 16.8).

Fishbone diagrams (Section 16.9).

Tally charts and other simple frequency distribution curves (Section 11.2).

Simple quality control charts, such as the pre-control (Section 13.17).

10.8   The structure of a quality circle

The circle members should be a representative cross-section of the work supervised by the leader. They can be elected by their colleagues, but probably the initial membership for the first few circles will be invited. They must accept the task voluntarily, although some gentle persuasion is permissible. If more people are interested than can be accommodated, so much the better. Let them rotate from time to time, so that all who are willing to serve have a chance to do so. Circle members must anyway keep their colleagues informed about their activities.

Find a suitable meeting place, preferably near the workshop, but ensure that meetings will not be disturbed by shop floor queries. For many meetings only a table and chairs will be required, but for some a marker board and/or an overhead projector will be needed.

The co-ordinator must attend initial meetings, to explain in detail what is intended, provide circle members with instruction, etc. However, he must be conscious from the start that the circle leader is the person in charge. At the earliest opportunity the co-ordinator must fade into the background, and let the leader take over. As soon as the circle is self-supporting, he should stop attending meetings. No doubt he will look in on a meeting from time to time, to see if he can help, and he will always be available to provide advice and assistance in any way he can.

10.9 The operation of a quality circle

From the first meeting it will be necessary to discuss with members what problems should be tackled and in what order. In Section 10.7 we said that circles should be started where suitable problems exist, and it may be that members will need some guidance about where to start. As far as possible, however, they should be allowed to decide for themselves. It may be that a job which really niggles them, e.g. because it is dirty or tiring, is not regarded as serious by management, in the sense that no large loss of money is involved. Nevertheless it is good for morale if such irritations are removed, and money should not be regarded as the only objective, particularly in the early stages. Overall quality circles will reduce costs considerably.

Steer the circle away from technically complicated problems, and from those whose solutions are likely to be expensive to implement. Top management may be reluctant to spend a lot on a circle idea in the early stages, when it is still not fully convinced that circles are of value, whilst the shop floor will soon lose interest if their ideas are rejected. Similarly, avoid problems whose solutions can only be implemented on a long-term basis. We need a quick success which members can feel they have achieved themselves. Introduce members to quality control techniques as they are ready to use them on an actual problem. This helps them to see the relevance of what they learn.

Brief notes should be kept of decisions, etc., taken by the circle.

10.10 Dealing with a problem

Once circle members have agreed on a problem, they must start the process of solving it. The steps will be similar to the way in which any quality problem is solved, but it usually also includes the brainstorming technique of value analysis. Typically the steps will be as follows:

1 Set out clearly the required quality standard in variables and standards, etc. (Sections 3.3 to 3.8). The members must be quite clear about what is acceptable quality. However, many problems are not clear-cut. For example,
'It is difficult to get the casting firmly in the hoist sling. If it slips it's dangerous, as well as getting chipped or cracked, which means it's scrap.'
'It's almost impossible to solder that inaccessible joint neatly, without bits of solder dropping onto the PCB below.'
Methods often have to be considered as well as quality. It may help if members return to the shop floor to see for themselves what the difficulties are, unless of course it is a job all of them do. The circle leader must keep asking questions until he and other members are quite clear what the problem is.

2 Often it will be necessary to collect data, which will then be analysed. If actual measurements have been recorded, a tally chart may be used (Section 11.2); if it is in attribute form, such as numbers scrap, a Pareto chart will be useful (Section 16.7). If the position of the fault on the work is important, a measles chart may be used (Section 16.8). If it is necessary to investigate possible sources of difficulty, a fishbone diagram will be appropriate (Section 16.9). The circle must have access to whatever data it needs, e.g. drawings, planning sheets, method study records and costs. It must also be able to co-opt expertise as required, e.g. production engineer, quality engineer and safety officer. Probably the leader will have to gently restrain his members so that they consider all possibilities and do not jump to premature conclusions.

3 When all or most of the facts are known, possible solutions can be considered; this will be done by a brainstorming session. As far as practicable, all the data plus an example of the work itself will be on view at this meeting. Everyone is invited to make suggestions and these are recorded. Often the leader will write them on a marker board or even better an overhead projector, so that everyone can see them. The 'rule' is that no discussion or criticism is permitted at this stage, because this may impede the flow of ideas. Thus if someone says, 'Let's turn it upside down, it will make it much easier to machine', someone else is not permitted to retort: 'Don't be daft, it weighs half a ton'. They may however say: 'If we do it on the other machine, we can use the hoist above it'. The point is that wild ideas are often precisely those which form a bridgehead onto more practical suggestions. If we stop them, the practical ideas just don't come, and the meeting dissolves into silence. The leader must keep the flow of ideas going. When a lull comes, he can draw attention to an aspect of the problem for which no suggestions have yet been made, or he may recapitulate, by reading back the suggestions made so far. At the end of the brainstorming session he will let ideas incubate for a day or two.

4   Next the ideas must be sorted out. A lot will be discarded, but this should not be done too hastily. Beware of discarding an idea, merely because it has an unusual approach, or because it has an obvious snag, even though it is basically sound. Perhaps the snag can be overcome quite easily. From what is left the best will be selected, combined together, rearranged, simplified, etc., until they are as simple, cheap and practicable as possible. The circle members must first agree amongst themselves about what should be done, and then explain it to, and get the agreement of, other members of the section concerned.

5   Now the proposals must be sold to management. As far as possible let the circle members explain them themselves. Usually several members each explain one section of the proposals, and use the marker board, diagrams and maybe the overhead projector to do it.

6   Once approval has been given, the proposals can be implemented. Make sure that before and after results are recorded, so that the improvement achieved can be clearly demonstrated, and then ensure that circle members get credit for it.

10.11   Enlargement

As the initial circles become self-supporting, so the co-ordinator will move on to start others. The principles discussed in Section 10.7 still apply. A solid area of committed circles is usually better than a scatter across the company. However, once interest has been aroused, it is likely that other sections will ask to be allowed to form a circle. Such requests should be granted if at all possible. Indeed they may pinpoint a second area in which a group of circles should be encouraged. Do not forget the nightshift; they need circles too.

We have discussed quality circles in terms of the production shop floor, because it is there that they have already been so successful. However, they are by no means limited to manual work, or to the lowest status levels. Office work could benefit, and so could the design departments. There are also possibilities outside the manufacturing industry, for example in government offices and colleges.

10.12 Questions

1a Outline the principle of quality circles. *(13 marks)*
1b Explain how circles could be, or have been, used in
a department with which you are familiar. *(12 marks)*
2 Compare the contribution to quality which can be made
by operator control, with that made by quality circles. *(25 marks)*

PART THREE

QUALITY CONTROL OF THE ACTUAL PRODUCTION OPERATIONS

CHAPTER 11

FREQUENCY DISTRIBUTION CURVES

11.1 Recapitulation

In Section 1.10, we set out the five basic stages of any quality control system, and in the subsequent chapters we have considered the first two stages in detail. Thus, in Chapter 3, we discussed the first stage, that of setting our quality standard in clear practical terms. Next, in Chapters 4 to 10, we elaborated upon the second stage, which was how to plan to achieve the required quality.

Now we must carry out our plan. We must attempt to make everything right first time and the better we have planned our quality the easier this will be.

11.2 The concept of machine or process variability

We may wonder why we are so often plagued with a small percentage of defective work, say 5 per cent. After all, if an operator can make 95 per cent of his work correctly, why does the other 5 per cent have to be wrong?

To try to understand this problem, suppose we have a close look at the output from any machine or process which happens to be making a quality which we can observe as a variable, i.e. in figures. It need not be a machine, but to make the example clear, suppose that a lathe is producing a diameter, whose nominal size is 10.75 mm. However, all the pieces produced will not have a diameter of exactly 10.75 mm. They will vary a little, depending on various factors, for example:

1   How good the machine is.
2   How skilled the operator is.
3   Whether the materiel is easy or difficult to work, etc.

Suppose we take fifty successive pieces, just as they come off the machine, and measure them. We might get the following readings in millimetres:

10.77	10.76	10.73	10.75	10.78
10.76	10.79	10.75	10.75	10.76
10.77	10.78	10.76	10.78	10.75
10.80	10.77	10.74	10.79	10.74
10.72	10.75	10.82	10.76	10.73
10.76	10.77	10.79	10.76	10.77
10.75	10.76	10.77	10.78	10.75
10.81	10.74	10.81	10.74	10.73
10.75	10.78	10.76	10.80	10.77
10.74	10.79	10.78	10.77	10.80

What can we make of these figures? Probably not very much as they stand. We can see that the diameter is varying a bit, but we can say little about how. Suppose that instead of putting the figures down as they come, we collect all the 10.75 mm readings together, then all the 10.76 mm and so on. If we put an X for each piece, we would get what is called a *tally chart* as shown in Figure 11.1. Alternatively we can draw our results as shown in Figure 11.2, in which case it would be called a *histogram*.

We can now begin to see some sort of pattern. Thus:

1   Although the nominal diameter is 10.75 mm the most numerous observation is 10.76 mm and, in fact, far more pieces are larger than nominal than are smaller.
2   Above 10.80 mm, the histogram has a tail marked CD. Although diameters are seldom more than 0.03 mm below nominal, a proportion are appreciably greater than this above nominal.

Thus, we have now got some idea how our lathe varies, and therefore of what sort of precision it is capable of achieving. Whether or not this is good enough will depend on the limits called for on the drawing. Suppose it says that all diameters must be between 10.70 and 10.80 mm. We therefore draw two vertical lines at these values, as is shown in Figures 11.1 and 11.2.

We can now see that our lathe is keeping well inside its bottom drawing limit of 10.70 mm, but that some of its work exceeds the top limit of 10.80 mm. Indeed, we can infer that:

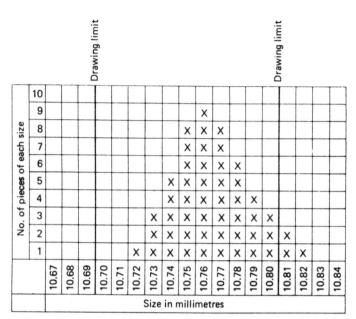

Figure 11.1 Example of a tally chart

1 Most of the work would be within limits, if the operator was asked to centre his work just below 10.75 mm rather than at 10.75 mm.

2 As three pieces (those reading 10.81, 10.81 and 10.82 mm) are over top limit, out of fifty pieces, we can estimate that three in fifty or 6 per cent of the whole production is over top limit. This would not be an accurate deduction, because our sample of fifty may not be truly representative of production as a whole, but it gives us a first indication.

11.3 Frequency distribution curves

In Figure 11.2 we drew the variations in diameter from our lathe as a series of steps or intervals each 0.01 mm wide. If we had had more observations we could have decided to make the interval smaller. Thus the shape of a histogram depends partly on personal decisions and partly on the amount of data available. In general it is convenient to think of a smooth curve, called a frequency distribution curve. Strictly speaking it now relates to an infinitely large sample, and shows the probability that any given observation will occur. The following are examples of what we might find in practice.

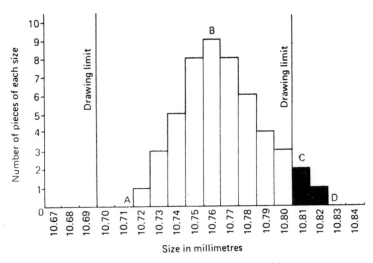

Figure 11.2   Histogram for the example described in text

In Figure 11.3 the specification or drawing limits are much wider than our frequency distribution curve marked ABC. Therefore, we should expect this process to give us very little trouble on the shop floor. The setting can drift as far as XYZ in either direction before we need worry about the risk of making out-of-limit work. Indeed, our curve indicates that the machine or process is really too good for the

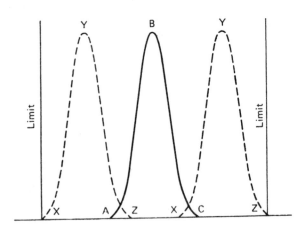

Figure 11.3   Frequency distribution curve for a process that is able to do much better than the specification demands

122

job in question, and we should consider whether there is a more exacting job which it could do.

Figure 11.4 shows the case where the frequency distribution curve just fills the whole of the drawing limits. At first sight it is just all right, but in practice it is unlikely to be entirely satisfactory, because it will be difficult to keep the process centred exactly at B, and the slightest drift one way or the other will result in out-of-limit work. For example, if the peak of the curve drifts from B to Y, then the part of the curve shown in black will be out of limit.

In Figure 11.5 we have an incorrectly set process. The frequency distribution curve shows that the variability is from A to C. If we reset the process so that the peak of the curve is in the centre of the drawing limits at Y, then the whole production is within limits, as shown at XYZ.

Finally in Figure 11.6 we have a frequency distribution curve which is actually wider than the width between the drawing limits. Clearly, no

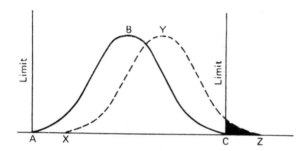

Figure 11.4 Frequency distribution curve for a process whose variability just equals the specification limits

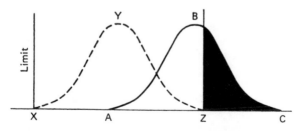

Figure 11.5 This frequency distribution curve indicated that the process is incorrectly set

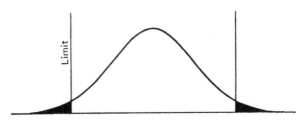

Figure 11.6 Frequency distribution curve indicating that the process is too variable to achieve the limits demanded

matter where we set our process, some of the work produced is bound to be out-of-limit. This means that our present combination of machine, materiel, operator, etc., is just not good enough to achieve the drawing or specification limits required. If we carry on with production, some of the work made is bound to be outside limit. In principle, therefore, there are two lines of action open to us:

1   We can improve the process or machine, etc., so that the frequency distribution curve is narrower. We might do this by moving the job to a more precise machine, giving it to a more skilled operator, or using better quality materiel, etc.

2   Alternatively, if (1) is difficult or expensive, we may approach the designer or customer with a request that the drawing or specification limits should be widened.

Meanwhile, if production is urgent, we might be forced to produce with the conditions shown in Figure 11.6, and then carry out 100 per cent inspection of the work produced, in order to remove those which are outside limit. If our sole object is to keep out-of-limit work to a minimum, then we shall centre the curve symmetrically, so that equal tails protrude beyond each limit.

However, it often happens that, whereas work outside one limit is scrap, that outside the other limit can be corrected. In such a case, it may pay us to bias the process in favour of more correctable rejects, in return for less scrap. Some caution is necessary, however, because when the process is moved off centre the increase in correctable rejects will exceed the reduction in scrap. If it is moved too far, it is possible to find that we have let ourselves in for a huge number of corrections, just to avoid a few, and in some cases not very expensive, scrap pieces.

11.4   Normal and non-Normal frequency distribution curves

So far we have assumed that our frequency distribution curve will have a regular bell shape, as shown in the figures in Section 11.3. Indeed this bell shape is very common in practice, so much so that it is called a

Normal frequency distribution curve or cometimes a Gaussian curve. Its shape can be deduced mathematically, if we make two assumptions:

1   All the variables in our process are very small.
2   They are all just as likely to be positive as negative about the mean.

The first condition implies that there must be no single source of variation which is much larger than all the others. For example, the output from a machine may vary in, say, diameter because there is very slight play in all its bearings. Our condition, however, implies that there is no *one* bearing with a *lot* of play in it giving rise to a single large source of variation.

The second condition, applied to our example, would mean that the play in each bearing was just as likely to make the diameter a little larger as to make it a little smaller.

To us, as quality engineers, the importance of these two conditions lies in their converse. Suppose that when we plot an actual frequency distribution curve we find that it is nowhere near Normal in shape. This tells us that our process must be breaking one, or both, of these two conditions. Either it contains one or more large variables, or there is some bias which prevents the variables from being just as likely to be positive as negative about the mean. It should not be too difficult to identify them, and then eliminate them. Thus, if one bearing has excessive play, we must renew it; if swarf occasionally gets jammed in a diecast machine, causing excessively thick diecastings, we must prevent this from happening, and so on.

Similarly, if we have a process in which variables are more likely to vary positively than negatively, or vice versa, we must identify and eliminate them. There is one exception to this however, and this occurs when a process has been deliberately biased in a favourable direction. For example, in the manufacture of semi-conductor rectifiers, the forward resistance should be as low as possible. Therefore, the production engineer will deliberately bias his process in favour of low resistance, and this may result in a non-Normal frequency distribution curve.

Apart from exceptions of this sort, however, whenever we find a non-Normal frequency distribution curve we shall do our best to discover the causes, and eliminate them. This may sound difficult, but when we are dealing with processes with which we are familiar it is often quite easy. For example, if we tell the foreman of a department that there is a distinct tendency for his forgings to be too soft, he may reply at once, 'Oh, that's Fred being too slow quenching them'. By eliminating these variables, we not only come back to a Normal frequency curve; we also reduce the variability of the process so that it is capable of working to tighter specification limits.

In some cases, the shape of a non-Normal curve can give a pointer as to what is wrong, and the following examples illustrate this.

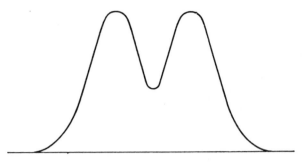

Figure 11.7   Bimodal frequency distribution curve

1   Bimodal   If our curve has two or more peaks, as shown in Figure 11.7, this means that our output is a mixture of two, probably Normal, frequency distributions. Possible explanations for this are that:

1   The outputs of two similar machines or processes have been mixed together, or that two separate runs on the same machine have been mixed.
2   The setting of a single machine or process suddenly changed in the middle of the run.
3   The machine or process is able to take up either of two settings at will.

If the two peaks are of unequal height, then we conclude that the process has run longer at the high peak setting than it did at the other.

2   Flat-topped curve   If our curve is flat topped, as in Figure 11.8, this probably means that the setting of our process is inclined to drift. Unlike our first example, it is not limited to two fairly distinct settings but can drift through a variety of positions.

3   Curve with a long tail   If our frequency distribution curve has a long tail, as shown in Figure 11.9, it is said to be *skewed*. This probably means that our process has at least one large variable, which is biasing it to the right. Its elimination will probably bring the curve back to the broken line.

4   The presence of observations which do not belong to the frequency distribution curve   In Figure 11.10 the frequency distribution curve itself is Normal but in addition there are a small number of observations, marked ●, which do not belong to the curve at all. For example, in some electrical components, their resistance will in general form a Normal curve. Here and there, however, our inspector may find a near short circuit (i.e. the resistance is zero). These oddities are often very trouble-

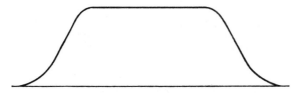

Figure 11.8   Flat-topped frequency distribution curve

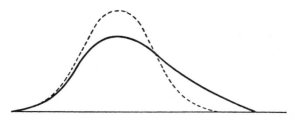

Figure 11.9   Frequency distribution curve with a long tail

Figure 11.10   Observations that do not belong to a frequency distribution curve

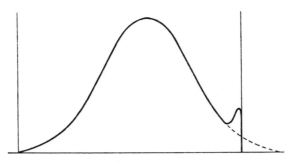

Figure 11.11   Effect of a lenient inspector on a frequency distribution curve

127

some, so the best solution where possible is to refine the process, so that they are not made. Where this is not possible, then:

1   The information given in Chapters 11 to 14, dealing with variables, will apply only to the distribution curve proper, and not to these odd observations.
2   The oddities can be treated as attributes, as discussed in Chapter 15.
3   Their complete removal will involve 100 per cent inspection.

5   *Inspection effects*   In Figure 11.11, the distribution curve has an odd 'spike' just before it crosses the specification limit, and then the part of the curve which we would expect to be just outside the limit does not exist. Usually, this is caused by a lenient inspector who, on finding work just outside limit, has recorded it as just within limit.

6   *Alternate peaks and troughs*   This is usually associated with the calibration of the measuring instrument. In Figure 11.12 the weighing device was scaled in units of 0.2 g, and the inspector had to interpolate between the divisions, to read to 0.1 g. If the needle was near to 17.0 he recorded 17.0 g. Similarly if it was nearer to 17.2 he recorded 17.2 g. Only if it was so near to midway that he could not make up his mind, did he record 17.1 g. Hence peaks occurred for 17.0, 17.2, 17.4, etc., and troughs for, 17.1, 17.3, 17.5, etc.

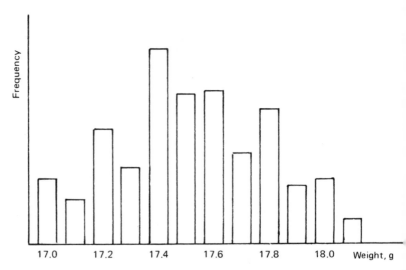

Figure 11.12   Example of alternate peaks and troughs

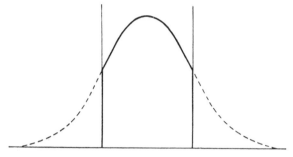

Figure 11.13 Effect of 100 per cent inspection when a process is unable to meet its limits

7 A nearly rectangular frequency distribution curve In Figure 11.13 the distribution curve is not far off rectangular. This can occur if the manufacturing process was much too variable to meet the specification limits and someone decided to do 100 per cent inspection on the output to eliminate work which was outside limit. Thus, the original output included the two sections of the curve drawn in broken lines.

Plotting a frequency distribution curve Care is needed in drawing a frequency distribution curve, if information is not to be lost or bias introduced. The following are guidelines.

a   If the raw data will plot satisfactorily as it is, do not attempt to group it. In Section 11.9 it was possible to plot in the 0·1 ohm steps created by the method of measurement. If measurement had been in 0·01 ohm steps however, grouping into cells would have been necessary unless a large number of observations had been available. Too many cells and insufficient data result in cells being inadequately occupied. Beware of losing data by grouping. In the example in Figure 11.12, if each pair of cells had been merged into one, the alternate peak and trough effect would have been lost.

b   Aim for a minimum of about 12 cells, and a few more if possible. If the number of cells is reduced to say 4 or 5, almost any data can be made to look Normal.

c   Make all cells equal in width.

d   Choose scales carefully. A variable process can be made to look quite reasonable by cramping the horizontal scale. If two curves are to be compared, they must be drawn to the same scale.

11.5 Average and standard deviation

For each frequency distribution curve, we can work out two useful quantities, called the average and the standard deviation respectively.

11.5.1 The average

We can calculate the average, or mean value, at which our process is working in the usual way. For simplicity, suppose that we have ten observations of the weights of some pellets, as follows (in practice we should prefer more than ten observations, in order to get greater precision):

21, 20, 20, 19, 21, 22, 20, 18, 19, 20 g

The average weight of these pellets is 200/10 = 20 g.

The average tells us the machine or process setting. Thus, our pellet-making machine is set nominally at 20 g although individual pellets may vary from this value.

In Figure 11.14, frequency distribution curve A has an average value of 13 g, while B has an average value of 20 g. (If our curve is Normal, the average is at the peak of the curve.)

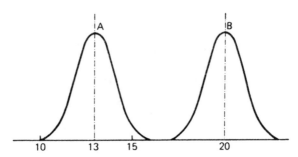

Figure 11.14 Frequency distribution curves indicating that the process average has changed

Thus, if we know our machine or process average, we know the value at which our frequency distribution curve is centred. If the machine or process setting moves up or down, then the whole distribution curve, including the average value, moves up or down with it.

11.5.2 The standard deviation

The standard deviation measures the variability of our observations about their mean value. In Figure 11.15 both curves have the same mean at 20 g, but A is more variable than B, and so will have a larger

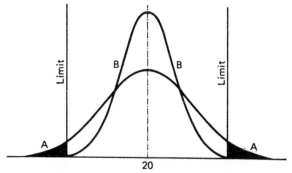

Figure 11.15 Frequency distribution curves indicating that the variability has changed

standard deviation. To estimate the standard deviation, the steps are as follows (the values are for the pellet example, started in Section 11.5.1):

1 In column A below, set out all the observations that differ in value. Although we have 10 observations, there are only 5 different values, i.e. 18, 19, 20, 21, 22.
2 Subtract the mean of 20 g from each, giving column B.
3 Square the values in column B to give column C.
4 Allow for the fact that some values occur more than once, e.g. 19 occurs twice and 20 four times. Set out the number of times each occurs, i.e. the frequency, in column D.
5 Multiply column C by column D to give column E.
6 Total column E.
7 Divide this total by the original number of observations less one. As there are 10 observations, we divide by $(n-1) = (10-1) = 9$.
8 Take the square root.

A Observations $= x_i$	B $(x_i - \bar{x})$	C $(x_i - \bar{x})^2$	D f	E $f(x_i - \bar{x})^2$
18	−2	+4	1	4
19	−1	+1	2	2
20	0	0	4	0
21	+1	+1	2	2
22	+2	+4	1	4
				12

Therefore the best estimate of the standard deviation is

$$\hat{\sigma} = \sqrt{[12/(10-1)]} = \sqrt{1.33} = 1.15g$$

The steps for estimating the standard deviation can be expressed mathematically as follows. Suppose there are n observations, so that the general term x_i takes the values $x_1, x_2, x_3 \ldots x_n$. Let the mean of the observations be $\bar{x}$. Then the best of the standard deviation is

$$\hat{\sigma} = \sqrt{\left[\frac{\sum\limits_{1}^{n}(x_i - \bar{x})^2}{(n-1)}\right]} \qquad (11.1)$$

11.5.3 Errors in calculating the mean and standard deviation

In the above example, we attempted to estimate the mean and standard deviation of the whole process, using observations taken on a sample of 10 pellets. If we had used a sample of 100 pellets, we should have expected our estimate to be nearer to the correct value, but still not as near as if we had used a sample of 1,000. Thus when we calculate the mean and standard deviation from a sample, our result is only an *estimate* of the true value. We hope our estimate will be reasonably correct, but in order to distinguish it from the true value of the whole process, it is usual to use:

$\hat{\sigma}$ or s = the best estimate of the process standard deviation which can be made from the sample data available.
σ = the true standard deviation of the whole process.

This is the reason why the denominator of Eqn 11.1 is $(n-1)$ and not (n) as we might expect. The term $(n-1)$ is called the *number of degrees of freedom,* in which the (-1) is a correction factor which ensures that we get an unbiased estimate of the process standard deviation. If, as often happens in quality control, we have a small sample of say 5, whether we divide by 5 or 4 makes a considerable difference. If the sample exceeds about 30, it usually makes little difference whether we divide by (n) or $(n-1)$. Nevertheless when dealing with samples, it is always correct to use $(n-1)$, however large the sample.

11.6 Properties of a Normal frequency distribution curve

Notice that the standard deviation is in the *same units* as the original data. Thus, when we had pellet weights in grammes our standard deviation was in grammes; if we had been observing a diameter in millimetres our standard deviation would have been in millimetres, and so on.

Consider the frequency distribution curve for our pellets as shown in Figure 11.16 and bear in mind that the horizontal or x axis is in grammes. Starting from the average line at O, count 1 standard deviation in grammes on either side, and draw two vertical lines as shown at A and A. From A and A, then count another standard deviation on either side and put two more verticals at B and B, and repeat yet again to get C and C. We have now cut our curve into six sections and, assuming that it is Normal in shape, each section will contain a predictable percentage of the total production, as shown in Figure 11.16.

Thus, in our example, the average pellet weight is 20 g, and the standard deviation is 1.15 g. Therefore, as Figure 11.16 shows, 34.1 per cent of pellets will have a weight between 20 g and $(20 + 1.15) = 21.15$ g. Another 34.1 per cent will have a weight between $(20 - 1.15) = 18.85$ and 20 g. Similarly, 13.6 per cent will have a weight between 21.15 and $(21.15 + 1.15) = 22.30$ g, and a further 13.6 per cent between 17.70 and 18.85 g, and so on. In theory, about 0.13 per cent of pellets lie outside three standard deviations on each side, although such pellets may or may not be found in any actual sample. It is usual to assume that the curve ends at 3.09 standard deviations from mean, since only 0.1 per cent of production is theoretically beyond this.

An important application of the above is that it enables the quality

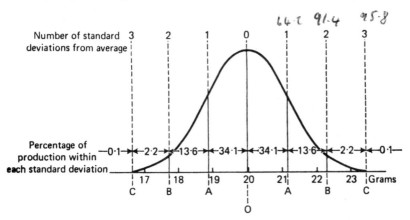

Figure 11.16 For a Normal frequency distribution curve, the percentage of observations between each standard deviation is as shown

133

engineer to predict the performance of his machines and processes. Thus, suppose that we have a capstan lathe which when working on a given materiel can produce diameters with a standard deviation of 0.01 mm. One day, the factory manager rings us up saying that a customer has requested an urgent delivery of components from this lathe, and has asked that all diameters should be 18.00 ± 0.02 mm. Can we do it? A quick calculation tells us that, as the standard deviation is 0.01 mm, the customer is asking us to work to within +2 and −2 standard deviations. Figure 11.16 shows us that the percentage of work between these limits will be 13.6 + 34.1 + 34.1 + 13.6 = 95.4 per cent and that, therefore, the remaining 4.6 per cent will be outside limits. It is then a question of economics, whether what our customer is prepared to pay will make the order profitable with at least 4.6 per cent out-of-limit work. (The actual percentage out-of-limit may be a shade higher, if we have any difficulty in holding the average value of our production, centrally within the drawing limits.)

Tables have been prepared giving the areas in the tail of the Normal distribution, e.g. *Statistical Tables for Science, Engineering, Management and Business Studies* by J. Murdoch and J. A. Barnes. Using these we can predict the percentage of our production which will be\out-of-limit, when the number of standard deviations from mean is\fractional. (Tables give the area in *one* tail. When both are concerned, the areas in each must be added together.)

11.7 The mode and median

In addition to the mean, there are two more ways in which what the statistician calls *central tendency* can be measured. They are *the mode* and *the median*.

11.7.1 The mode

This is the observation which occurs most frequently. Suppose, for example, that the observed weights of our pellets had been 19, 21, 18, 22, 21, 21, 20, 19, 20, 17, 21, 16, 21, 20, 18 and 19. We count how many there are of each:

Observation	Frequency (how many there are of each)
17	1
18	2
19	3
20	3
21	5
22	1

The mode is therefore 21, because this occurs more frequently (5 times), than any other value. In a frequency distribution curve, the mode is at the peak of the curve.

11.7.2 The median

When the observations are in strict ascending or decending order, the median is the middle one. Putting our example in ascending order we get:

17, 18, 18, 19, 19, 19, 20, *20,* 21, 21, 21, 21, 21, 22
Hence the median is 20

Since the average of these figures is 19.6, we find that the mean, mode and median all have different values. This is generally the case, except for symmetrical curves with a central peak. Thus for a Normal frequency distribution curve, the mean, mode and median all have the same value.

11.8 Assignable and unassignable causes of variation

Some of the sources of variation which affect a process are always known, and we do our best to minimise their effect. These the quality engineer calls the 'assignable' causes of variation.

However, even when all the assignable causes of variation are under control, some variability always remains unexplained. These are called 'unassignable' causes of variation, by which we mean that we do not at present understand what causes them. From time to time, the reason for an unassignable variation will be discovered and controlled, after which that particular variation will be assignable.

11.9 Cumulative frequency distribution curves

It is sometimes useful to plot a *cumulative frequency distribution curve.* By this we mean that we plot the total percentage of observations so far. Suppose we have a coil winding machine from which we take a sample of 60 successive coils, and measure their resistances to the nearest 0·1 ohm. This gives columns A and B of the table overleaf.

A	B	C	D
Observed resistance, ohms	No. of coils with each resistance	Cumulative total (= i)	Cumulative %
9·6	1	1	1·15
9·7	1	2	2·8
9·8	5	7	11·1
9·9	10	17	27·6
10·0	16	33	54·1
10·1	14	47	77·3
10·2	9	56	92·2
10·3	3	59	97·2
10·4	1	60	98·8

Next we cumulate the numbers of resistors, usually from the lowest value upwards, as shown in column C. Thus for 9·6 ohms we write 1, for 9·7 we put $(1 + 1) = 2$, and for 9·8 we put $(2 + 5) = 7$, etc. Clearly when we get to 10·4, the total must be the whole sample of 60.

Next we convert column C into percentages. We could do this in the usual way, but it is better to include a correction factor. The reason is that our information comes from a sample, but we would really like to know about the machine in general over a long run. For example, when we reach 10·4 ohms, we have undoubtedly accounted for 100% of our sample, but it would be wrong to infer that if we could check a long and representative run of many thousand coils, nothing above 10·4 would ever be found. Almost certainly a few exceed this value. Similar arguments apply to the rest of the sample. To correct for this in an unbiased way requires the use of median ranks, but these are difficult to work out, so unless tables are available, it is easier to use an excellent approximation devised by Bernard, which is

$$\text{Cumulative percentage} = \frac{i - 0.3}{n + 0.4} \times 100\%$$

where i is the cumulative total so far and n the number of observations in the sample. Thus for 9·6 ohms we have $i = 1$ and $n = 60$. Therefore,

$$\text{Cumulative percentage} = \frac{1 - 0.3}{60 + 0.4} \times 100 = 1.15\%$$

and for 10·4 ohms where $i = n = 60$, we have

$$\text{Cumulative percentage} = \frac{60 - 0.3}{60 + 0.4} \times 100 = 98.8\%$$

This means that on an unbiased basis, we estimate that $(100 - 98.8) = 1.2\%$ of our production will exceed 10·4 ohms. Working all the data gives column D. We now plot column A horizontally versus column D vertically on ordinary graph paper, as shown in Figure 11.17, to get a

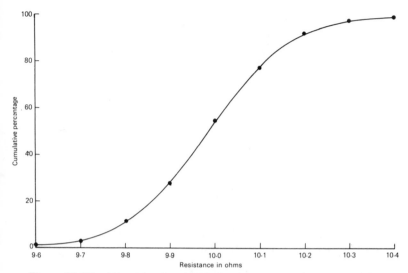

Figure 11.17 Example of a cumulative frequency distribution curve

cumulative frequency distribution curve or *ogive*. The steeper it is, the less the variability of the process concerned.

If we wish to check whether the variable concerned appears to be Normally distributed, we replot Figure 11.17 exactly, using *equal divisions versus probability graph paper*, sometimes called *arithmetic probability paper*. This is shown in Figure 11.18. Notice that the vertical axis is not evenly spaced. Starting at 50% and going towards either 0% or 100%, the divisions are at first close, but progressively space out, and this spacing has been carefully arranged so that if the data plotted are Normally distributed, a straight line results. Since our data form a reasonably straight line, we conclude they must be roughly Normal. In drawing the line, do not worry too much about outlying points. Thus the 98·8% point appears to be a little adrift, but the scale shows that it is only 0·8% from the line, whereas the 54·1% point is over 2% out, but appears less due to the cramping of the scale in the central region.

Where data are Normally distributed, the mean and standard deviation can easily be read from the graph. Since the Normal curve is symmetrical, the mean must correspond to 50% on the cumulative axis, which gives almost 10 ohms horizontally. Reference to Figure 11·6 shows that at lower point B, the cumulative area under the Normal curve is (0·1 + 2·2) = 2·3%. Similarly at upper point B, it is 2·3% short of 100%, which is 97·7%. Between the lower and upper B's there are four standard deviations on the horizontal axis. Applying this to Figure 11·18, we enter 2·3% and 97·7% on the vertical scale, and read 9·685 and 10·297 ohms, respectively, horizontally. Therefore

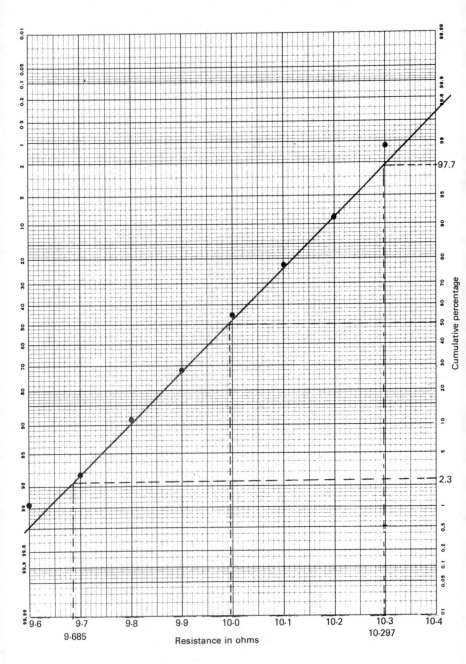

Figure 11.18 Use of equal divisions v. probability graph paper

138

Estimated standard deviation = $\dfrac{10\cdot297 - 9\cdot685}{4}$ = 0·153 ohm

Readers who check the above with the usual method, given in Section 11·5, will find that the standard deviation is reasonably correct, but the mean is a bit low. Primarily this is due to our grouping the data into cells, and cumulating upwards. If we cumulated from the highest value down, we would get a corresponding error in the opposite direction.

11.10   Statistical tolerances

Suppose that two parts A and B are required to fit together as shown in Figure 11.19, and that the pair will function correctly provided the total clearance between them is not less than 0.01 mm and not more

Part A

Part B

Figure 11.19

than 0.07 mm. Traditionally half this tolerance would be allocated to each part, e.g.

Total permitted tolerance = (0.07 − 0.01)   =   0.06
Tolerance on each part   =   0.03 mm

This ties the factory down unnecessarily, because the chances are remote that in practice a part A on top limit, will be mated with part B on bottom limit, or vice versa. In effect we are adding the variability of part A to that of part B, and are only concerned with their combined variability. Let

σ_o = Overall standard deviation
σ_A and σ_B = Standard deviation of each part respectively

139

Then statisticians have shown that:

$$\sigma_o{}^2 = \sigma_A{}^2 + \sigma_B{}^2 \qquad (11.2)$$

The square of any standard deviation is called the *variance*, so we are in effect adding the individual variances to get the overall variance.

If the frequency distribution of each part is Normal, and roughly fills the whole of the tolerance band we allocate to it, then:

$$\text{Tolerance} = T = 6 \times (\text{Standard deviation}) \qquad (11.3)$$

and Eq. (11.2) can be rewritten,

$$\left(\frac{T_O}{6}\right)^2 = \left(\frac{T_A}{6}\right)^2 + \left(\frac{T_B}{6}\right)^2$$

Therefore

$$T_O^2 = T_A^2 + T_B^2 \qquad (11.4)$$

Applying this to our problem gives,

$$(0.06)^2 = T_A^2 + T_B^2$$

If the tolerances are to be equally shared, therefore:

$$(0.0036) = 2 \times (\text{Tolerance on } A \text{ or } B)^2$$

Therefore

$$\text{Tolerance on } A \text{ or } B = 0.042 \text{ mm approx.}$$

If the frequency distributions are not Normal, then Eq. (11.3) is invalid. If they do not fill the whole of the tolerance band, there is no problem provided they are well centred within them. Otherwise a preponderance of extra large or extra small pieces will be made, and these will increase the risk of a mismatch between A and B.

When tolerances are based on the probabilities that certain measurements will occur, as in this example, they are said to be *statistical tolerances.*

11.11 Questions

1a Sketch frequency distribution curves to show the general shape of

each of the following:
- (i) Normal distribution *(2 marks)*
- (ii) Skewed Normal, marking the approximate positions of the mean, mode and median. *(5 marks)*
- (iii) Poisson or binomial distribution. *(3 marks)*

1b The variability of a dimension produced by a manufacturing process is Normally distributed with a standard deviation of 0.05 mm. The mean can be held practically constant. If this dimension is to be as high as possible, provided that hardly any exceed 60 mm, at what value should the mean be set? *(2 marks)*

1c If in the same process the components are required to be 60 ± 0.12 mm, what percentage would be out of limit:
- (i) if the mean is correctly set at 60.00 mm? *(3 marks)*
- (ii) if the mean is incorrectly set at 60.05 mm? *(3 marks)*

1d Quality engineers sometimes use arithmetic probability paper (probability versus equal divisions).
- (i) What is the most common purpose for which they use it? *(1 mark)*
- (ii) How is the graph paper designed? *(3 marks)*
- (iii) What are the steps involved in using it? *(3 marks)*

2 In order to estimate the process capability of a machine making resistors, the resistances of 1000 successive items from it were checked as follows:

Resistance in ohms	No. of resistors
150.00 – 150.49	5
150.50 – 150.99	17
151.00 – 151.49	44
151.50 – 151.99	92
152.00 – 152.49	150
152.50 – 152.99	192
153.00 – 153.49	192
153.50 – 153.99	150
154.00 – 154.49	92
154.50 – 154.99	44
155.00 – 155.49	17
155.50 – 155.99	5

2a Plot the above data as
- (i) an ordinary frequency distribution curve,

141

(ii)   a cumulative frequency distribution curve, i.e. an ogive,
(iii)   a cumulative frequency distribution curve on arithmetic
        probability paper, i.e. probability versus equal divisions.

(9 marks)

2b   State whether the data appears to be Normally distributed, giving
your reasons.   *(2 marks)*

2c   Use the curves to estimate the mean and standard deviation.

(6 marks)

2d   If a customer demands that resistors should be between 140 and
145 ohms
    (i)   to what mean value should the machine be adjusted?
    (ii)   approximately what percentage of resistors would be out-
           side limits?   *(8 marks)*

CHAPTER 12

THE PRINCIPLES OF QUALITY CONTROL CHARTS, CONTROLLING VARIABLES TO SPECIFICATION OR DRAWING LIMITS

12.1 Controlling a process over a period of time

In Section 11.5, we agreed that:
1   *The average* tells us the central value at which our machine or process is set. Our pellet machine was set at 20 g. We could, if we had wished, have set it at, say, 13 g in which case the average would have been 7 g less, but the variability would still have been much the same. (See Figure 11.14.)
2   *The standard deviation* is used to measure variability about the average. If a bearing on our machine became very worn, the variability and, therefore, the standard deviation might increase, but the average would probably stay the same. (See Figure 11.15.)
   In Section 11.6, when we were considering the capabilities of our capstan lathe, we assumed that once our machine was set up it would continue to produce with the same average and standard deviation until the production run was finished. In practice, however, we can seldom rely on this and, if we wish to work within specification or drawing limits, our quality control system needs to be able to detect when our machine or process reaches these limits.
   In order to do this economically, it is worth spending a little time observing the performance of our machine or process. Thus, suppose we choose one or two typical variables and then measure every piece made over, say, a morning or a shift. For example:
1   On a lathe we might observe a diameter.

143

2   On a diecast machine, the thickness of castings.

3   On a coilwinding machine, the resistance of the coils.

(For the moment, we are only dealing with variables; attributes will follow in Chapter 15.)

We plot our results as an ordinary graph, with the observed variable vertically, i.e. on the y axis, and successive pieces or time horizontally on the x axis. We then compare our graph with the six basic possibilities described below. In many cases, we can save ourselves a lot of inspection effort, if we can identify our pattern of variation with one of these.

Type 1   Figure 12.1 illustrates the ideal case, in which the machine or process goes on making piece after piece with very little variation at all. Practical examples of this are rare but, if we are lucky enough to have a very good machine or process, it would be foolish to waste money doing a lot of inspection. An occasional check to make sure that it is still all right should be sufficient.

Type 2   In Figure 12.2 our machine or process is very consistent for a time, but sooner or later at some random unpredictable moment, it suddenly goes wrong, e.g. perhaps it jams up, and after that the setting changes to a new level. Thus, the average value changes, but the variability and, therefore, the standard deviation, remain much the same. This pattern of behaviour is quite common, a typical example being that of automatic lathes, when they are working to reasonably wide drawing limits.

Type 3   In this type, illustrated in Figure 12.3, we have a fairly constant drift either upwards, as shown, or downwards. Successive points lie roughly in a straight line, and the moment the machine or process will go out of limit can be approximately predicted.

Type 4   The pattern of variation in Figure 12.4 is similar to that in Figure 12.2 in that the machine or process has one average setting for a time, and then at some unpredictable moment it suddenly changes to a new average. However, its variability about this average is much larger than before, and is now appreciable when compared with the specification limits.

Type 5   Figure 12.5 shows a corresponding variation to Figure 12.3. The average setting is gradually drifting up or down. About this average setting, however, we have a variability which is constant, but appreciable when compared with the specification limits.

Type 6   In our last example, illustrated in Figure 12.6, we have a

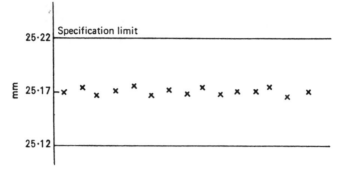

Figure 12.1 Plot of successive pieces from a machine or process that varies little compared with its specification limits — Type 1

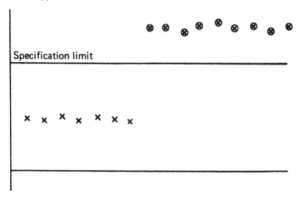

Figure 12.2 Machine or process with small variability and which is liable to change suddenly to a new average setting — Type 2

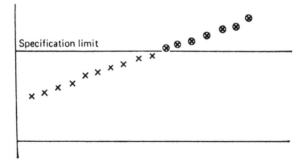

Figure 12.3 Machine or process with a small variability but a steady drift towards one limit — Type 3

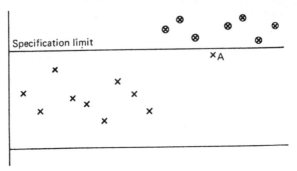

Figure 12.4 Machine or process with appreciable variability which is liable to change suddenly to a new average setting — Type 4

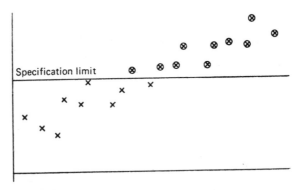

Figure 12.5 Machine or process with appreciable variability and a steady drift towards one limit — Type 5

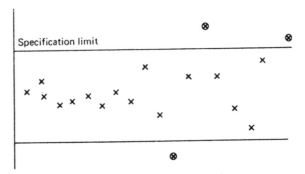

Figure 12.6 Machine or process in which the variability starts small but is liable to increase suddenly — Type 6

machine or process in which the average level remains fairly constant, but at some unpredictable time the variability and, therefore, the standard deviation increases suddenly or gradually.

12.2 Quality control of machines or processes which vary as Types 1, 2 or 3

If we can identify our machine or process with variation patterns of Types 1, 2 and 3, then we can make use of a simple method of quality control. Fortunately, a very considerable number of industrial processes belong to one of these types.

If our process is really Type 1 and never varies, then it hardly needs any shop floor quality control at all. In practice, of course, such perfection is seldom attained and occasional lapses will occur which result in either of Types 2 or 3.

Types 2 and 3 have one very important common feature. If at any moment we wish to know how our machine or process is doing, we have only to check the last piece made, for:

1   If the last piece made is within limits, then all the pieces made so far will in general be satisfactory, and in many cases it will be unnecessary to carry out any further inspection on them.

2   If the last piece made is out-of-limit, then the work made since the last satisfactory check will consist of a mixture of good and bad, the proportions of each depending on just when the machine went wrong.

Notice that there is an implied assumption here, that once the machine has gone out of limit it will not return by itself, without assistance from someone like the operator or setter. If this assumption is not justified, then the fact that the last piece is all right is no guarantee that all the work made since the last inspection is acceptable. However, do not be put off too easily. There is always the pessimist who will tell you that it will not work because, for example, 'A piece of swarf may get stuck on the stop for a short while, and then get pushed out again.' It may be *possible* for this to happen, but in many cases such an occurrence is very unlikely, and each case must be judged on fact, and not on opinions.

For machines and processes which are of Type 1, 2 or 3, therefore, we can come to several useful conclusions:

1   Each time we inspect, we only need to check a sample of one piece, the last made.

2   We can plot our results on the simplest of quality control charts, basically like any of Figures 12.1 to 12.3.

Vertically we put the variable we are plotting, and we draw two horizontal lines to represent the specification or drawing limits. Horizontally we plot successive samples which might be, say, once per hour. We do not need to use control limits, as discussed in Sections 12.3 to 12.6. Indeed, in cases where the pattern of variation is a well-defined Type 1 or 2 it may be possible to dispense with plotting variables, and plot attributes instead. Thus we merely plot √ for within limit, and ⊗ for out-of-limit, and our quality control chart will look like this:

Length 38.00 ± 0.12 mm √√√√√√√√ ⊗ √√√√√√√√

Attributes are not only quicker to plot, they also save a lot of space. As we may have a dozen or more qualities to check on each piece made, if we can plot them as attributes, then it will not be too difficult to get them all on to one chart by putting one row underneath the other. As a general rule, it is not convenient to put more than two, or at the most three, variables charts one under the other, since this requires a very large sheet of paper to avoid cramping them.

3   We only need to control for average. The variability is small enough compared with the specification or drawing limits to be omitted.

4   Remember that any actual quality control system must be designed to suit the production line for which it is intended. Do not be afraid to modify any of these suggestions to suit your needs.

12.3   Quality control of processes which vary as Types 4, 5 or 6

In this section, we can include not only processes that are obviously Types 4, 5 or 6, but also those which have a pattern of behaviour which does not exactly match any set type. All these have one feature in common, and that is that their variability is appreciable compared with the width between the specification or drawing limits. This means that it is no longer possible to check the last piece only and assume that, if that is all right, the rest are also acceptable. In Figure 12.4 we can see that if piece A happened to be checked as the last piece made, it would be within limits, even though practically all the pieces being made are over limit. Similar arguments apply to Figures 12.5 and 12.6. To meet this problem we need a different approach.

Now a quality control chart is rather like a frequency distribution curve turned on its side. The two specification limits are horizontal, instead of vertical, and the corresponding frequency distribution curve sits inside as shown in Figure 12.7.

If our machine or process is centred at mid-limit, the points which we plot will correspond to the frequency distribution curve marked A.

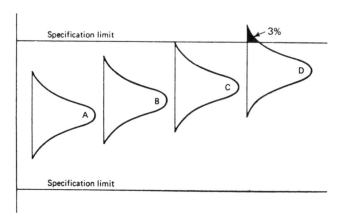

Figure 12.7 Movement of the frequency distribution curve when a process drifts towards one limit

Suppose that as manufacture proceeds the average level of production moves up. Thus, the plotted points will move up and with them the frequency distribution curve, which may now be as B in Figure 12.7.

The question is, 'How far do we dare to let this curve move up, before we stop it?' The answer must obviously be that it can move until it reaches position C, where one tail is just touching the specification limit. Thus:

1   If we let it drift any further, one tail of the curve will project over limit, as shown in D, and a proportion of out-of-limit work will be made.

2   If we stop the process or machine, and reset appreciably *before* the tail touches the limit, i.e. before position C is reached, then we shall waste time and money in unnecessary resetting.

This argument does, of course, apply equally to a movement of the frequency distribution curve towards the lower limit. (We have assumed here that the frequency distribution curve comes to a precise end on either side. In the mathematical sense, each tail does in fact continue to infinity, but its values become so low that for all practical purposes we can consider that it finishes at 3.09 standard deviations out from the mean. Even in theory, only 0.1 per cent is beyond that, on each side.)

Consider now the difficulty of detecting when the tail reaches and goes over limit. Suppose that the machine or process has actually reached position D in Figure 12.7, in which case 3 per cent of the production, i.e. the part of the curve shown black, is outside limit, and therefore 97 per cent is within limit. Now 3 per cent is a lot of out-of-limit work to incur

149

on one quality, on one operation. If we have say five or six operations, and several qualities to be controlled at each operation, we shall soon approach 100 per cent overall defectives.

However, the difficulty in detecting when 3 per cent of production is out-of-limit is a real one, because 3 per cent means that 3 pieces in 100 are wrong. If we say to an operator or inspector, 'Check one piece, and see that our process is all right', the chances will be only 3 in 100 that he will draw an out-of-limit piece. It is far more likely, i.e. 97 chances in 100, that he will get a satisfactory piece, and conclude that nothing is amiss. Even if we ask him to check five pieces, the odds are still against his finding an out-of-limit piece. Indeed, to have an average chance of finding one out-of-limit piece, he must check 33 pieces! Clearly, this is uneconomic, and we must find a more powerful method.

12.4   The effect of averaging samples

Suppose that we want to study the varying heights of men, so we decide to go down into our town centre one morning, select men at random, and assuming that they will let us, measure and record their heights. Next, we plot our observations as a frequency distribution curve, as shown in Figure 12.8. The curve we get will be Normal, because the factors which control our height obey the two conditions given in the first part of Section 11.4. Thus:

1   Our height is determined by many small variables, contributed by our parents, grandparents, upbringing, etc.
2   These variables are just as likely to make us a little taller, as a little shorter than average.

Thus, as Figure 12.8 shows, most men will be somewhere about average height, but here and there we shall find a very tall man, and his height will contribute towards tail C. Similarly, we shall come across the occasional very short man, whose height will contribute to tail A. (If we should find a deformed man only 3½ft high, his height will not be part of our curve because he has suffered some mishap which is the nature of a large variable, infringing the conditions for a Normal curve.)

Now suppose that when we go into our town centre, instead of taking men one at a time we take them five at a time, measure the height of each and average the five readings together. If we do this enough times, we shall be able to plot a new frequency distribution curve, based on *average of samples of five* and DEF in Figure 12.8 shows the sort of curve we might get. Notice that DEF has a shorter base and steeper sides than curve ABC for men taken one at a time.

The reason for this is as follows. When we took our men one at a time, we occasionally found a very tall man who contributed to tail C. However,

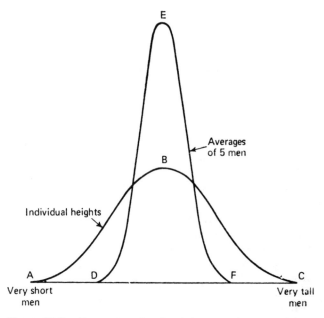

Figure 12.8 Frequency distribution curves for the heights of men

when we take men five at a time, the chances that we shall find five very tall men all together in the sample is so remote that it will hardly ever occur. Almost certainly, the height of each very tall man will be averaged with the heights of four men of more normal height. Hence, the average will be less than that of the tall man, and tail C of our original curve for men taken one at a time moves into position F. The same argument applies to very short men. The chances that we shall find five very short men all together in the same sample of five is so remote that we can dismiss them, and therefore tail A moves into D.

Clearly, the frequency distribution curve for averages of samples of five will have a smaller standard deviation than the original curve, and we can estimate its value from the following relation:

Let σ = the true standard deviation of the original samples of one, as discussed in Section 11.5.

n = the number of observations we propose to average together each time. This is five in the above example.

σ_n = the standard deviation of the averages of samples, taken n at a time. Statisticians call σ_n the *standard error of the mean*.

Then,

$$\sigma_n = \sigma/\sqrt{n} \qquad (12.1)$$

Our new curve will still be Normal in shape. Indeed, if the original curve ABC was not quite Normal, the new curve DEF will be nearer Normal than the original one.

12.5 The use of control limits

We now return to the problem which we posed in Section 12.3, of detecting quickly when a process or machine starts to make a proportion of out-of-limit work.

In Figure 12.9 the curve marked C is the same as is marked C in Figure 12.7. Thus, it is a frequency distribution curve for individual samples of one, and its position is such that it just touches one specification or drawing limit. Inside curve C is another curve E, which would be formed by taking samples of five, measuring each piece, and then drawing a new curve of averages of samples of five. Because this new curve is plotted from the same information as the curve for samples of one, it must always sit inside it as shown. If the curve for samples of one moves up or down, then the curve for averages of samples of five moves up or down with it.

Now, when the curve is in position C, so that it just touches the specification or drawing limits, we draw what is called a control limit as shown. Its position is just below the tip of the upper tail of curve E and it is, in fact, 1.96 standard deviations of curve E above its average value. We also draw a corresponding lower control limit, based on the lower specification or drawing limit.

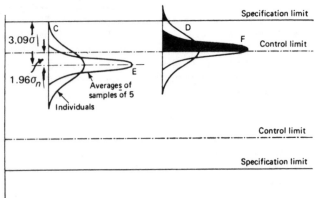

Figure 12.9 The principle of control limits

152

We now instruct our inspector that each time he visits the process or machine he is to take a sample of five pieces, measure them, average the results together and plot this average on the quality control chart, using the control limits as his limit lines. Consider now what happens:

1   If the average of the process or machine is comfortably in the middle of the specification or drawing limits, then the averages of samples of five will plot comfortably inside the two control limits.

2   When the process is in position C, so that the curve for samples of one just touches the specification or drawing limit, almost all the averages of samples of five will still be within the control limits. The only exception will be if the inspector happens to draw a sample of five which, when averaged, comes from the little bit of curve E, which is above the control limit. The chance that this will happen is only one in forty but, if it should occur, it will be a warning that the process is just about to go out-of-limit and so should be reset.

3   Suppose now that our curve gets into position D, where 3 per cent of individual pieces are outside limit. Notice what has happened to curve F, for averages of samples of five. Because of its short base and very steep sides, the same movement which took 3 *per cent of curve D* outside *specification limits*, has taken some 77 *per cent of curve F* outside *control limits*. This means that the inspector has a 77 per cent chance, which is better than two chances to one in favour of detecting this shift on his first sample of five. This enormous improvement over that discussed in Section 12.3 has been achieved merely by *averaging the five readings together, and plotting the result against control limits*.

Of course, the larger the sample which is averaged, the more curve E contracts, and the more powerful the method becomes. There are limitations, however:

1   The improvement is not proportional to the increase in sample size. Equation 12.1 shows that the square root is involved.
     Thus, if we use a sample of six, instead of five, the improvement is proportional to $\sqrt{6}$ compared with $\sqrt{5}$.
2   There are in any case objections to very large samples, and we shall discuss these in Section 13.8.

12.6   Detecting changes in variability

The quality control chart which we have just discussed will be very useful for detecting when the *average* level of our process changes. Thus, referring back to Figure 11.14, it will easily tell us when our process changes from that of curve A to that of curve B. It is, however, unlikely to tell us if the variability suddenly increases without a change of average. For example, a change from B to A in Figure 11.15 would probably go undetected, and for this we need a second chart, which we call a range chart.

In any sample, of say five observations, the range is the difference between the largest and the smallest. Thus, suppose we are measuring the resistance of five resistors. We might get:

40, 41, 38*, 42*, 39 ohms
Now range = (Largest − Smallest) = (42 − 38) = 4 ohms

Clearly, the greater the variability of the process, the greater the range will tend to be, although a single calculation of the range will give us no more than a rough indication of its variability. If, however, we observe the range of a lot of samples of say five each and average our results together, the mean range we shall obtain will give us a good indication of the variability. Indeed, there is a precise relation between true mean range and standard deviation. Thus to convert the mean range to the corresponding standard deviation, we multiply it by the appropriate constant, depending upon the sample size.

Sample size	2	3	4	5	6	7	8
Constant	0.90	0.59	0.49	0.43	0.40	0.37	0.35

On the shop floor, range is easier to use than standard deviation.

Detailed instructions for drawing up a range chart are given in Sections 13.2 and 13.3. We need only note here that the range chart has its own control limits, similar in principle to those of the average chart.

12.7 Quality control charts using 'modified limits'

Historically, the first quality control charts to be developed were those working to process capability, as described in Chapter 14. Later this method was 'modified' to permit charts to work to specification or drawing limits. Hence, the type of quality control chart which we have described in this chapter and in the next is commonly referred to in quality control literature as charts working to 'modified' limits, even though the term is not really appropriate.

CHAPTER 13

THE PRACTICAL USE OF QUALITY CONTROL CHARTS WHICH CONTROL VARIABLES TO SPECIFICATION OR DRAWING LIMITS

13.1 Machines and processes whose variability is small compared with the width between the specifications or drawing limits

If by an observational run we can identify our process as Type 1, 2 or 3, as shown in Figures 12.1-12.3, then our whole system of quality control, including the quality control chart, can be simplified as explained in Section 12.2 since:

1   Only one piece need be checked at each inspection.
2   The quality control chart need only consist of the two specification or drawing limits, as shown in Figures 12.1-12.3.
3   No control limits are required.
4   This method can be used for very short runs.

13.2 Machines and processes whose variability is comparable with the specification or drawing limits

If our observational run shows a pattern of variation like that in Figures 12.4 - 12.6, or if we are uncertain about the form it takes, then we should start off with average and range charts, even though some simplification may be possible later. We proceed as follows:

1   Draw outline quality control charts as shown in Figure 13.1. At this stage our chart will only show:

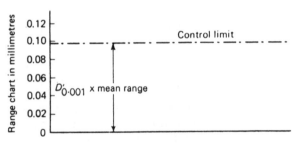

Figure 13.1 Construction of average and range charts for controlling a process or machine to specification or drawing limits

a   *Average chart*   The left-hand y axis, scaling the variable to be observed, and the two specification or drawing limits.

b   *Range chart*   The left-hand y axis, and a horizontal line at zero range. Notice that all range measurements are counted upwards from zero range.

2   Instruct the inspector to start plotting points on the blank chart. Thus, if the sample size is to be five pieces, taken once per hour, he will, every hour:

a   Take a sample of five pieces, from among those most recently made.

b Measure each piece, and calculate the sample average and the sample range.

c Plot the average and range so obtained on the quality control chart.

3 When we have at least ten, and preferably twenty settled points on the chart, we are ready to set the control limits. Sometimes at the start of a production run, particularly if it is a relatively new process, the variability is higher than it should be, or indeed will be, when the process has settled down. Hence, the reference to 'settled points'. Any obviously unsettled points should be discarded. Setting the control limits should not, however, be unduly delayed, because they can be useful in persuading the process to settle. In such cases it may be best to set provisional control limits early on, and then recalculate them later when the process has settled down.

4 To calculate the control limits we:

a Work out the range of each settled sample, as 2*b* above.

b Average each of these range values together to give the mean range.

c Multiply the mean range by the constant $A''_{0.025}$ below, choosing the value which corresponds to the sample size used.

Sample size	2	3	4	5	6	7	8
$A''_{0.025}$		1.51	1.16	1.02	0.95	0.90	0.87	0.84

d On the average chart, draw each control limit so that it is a distance

$$[(A''_{0.025}) \times (\text{Mean range})]$$

inside each specification or drawing limit, as shown in Figure 13.1.

e Multiply the mean range by the constant $D'_{0.001}$ below, which corresponds to the sample size used.

Sample size	2	3	4	5	6	7	8
$D'_{0.001}$		4.12	2.98	2.57	2.34	2.21	2.11	2.04

f On the range chart, draw the control limit a distance

$$[(D'_{0.001}) \times (\text{Mean range})]$$

up from zero range, as shown in Figure 13.1.

5 Our quality control chart is now complete. The constants $A''_{0.025}$ and $D'_{0.001}$ are repeated for your convenience in Table 3.

13.3 Example of the calculation of control limits for a quality control chart, working to specification or drawing limits

Suppose we wish to control a dimension to drawing limits of from 14.34 to 14.54 mm. Therefore, we draw our chart as shown in Figure 13.1, except that at this stage, it will have no control limits on either average or range. We set up our machine and start producing, and take a sample of five once per hour. As it happens, the machine settles down immediately, and the inspector's results over the first 10 hours are as follows:

Hour	1	2	3	4	5	6	7	8	9	10
Five	14.43	14.45	14.47	14.42	14.44	14.45	14.43	14.42	14.44	14.46
readings	14.45	14.44	14.45	14.43	14.42	14.44	14.43	14.44	14.44	14.41
on	14.43	14.44	14.43	14.46	14.47	14.44	14.46	14.44	14.46	14.44
each	14.42	14.45	14.43	14.47	14.44	14.43	14.45	14.48	14.46	14.45
sample	14.46	14.42	14.44	14.44	14.45	14.45	14.47	14.43	14.47	14.45
Range	0.04	0.03	0.04	0.05	0.05	0.02	0.04	0.06	0.03	0.05

Therefore, mean range = w = 0.41/10 = 0.041 mm

1 On the average chart

We set the control limits at $(A''_{0.025} \times$ mean range) from the drawing limits

$$= 0.95 \times 0.041 \text{ mm}$$
$$= 0.039 \text{ mm}$$

2 On the range chart

We set the range limit at $(D'_{0.001} \times$ mean range) up from zero range
$$= 2.34 \times 0.041 \text{ mm}$$
$$= 0.096 \text{ mm}$$

These quantities are now used to draw the control limits, as shown in Figure 13.1 and explained in Section 13.2, paragraph 4.

13.4 Making use of the quality control chart

To be of maximum use, the quality control chart must show the state of the process or machine at a glance. Therefore:

1 Provide the person who will fill in the chart with a red ball-point pen,

as well as a black one. All points, etc., are entered in black but, whenever
a point is out-of-limit, it is ringed in red. This makes it stand out and so
encourages corrective action.

2   Make sure that a note is made on the chart of all changes in the process settings, resets, adjustments, etc., indicating the time at which the
change occurred, even if the change is not believed to affect the quality.
It is not uncommon to find that some believed harmless change does in
fact affect the quality and, if the change has been noted down on the
chart, it is easy to relate it to the resultant change in quality.

3   Ensure that everyone concerned is clear about the action to be taken
when a point plots outside limit. It is no good the chart drawing attention
to unsatisfactory quality, if nothing is done about it.

13.5   Practical points about control limits

Consider the quality control chart of Figure 13.1. The greater the variability of the process, the greater will be the value of the mean range.
Now this means that:

1   On the range chart, the control limits will be higher up the chart
giving us more 'room' in which to plot our points before they go outside
the control limit. Clearly, this will not worry us at all.

2   However, on the average chart, the greater the mean range, the further
each control limit is from its specification or drawing limit, and therefore,
the *less* the room between them, within which we hope our points will
plot. If the specification or drawing tolerances are very narrow, or if the
variability of the process is very large, the control limits may be so close
together that we cannot possibly work between them. Indeed, in extreme
cases, it is possible for the control limits to cross over, and then we are
completely snookered!
    Now when this happens, it does not mean that quality control has
failed. It is simply the chart telling us that, with that combination of
machine or process, materiel and operator, etc., we cannot possibly hold
those specification or drawing limits.

13.6   The control routine

Having taken some considerable trouble to set up our quality control chart, we must be careful not to assume our job is done. The chart is not an end in itself. Our job is to produce within specification or drawing limits, as cheaply and as easily as possible. If our chart assists in doing this, it justifies its existence. If it is of no help, it should be modified or discarded. Be careful before you discard, however. Most charts have uses which are not immediately apparent.

In order to reduce inspection to a minimum, the routine already discussed in Sections 8.10 to 8.16 is most useful. Thus:

1 Prepare a quality schedule, to tell inspector, setter and operator, etc., which qualities are to be inspected.
2 When each new run has been set up, check the 'first-off', to ensure that the set-up is satisfactory, for the first period's production.
3 Periodically check samples of the work produced, to ensure that the quality is still all right. Arrange that all work made between one inspection and the next is kept separate from the bulk of the production, until the check at the end of that period has proved satisfactory. If this check should be unsatisfactory, that period's work is isolated for 100 per cent inspection of the quality which is wrong, and the machine or process is readjusted for the quality which is out-of-limit. A further check is then made, before production recommences.
4 Check the last piece made in a production run, to check the condition of tools, etc.
5 Use final inspection only where economically justified. Consider whether operator control, as described in Sections 9.7 to 9.10, could with advantage replace some of the patrol inspection in (3) above.

13.7 Taking samples

When we require a sample of one only, we shall take the last, or almost the last, piece made. This is because we want to know the latest news about our process. We want to know whether it is all right now, and not whether it was all right some time ago.

When we take a larger sample of, say, five we shall still include the last, or almost the last piece made, but we have a choice about the other four. We can either take them from among the most recent work, or to be representative of the whole period's run. Our decision will depend upon what we want to know.

1 Most probably our desire will still be to get the latest news about our process, in order to keep it within specification limits, and, in this case, we shall take the whole sample from the most recent work.

2   It is just possible, however, that we may wish our sample to be representative of the whole of that period's work, so that we can use it to judge whether the period's work should be accepted without further, say 100 per cent, inspection. In this case, we shall take our sample from the whole of that period's work.

13.8 Sample size

The general rule for sampling a machine or process using variables, is 'little and often'. 'Often', because if a process approaches or goes out of limit, the sooner we find out about it and make a correction, the less out-of-limit work we shall make. The sample size must be sufficient to tell us the quality condition of our process, but should be no more. Thus, if a sample of five tells us all we need to know, a sample of ten merely tells us all we need to know twice over! In such a case, a sample of five every half hour is better than ten every hour, because when the process goes out of limit, we catch it, on average, in half the time.

As we have already shown in Section 12.2, if the pattern of variation of our process is as Figures 12.1, 12.2 or 12.3, then a sample of one, the last off, is usually sufficient. However, if our pattern is like Figures 12.4, 12.5 or 12.6, or if we are uncertain what it is, then a sample of one is unlikely to be enough. In such cases, a sample of two or three may also be too small to tell us how the frequency distribution is varying, and we must usually consider samples of, say, four upwards. Now, beyond about seven the relation which connects range and standard deviation (see Section 12.6) becomes insensitive and, therefore, we try not to go beyond this. This leaves us, in general, with a useful range of sample sizes of four, five, six and seven.

Since five is a convenient sample size to handle, we often settle for five, almost as a standard. It is easier for the inspectors, etc., if the sample size is always the same. However, there is nothing magic about five, and if another sample size is more appropriate, we should use it. For example:

1   Suppose a coilwinding machine has three heads. In this case, a sample of five has no meaning. We should either have a sample of three, i.e. one from each head, or six, i.e. two from each head.

2   On a plastics press, or a diecast machine, we may have a four impression tool, and again a sample of five has no meaning. This demands a sample of four, one from each impression.

3   Suppose we have a multi-impression die, with say sixteen impres-

sions. We shall probably decide to sample the sixteen from a single load. If we know nothing about the way the impressions vary one from another, we may take a random sample of five. Very often, however, there is some relation between the impressions. Probably the outside impressions always exhibit the largest variation from mean, and we might decide to have a sample of four, one from each outer row.

This again emphasises the desirability of finding out the variation patterns and characteristics of each type of machine or process we use, because this so often enables us to simplify the quality control system and increase its effectiveness.

13.9 Frequency of sampling

Like so much of quality control, deciding how often to sample is essentially an economic problem, since:
1   The more often we sample, the more our inspection costs us.
2   The less often we sample, the more the cost of out-of-limit work which is made from the moment the machine or process goes out of limit until the moment that we detect that it has done so.
Our object must be to choose a frequency of inspection which will make the total of the above two costs a minimum.

Now our machine or process can go out of limit in two different ways, and we must consider them separately, as follows:
1   It can drift out, in the manner shown in Figures 12.3 and 12.5.
2   It can go suddenly out of limit, at some random and unpredictable moment, as shown in Figures 12.2 and 12.4.

13.10 Drifting out of limit

If our machine or process always drifts towards one limit, then we can increase the length of run between adjustments or resets, by making sure that it is always set as near as possible to the other limit. Thus:
1   For a sample of one used without control limits, set the machine or process so that the first point is just comfortably inside the specification limit away from which it will drift.
2   For samples larger than one used with control limits, set the machine or process so that the first average point is just comfortably inside the control limit away from which it will drift.
We must now estimate how long it is safe to leave it between inspections. Our object is clearly to catch the machine or process just before it runs out of limit. In practice, at the start of a run little information

may be available, and we may have to set a provisional time between inspections. In this case, we play safe and set the frequency of inspection on the short side. As production proceeds, we can easily see whether our judgement was correct, since:

1   If most inspection points are near, but not over, the limit towards which the process is drifting, our estimation was probably correct.

2   If most points are well inside limit, we can afford to lengthen the interval between inspections.

3   If an appreciable proportion of the points is over the limit, we must shorten the interval between inspections.

If we decide to adjust the interval between inspections, then we must inspect the quality control chart again after a while, to see whether our change has been correct, and to adjust further as necessary. Where our sole problem is a predictable drift, it should be possible to control so that very little out-of-limit work is made and, at the same time, to ensure that inspection costs are a minimum. If an observational run has been carried out, this will of course give a first indication of what frequency of inspection will control the drift.

13.11   Going out of limit, at some unpredictable moment

Where at some unpredictable moment our machine or process may suddenly go out of limit, we cannot hope to run without any out-of-limit work at all, and we must settle for minimum total cost. In order to start production, we set some frequency of inspection based on experience. Thus, very often, one inspection per hour is a suitable basis on which to start. Once production is going, we calculate the average cost of defective work, i.e. of scrap and rework, say per week or over any other convenient period. We also work out what patrol inspection is costing, including overheads, over the same period. Strictly speaking, if the patrol inspector spends any of his time doing 100 per cent inspection on work which has plotted out of limit on the quality control chart, then the cost of this should be included with the cost of defective work, and not with the cost of patrol inspection.

Suppose that at the moment, we carry out one inspection per hour, and further suppose that we decided to change this to one inspection every half hour, i.e. we decide to inspect twice as often. The effect on costs would be as follows:

1   The cost of patrol inspection would roughly double, because twice as many inspections would require twice as many inspectors.

2   The cost of out-of-limit work would roughly halve. In order to see why this should be, consider the machine when it is checked once per hour. Now the machine may go wrong at any moment, giving rise to varying amounts of defective work on each occasion, depending on how long the machine falters before the patrol inspector is due to come along. However, there are two extreme cases:

a   When the machine goes wrong just as the inspector comes up to it. As he will catch it at once, almost no out-of-limit work will be made.

b   When the machine goes out of limit immediately the inspector has left it, and so runs for practically an hour before he returns and finds out.

Therefore, balancing these two extremes and all other possibilities together, we conclude that if we check once per hour, every time the machine goes out of limit we shall, on average, make half an hour's out of limit work. Thus, if we check every half hour we shall, on average, make a quarter of an hour's out-of-limit work, every time the machine goes off limit, and so on.

In order to determine the frequency of inspection that will give us minimum overall cost, we must do a short calculation. Let S be the cost of out-of-limit and, therefore, defective work, say per week, at our present frequency of inspection, and I the cost of patrol inspection over the same period (which should include overheads). Now suppose that we increase our frequency of inspection by a factor f. Thus if $f = 2$, we shall inspect twice as often, and so on. Therefore

Cost of out-of-limit work per week $= S/f$
Cost of patrol inspection $= If$

Therefore

Total cost $= C = If + (S/f)$

Now, we wish to find the value of f at which C is a minimum, bearing in mind that I and S are both constants, because they relate to the frequency of inspection at which we work. We therefore differentiate C with respect to f and put the result equal to zero. Thus

$$\frac{dC}{df} = I - (S/f^2) = 0$$

from which

$$I = S/f^2$$
$$f^2 = S/I$$
$$f = \sqrt{(S/I)} \qquad (13.1)$$

This means that we must increase our frequency of inspection by the square root of the present cost of out-of-limit work, divided by the present cost of patrol inspection, over the same period. If f comes out to 2, we shall inspect twice as often, and if it comes out to 0.5, we shall inspect half as often, and so on.

Notice that Eq. (13.1) means that the best frequency of inspection occurs when the cost of out-of-limit work equals the cost of patrol inspection. Indeed, you may be surprised to find that Eq. (13.1) may sometimes recommend *less* patrol inspection, because this will clearly increase the proportion of out-of-limit work. We can explain this with an example.

Suppose that at the moment, on a machine section where we check once per hour, the cost of patrol inspection, including overheads, is £160 per week, and that the value of out-of-limit work, which in this case is scrap, is £40 per week. We can draw up a table to show what happens, if we change the frequency of inspection.

Frequency of inspection	Cost of inspection	Cost of out-of-limit work	Total cost
Present once per hour	£160	£ 40	£200
Every half-hour	£320	£ 20	£340
Every 2 hours	£ 80	£ 80	£160*
Every 4 hours	£ 40	£160	£200
Every 8 hours	£ 20	£320	£340

Therefore, the minimum cost, among the frequencies which we have chosen, occurs when inspection takes place every two hours. We can confirm that this is in fact the minimum by inserting S = £40 and I = £160 into Eq. (13.1). Thus,

$$f = \sqrt{(S/I)} = \sqrt{(40/160)} = \sqrt{(1/4)} = \tfrac{1}{2}$$

Thus, our equation confirms that for minimum overall cost, we should inspect half as often as we do now; in other words, we should inspect every 2 hours, as denoted by an asterisk in the table.

There are a few practical points about the use of Eq. (13.1):

1 Inevitably f often works out to an awkward quantity. For example, it might come out to 3.16, in which case we might round it off to, say, 3.

2 The best frequency of inspection often calls for a fraction of an inspector! We must then either round off to the nearest whole inspector, or find the under-employed inspector something additional to do.

3 If our section or department does a variety of work then, in principle,

each type of work will have its own best frequency of inspection. However, it tends to get very complicated, if we say to our inspector, 'This job is to be checked every twenty minutes, that one every hour and a half, the next one to it every hour, and the one on the end every two hours and a half, etc.' Our inspectors would soon be in the most dreadful muddle. In such a case, if all work is reasonably similar, we may decide to do an overall calculation, based on the cost of all defective work for the section per week.

13.12 Processes which both drift and go out of limit at random

In most processes, either drift as discussed in Section 13.10 or sudden random changes as in Section 13.11 predominate sufficiently to be able to neglect the other. Where, however, both effects are serious enough to be taken into consideration, we proceed as follows:

1 Deal first of all with drift, along the lines suggested in Section 13.10.
2 Only after out-of-limit work due to drift has been largely eliminated do we count the cost of the remaining out-of-limit work, in order to use Eq. (13.1). Unless we work in this order, our calculation for random changes will be influenced by those due to drift.
3 We now have two 'best' frequencies of inspection, and we settle for the most frequent, because this is bound to suit the other.

13.13 The effect of operator control on frequency

Where operator control is used, as described in Sections 9.7 to 9.10, that operator replaces the patrol inspector by doing some or all of the periodic checks. The principles for deciding the frequency of inspection remain the same, with the following additions:

1 Where the operator has enough idle time while the machine is working on one piece to check the previous piece, then the case for checking every piece is very strong. In terms of cost, the operator has to be paid anyway for machine cycle time, so we might just as well utilise it as leave him doing nothing.

2 Where the operator cannot do his checks during the machining or processing cycle, then production of the next piece or load is held up while he checks that which he has just made. Thus, strictly speaking, the cost of operator checks should include the value of lost production. In practice, the calculation tends to become complicated and, therefore,

unless a lot of money is involved, we shall probably decide to do it on the following basis:

a   The loss of production while the operator does his checks must be small. We therefore give time-consuming checks to a patrol inspector.

b   The routine must be simple enough for an operator to work. In one section of a department, it is usually convenient to have a fixed frequency of inspection, such as one piece in five, for all except perhaps special jobs. Operators then soon get into the routine of checking every fifth piece, and work measurement engineers get into the habit of allowing time for checks at this frequency.

c   Remember that the effect of operator control is to increase operator interest in quality, and this in itself reduces defective work, over and above the reduction to be expected from the routine itself.

13.14   Interpretation of a quality control chart for variables

Our quality control chart is a link in a chain. By means of various checks, we collect information about the state of our machine or process, and when we plot this information on to the chart we intend that:

1   The information shall be recorded for future use.

2   The chart shall be largely self-analysing, and show at a glance whether any corrective action is required.

However, we must ensure that this action is taken, otherwise our chart is no more than a decoration on the wall! I remember one case in particular, where three supervisors spent most of one day trying to correct some trouble they had on their production line. And the irony of it was that they already had a quality control chart which showed exactly what was wrong but, unfortunately, they had not been adequately taught to read it!

Now there are two important points about the interpretation of a quality control chart:

1   When the average chart is out of limit, this means something quite different from when the range chart is out of limit.

2   Interpretation must be related to the particular type of production, and to the way the chart itself has been designed.

13.14.1 Average chart

If the average chart goes out of limit while the range stays put, then our frequency distribution curve has moved as shown in Figure 11.14, in-dicating that our machine or process has moved to a new average setting.

1   Sudden changes of average   If the change is sudden, then the cause must also be sudden. Therefore, we consider possibilities like the follow-ing, which are appropriate to our type of work:

a   The machine jammed up, so altering its setting.

b   The process suddenly picked up an impurity.

c   There was an unauthorised alteration of switches, taps, valves, etc., on the control equipment.

d   There were sudden changes in the setting of a temperature controller.

There are also many other possibilities which should normally be accompanied by a note on the quality control chart, e.g.

e   The start of a new batch of materiel of quality different from usual.

f   The start of a different operator, especially if inexperienced.

g   Changes made by an engineer or supervisor for some other reason which he did not think would upset the process.

2   Drifts of the average   When the average drifts, this indicates a pro-gressive change in the setting, etc. Many processes always drift a little:

a   As the tool wears.

b   As chemical solutions become spent, etc.

We soon get to know if our process is of this type and allow for the drift as discussed in Section 13.10.

Suppose, however, that a process or machine which does not nor-mally drift, suddenly begins to do so or, if it does normally do so, it suddenly starts to do so at a much greater rate than usual, or in the opposite direction. This must indicate a progressive change and, again, we shall seek a cause which is applicable to our type of work. For example:

a   The tool is not tight, and keeps moving a bit farther during each operation or cycle.

b   A batch to be treated in a chemical bath has picked up some im-purity, and each time a piece goes into the bath, the impurity level in the bath increases.

c   The setting of a temperature or other controller is drifting.

Occasionally, something happens accidentally, which proves to be advantageous. Thus, a variable which causes a drift in the opposite direction from usual, might be useful in keeping the process average steady.

13.4.2   Range chart

Now the range is a measure of variability and, when it goes out of limit, it indicates that the frequency distribution has changed as shown in Figure 11.15.

On machine work, the range often indicates the general overall condition of the machine, e.g. the effect of play in its bearings, etc. It is therefore, not likely to increase suddenly unless perhaps one bearing suddenly deteriorates, or something equivalent. Where machines are well maintained, we may find that the range changes very little, and it may be possible to omit the range chart altogether and control solely on the average chart.

Sometimes the operator can affect variability, particularly if his work is not controlled by a machine to any extent. In photographic development, for example, careless timing of the immersion of the plates in the chemical baths, sometimes too long, sometimes too short, would cause the variability to increase. If, however, all times at one stage were say just two minutes too long, this would affect the average rather than the range.

Changes in the quality of materiel may affect the range. If the materiel being used suddenly becomes more variable, then the range chart may go out of limit. (If the materiel suddenly changes to a different level of quality, but is consistent within itself, this would show up on the average chart.)

13.14.3   Examples of particular applications

We have already said that a quality control chart must be interpreted, having due regard for the way it and its routine were devised. The following examples illustrate this:

1   Suppose we have a multi-impression tool which we use for moulding, for example, a diecast tool or one which is making plastics components. We might decide that every time the inspector visits the machine, he should take a sample of, say, five from among the various impressions of the same moulding load. Now, if we then find that our average chart goes out of limit, this suggests that all the impressions have gone out of limit together. Thus, if the sample average is too thick, this may indicate that a piece of swarf is jammed in the tool, so that it cannot close properly. However, if the range chart goes out of limit, while the average remains steady, this indicates an increase in the difference from one impression to the next. For example, if the two faces of the tool were no longer parallel, this would tend to make the impression on one side

of the tool yield pieces which were too thick, while those on the other side might be too thin.

2   If we have a multi-headed machine, for example a coilwinding machine with four heads, then we might decide to take a sample of four, one coil from each head. If then the average chart goes out of limit, this would mean that the change was one which affected all four heads together. However, if the range went out of limit, this would indicate a change which affected at least one head, but not all four. Notice that a large change which affected one head, while it would affect the range considerably, would probably alter the average a little as well.

3   Suppose that we have to heat-treat batches of components in a furnace. We may decide that each time a batch comes out of the furnace, the inspector shall take a sample of five components, measure their hardness and plot an average and a range chart. In this case, if the average chart goes out of limit, it probably indicates one of the following:
a   Wrong temperature.
b   Wrong timing.
c   Furnace atmosphere contaminated.
d   Incorrect quality of batch submitted for treatment.
    If the range chart goes out of limit, it might indicate:
a   Uneven temperature distribution within the furnace.
b   Variable quality of the original batch.
    Analysis of this example is discussed more fully in Section 16.9.

Notice how relatively simple these examples tend to be. Thus, your first reaction might be that it is easy with straightforward work, but that your type of production is much more complicated. This may be true, but in general, production troubles arise from comparatively simple causes. The problem usually is to locate the precise cause of a given undesirable effect, and this is where the quality control chart is so useful. Once the cause is known, correction is straightforward. Even in instances which do appear to be somewhat involved, the complication often arises because a number of simple effects are going on together, and it is difficult to distinguish them. Thus, suppose that on our quality control chart both average and range are constantly wandering, apparently with no underlying pattern. A good approach to this problem is to control every process parameter we can, regardless of whether it is supposed to affect the quality. Later, when we have found out which parameters are important, we may be able to relax a little.

13.15 Isolating each period's work

In Section 13.6, paragraph 3, we agreed that each period's work should be kept separate until the check at the end of the period has proved satisfactory. The way that we shall do this in practice will vary with the type of work involved, and the following are examples:

1   Where the components are small, a separate container can be provided to store them temporarily until they can be added to the bulk of the production. This applies to many small parts, for example the output from lathes, drilling machines, etc. Some care may be necessary, however, to avoid damage to the components.

2   Where work stacks easily, it may be convenient to place it in separately marked piles.

3   Sometimes it is convenient to mark the component when it is checked, or to put in paper markers at the points where inspection took place. If a period's work has to be isolated, the inspector or operator goes back to the last paper or other mark. Where an inspection is satisfactory the paper marker can usually be left, and thrown out during the next operation.

4   Sometimes unusual methods are possible. In forging, for example, the fact that the most recently made forgings are hot may be sufficient indication of the last period's work.

13.16 Review of control limits

Where runs are long enough, it may well be that experience gained, and the resultant improvements to the process, will have the effect of progressively reducing its variability. In such cases, it is desirable to recalculate the control limits from time to time. If variability has reduced, we shall find that the range control limit is lower, but as a compensation the average control limits have moved outwards, towards the specification or drawing limits.

Sometimes we may decide to issue instructions that control limits are to be recalculated at regular intervals. Now occasionally it happens that for some reason the variability of a process increases. If this should prove to be the case, the inspectors should be instructed to report the fact, so that the reasons for it can be investigated.

13.17 Pre-control charts

One of the drawbacks of the standard quality control chart is that control limits cannot be set until we have at least 10 reasonably settled points (see Section 13.2, paragraph 3). If these are taken at say hourly intervals, it may well be that a short production run is finished well before the control limits can be set, and even if the runs are long, 10 hours is still a long time to wait. The pre-control chart offers one possible solution to this problem.

At the start, we do not know how the variability of our process compares with the specification limits. We therefore assume that the specification limits represent ± 4 standard deviations of the process, as shown in Figure 13.2. This is probably about the worst situation which will be satisfactory, since the frequency distribution itself will require ± 3 standard deviations, and the extra standard deviation on either side allows for process drift, setting errors, etc. Next we draw two pre-control limits at ± 2 standard deviations from the mid-point 0. Notice that

Figure 13.2   An example of a pre-control chart

these will fall right at the start of the steep part of the distribution curve.

We now take samples of one, and plot them on our chart.

1   As Figure 11.16 shows, approximately 0.1 + 2.2 = 2.3 per cent of the points will plot outside each control limit. This is roughly 1 point in 40.

2   If the process average moves appreciably off-centre, the fraction of points outside the pre-control limit will increase sharply, because of the steepness of the curve. If for example, it moves a whole standard deviation either way, the percentage of points out of limit rises to 0.1 + 2.2 + 13.6 = 15.9 per cent, or roughly 1 point in 6, and this is easy to detect. Thus two successive points outside the pre-control limits mean that a change has almost certainly occurred.

3   Suppose however that the frequency distribution curve is not as we have assumed it to be in Figure 13.2. Then: *(a)* if the process variability is less than we have assumed, almost all the plotted points should lie within the pre-control limits, and we shall have no worries, or *(b)* if its variability is greater, then more than 1 point in 40 will lie outside the pre-control limits. If the average setting can be held steady in the centre of the specification limits at 0, then in theory we can accept up to 6.7 per cent or roughly 1 point in 15 out of limit. However if we exceed 1 point in 40 out of limit, we shall be immediately warned that the process is finding the specification limits uncomfortably tight. We shall then investigate and take action as necessary.

The frequency of inspection is often set so that there are about 20 samples between each reset of the process. If the run is long enough, we shall consider changing over to a standard quality control chart, as soon as sufficient information is available to draw the control limits for it.

13.18 Multi-vari charts

The multi-vari chart is useful where we have two sources of variation of the same quality. For example:

1   The diameter of machined components may vary not only from piece to piece, but also within a piece, due to say a taper along its length.

2   When components are heat treated in batches, we may wish to compare the hardness variations within a batch, with those from batch to batch. Suppose we ask the inspector to check the hardness of five components from each batch. He is then to plot his

Figure 13.3 Example of a multi-vari chart

results as shown in Figure 13.3. Thus he plots the value of the largest and the smallest and joins them with a vertical line. Hence the longer the line, the more variable the batch. (In some cases it will be useful to plot the intermediate values as well).

The interpretation of the chart is most easily seen from Figure 13.3. Thus:

Section AB shows excessive hardness variation within each batch, although successive batches are quite similar to each other.

Section BC indicates that there is little variation within each batch, but an excessive variation between batches.

Section CD shows little variation within each batch, but a considerable drift in average hardness with time.

13.19 Acceptance sampling inspection by variables

Most acceptance sampling inspection is done using attributes, in the manner described in Chapters 4 to 7. Even where items are actually measured, e.g. with a micrometer, the inspector still declares so many good and so many bad, which means that the measurements are being treated as attributes. However, it is possible to perform acceptance sampling inspection by variables, and full details for doing this are given in BSS6002 and in the American MIL-STD-414. The choice between the two methods depends on the following:

1 *Sampling inspection by variables:*
   Advantages
       Smaller sample sizes.
       Information about the mean and standard deviation becomes available.
   Disadvantages
       Can only be used if the frequency distribution curve is approximately Normal.
       More calculation is required, but with modern calculators this is no great drawback.
2 *Sampling inspection by attributes*
   Advantages
       Simpler to use than variables.
       Many checks can only be done as attributes.
       Several qualities can be checked and included in one AQL.
       The frequency distribution distribution curve need not be Normal.
   Disadvantages
       Larger samples are required, but they yield less information.

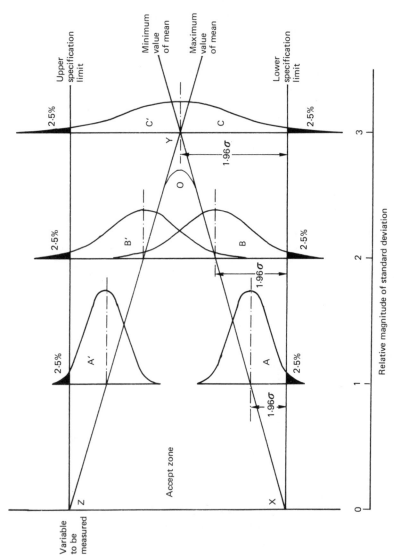

Figure 13.4 Theoretical situation when using acceptance sampling by variables

13.19.1 Principles of sampling inspection by variables

Various methods of sampling inspection by variables are available, but we shall confine ourselves to those given in BSS6002. So that each scheme using variables can be exactly related to its equivalent in attributes, all plans are called up by their AQL.

Suppose the AQL is to be 2·5%. This means that the batch can be accepted if no more than 2·5% of its items are out of limit, and curve A of Figure 13.4 shows a 'just acceptable' batch on this basis. Reference to Figures 11.16 and 14.1 shows that if 2·5% of the area under a Normal frequency distribution curve is outside specification limit, then the mean must be $1·96\,\sigma$ inside that limit, as shown in Figure 13.4. How this affects the practical situation depends on how we decide the AQL is to be applied, and there are four possibilities as follows.

1 Single Limit   If there is only one specification or drawing limit, for example the lower limit in Figure 13.4, then the mean must be at least $1·96\,\sigma$ above that limit, if the batch is to be accepted. Clearly the larger the value of the standard deviation, the further the mean must be kept above the specification limit. In Figure 13.4, the standard deviation of curve B is twice that of A, and for curve C it is three times A. Hence we can draw a line XY marking the minimum acceptable value of the batch mean, depending on the standard deviation. (If there is a single upper limit, the same argument applies to curves A', B', C', and the maximum value of the batch mean is shown by line YZ.)

2 Double Limits   If there are two limits, we must differentiate between:

a Separate limits where *each* limit is permitted to have the AQL value, e.g. 2.5%, out of limit.

b Combined limits where the total out-of-limit items from *both limits* together, must not exceed the AQL.

3 Separate Double Limits   This is equivalent to applying two entirely independent single limits, so that the bottom and top halves of Figure 13.4 both exist together. For a batch to be accepted, its mean must be on or above line XY, and on or below YZ. This gives accept zone XYZ. When the standard deviation is small compared with the width between the limits, as shown in position A, the frequency distribution curve cannot possibly have a tail outside more than one limit at a time. Curve C in the limiting position Y, however, has its full AQL (in this case 2.5%), outside each limit, and any larger value of standard deviation will cause the batch to be rejected. Hence any batch to the right of Y will be rejected.

4 Combined Double Limits   So long as the frequency distribution curve is sufficiently small so that it is impossible for it to have a tail outside both limits at the same time, it makes no difference whether the limits are separate or combined. At the other extreme position Y is obviously unacceptable, because it has 2·5% outside each limit, making 5·0% in all. Similarly positions near to Y, where the total of limit exceeds 2.5%, are unacceptable, and this has the effect of rounding off the accept zone from XYZ to XOZ as shown.

13.19.2   Practical use of sampling plans for variables

In order to use a variables sampling plan, we must in some form or other know or estimate the standard deviation. BSS6002 provides for three possibilities:

1 The standard deviation is already well established from previous deliveries. This is called the σ method, and it requires the smallest sample size of the three methods.
2 We estimate the standard deviation from the measurements on the sample, in principle using Eqn 11·1, although in practice the inspector would have a calculator. This is called the s method.
3 We estimate the mean range, which (as we said in Section 12·6) is exactly related to the standard deviation. This is called the R method.

BSS6002 provides tables for each of the above situations. Where there is only a single limit, or two which are to be treated separately, a decision can be reached by comparing the observed results with an acceptability constant given in the tables. Where two limits are combined, the solution must be found graphically, but again all necessary graphs are given in BSS6002.

13.20   Questions

1   Coils are wound four at a time on a four-headed coil winding machine, and are required to have an electrical resistance of 11.0 ± 0.7 ohms. A sample of four coils (one from each head) is checked for resistance value every hour, and over the first ten samples the following results (in ohms) are obtained:

Sample No.	1	2	3	4	5	6	7	8	9	10
Head A	11.2	11.0	10.9	10.9	11.2	11.0	10.9	11.2	11.1	11.2
Head B	10.8	10.9	10.8	10.9	11.0	10.8	10.9	10.8	10.8	10.9
Head C	10.8	10.7	11.0	11.1	11.1	10.5	11.1	10.9	10.8	10.9
Head D	11.1	11.0	11.3	11.2	11.3	10.9	11.5	11.1	11.2	11.1

1a Plot these results on average and range quality control charts, and insert control limits designed to control to specification limits, i.e. charts to modified limits. *(15 marke)*

Observations proceed as follows:

Sample No.	11	12	13	14	15	16	17	18	19	20
Head A	11.2	11.0	11.0	11.1	10.9	10.8	11.1	11.1	11.0	11.2
Head B	10.9	11.0	10.8	10.8	10.9	11.1	10.8	10.9	10.8	10.8
Head C	10.8	11.0	11.2	11.2	11.4	11.5	11.6	11.8	11.9	11.9
Head D	11.1	11.2	10.8	11.1	11.0	11.0	10.9	11.2	10.8	10.9

1b Plot these further observations on the charts and comment upon them. *(10 marks)*

2a For what purpose might a multi-vari chart be used? *(7 marks)*

2b Batches of raw materiel are each divided into five furnace loads which are processed and heat treated to produce electrical resistance elements. A sample of four elements is taken from each furnace load, and the resistance of each element is measured. Results from 20 successive furnace loads are given below (in ohms).

Batch	A					B				
Furnace load	1	2	3	4	5	6	7	8	9	10
	199.0	201.5	203.5	203.0	198.5	196.5	199.5	198.0	202.5	202.0
	203.0	198.0	200.0	201.5	198.0	203.0	197.0	200.0	202.0	201.0
	197.5	204.5	199.5	198.0	203.0	197.0	202.0	197.0	198.0	197.0
	198.0	202.5	198.0	197.0	203.5	203.0	200.5	202.5	196.5	197.5

Batch	C					D				
Furnace load	11	12	13	14	15	16	17	18	19	20
	198.0	199.5	200.0	199.0	201.0	204.5	199.0	203.0	199.0	205.0
	204.0	201.0	203.0	198.0	201.5	198.0	201.5	204.5	200.5	204.5
	199.0	203.5	197.5	201.5	198.0	199.5	205.0	198.0	198.0	198.5
	201.0	198.5	200.0	203.5	204.0	199.0	204.0	199.5	204.5	198.5

Specification limits are 200 ± 4 ohms.

(i) Plot a multi-vari chart of these observations. *(11 marks)*

(ii) Use the chart to discuss what can be learned about the process. *(7 marks)*

CHAPTER 14

QUALITY CONTROL CHARTS FOR CONTROLLING VARIABLES TO THE BEST THE PROCESS IS CAPABLE OF ACHIEVING

14.1 The need for process capability charts

So far, we have assumed that each variable has specification or drawing limits to which we must work. In some cases, however, we do not have such limits. For example:

1   Our process may be a new one, which we are still developing, and whose limits have yet to be decided. For the moment, we wish to control it to the closest limits which it is capable of holding.

2   Many processes contain a series of operations, each depending on the others, and a check on the quality of the product itself is only possible at the end. Thus, consider the manufacture of castings in a foundry. The specification and drawings may set the quality of the final casting in terms of dimensional tolerances, hardness, porosity, etc., but they are unlikely to tell us how accurately we must control the moisture content of the moulding sand, or the pouring temperature of the metal. Therefore we shall wish to control these secondary qualities, to the best they are reasonably capable of achieving.

3   Occasionally we may be obliged to produce with a process which is not capable of holding its drawing limits. We shall then need to control the process to the best it is capable of achieving, and since this will not be good enough, follow with 100 per cent inspection.

14.2 The basis of process capability control

To understand process capability charts, we must go back to the frequency distribution curves which we discussed in Chapter 11. We said that where a quality could be expressed as a variable, i.e. in figures, then we could represent its variability by a distribution curve, which in many cases would be approximately Normal. In Figure 11.16 we agreed that, within one standard deviation on either side of the average value, we should expect to find 34.1 + 34.1 = 68.2 per cent of all our production, and within two standard deviations on either side of the average, we should expect to find 68.2 + 13.6 + 13.6 = 95.4 per cent of all our production.

Now if 95.4 per cent of our production is within two standard deviations of the average value, the rest of our production, which is 100 − 95.4 = 4.6 per cent, must vary by more than two standard deviations from the average. We shall use this as the basis for our control system.

In Figure 14.1 the vertical line at O is the average, and two lines A and A′ have been drawn so that exactly one-fortieth of the area under the curve is outside each. Now one-fortieth is 2½ per cent, so this means that:

2½% of our production is below, i.e. to the left of, line A
2½% of our production is above, i.e. to the right of, line A′
Therefore, 95% of our production is between A and A′

Lines B and B′ have been drawn farther out, so that they each cut off only one-thousandth of the area under the curve. Thus:

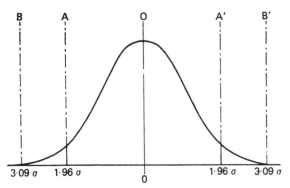

Figure 14.1 The principle of controlling to process or machine capability

0.1% of our production is below, i.e. to the left of, line B
0.1% of our production is above, i.e. to the right of, line B'
Therefore, 99.8% of our production is between B and B'

In order to draw these lines at such precise values as 1 in 40 (= 2½ per cent) and 1 in 1000 (= 0.1 per cent), we have to draw them at odd fractions of a standard deviation from the average line. Thus, lines A and A' are each 1.96 standard deviations from the average, and B and B' are each 3.09 standard deviations from the average.

Consider now how we can apply this knowledge in practice, and suppose that we have to produce a new electronic component with an active area which is nominally 30 mm^2. Suppose, further, that initial checks tell us that our production forms a frequency distribution curve which is approximately Normal, and which has a standard deviation of 1 mm^2. Applying this to what we have said above tells us that 95 per cent of our components should have an active area between

$$[30 - (1 \times 1.96)] = 28.04 \text{ and } [30 + (1 \times 1.96)] = 31.96 \text{ mm}^2$$

whereas, 99.8 per cent of our components should have an active area between

$$[30 - (1 \times 3.09)] = 26.91 \text{ and } [30 + (1 \times 3.09)] = 33.09 \text{ mm}^2$$

So long as the percentage of components in each group is approximately as predicted, then we know that our process has not changed much since we first measured its standard deviation. However, if the inspector suddenly finds that, say, 10 per cent of the components have an active area of 33 mm^2 or more, we know at once that our process has altered since we made our first observations on it.

This, then, is the basis of process capability quality control charts. *They tell us whether our process is continuing to perform as it did when the control limits were first set.*

We shall not, of course, expect our components to show the mathematical precision of the above calculation. Thus, being more realistic, we shall expect approximately 95 per cent of our components to have active areas between 28 and 32 mm^2, and almost all, i.e. 99.8 per cent, of our components to have active areas between 27 and 33 mm^2. Notice particularly the second point. Statistics tell us that, in theory, one component in 1000, i.e. 0.1 per cent, will have an active area exceeding 33.09 mm^2. However, whether we shall observe this in practice is very doubtful. In general, we can say that we shall expect all our production to have active areas between 27 and 33 mm^2, and the occurrence of any outside these limits must be investigated.

Even the 95 per cent limit will not often be exceeded, because statistics tell us that only 2½ per cent or 1 component in 40 should exceed this. Thus, from time to time, we shall find an odd component which is just outside this limit. However, if we find two such components together we must be very suspicious, because this is a probability of $\frac{1}{40} \times \frac{1}{40} = \frac{1}{1600}$. Now 1 in 1600 is a very remote possibility, and it is much more likely that our process settings have changed, rather than that this rare chance has occurred.

14.3 The construction of a process capability quality control chart

In order to achieve maximum sensitivity, we shall need an average and a range chart, with similarities to those described in Chapter 12. In this case, however, our control limits will show what our process is capable of achieving, instead of what the specification or drawing demands.

14.3.1 The average chart

If we instruct our inspector to take a periodic sample of, say, five pieces, measure them and average the results together, then the base of the frequency distribution curve for averages of samples of five will be a contraction of that for samples of one, exactly as described in Section 12.4. The position will, therefore, be as shown in Figure 14.2.

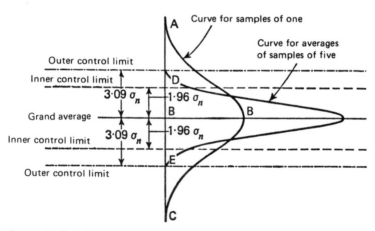

Figure 14.2 Derivation of the outer and inner control limits on the average chart when working to process or machine capability

Line BB represents the grand average of the whole process. As far as we are concerned, this will be the average of all the observations we take, at the time we are observing the capability of the process. Frequency distribution curve ABC has been drawn for all the individual observations, i.e. samples of one, and curve DBE is for the same data, but for averages of samples of five. We now draw two outer control limits, so that their distance from the grand average BB is 3.09 standard deviations of the curve for averages of samples of five, i.e. DBE, and a similar pair of inner control limits each 1.96 standard deviations from the grand average. If, now, our process continues to behave as it did when we set the limits, we shall expect to find that for points representing the average of samples of five:

1   Practically none (in theory 1 in 1000) will plot outside each outer control limit. Therefore, if points do in fact plot outside, this probably means that the process average has changed and that it should be readjusted.

2   Few (in theory 1 in 40) will plot outside each inner limit. Therefore, if we get two or more such points, close together, which are outside the limit, it probably means that the process grand average has changed and should be readjusted.

14.3.2   The range chart

The range chart is almost identical with the range chart already discussed in Section 13.2. The only difference is that for greater sensitivity it is usual to use two range control limits. The outer limit is the one discussed in Section 13.2 but, in addition, an inner limit is inserted to give earlier warning of any increase in variability.

14.4   Setting up a process capability quality control chart

The steps for setting up a quality control chart to control to process capability are similar to those described in Section 13.2 for a chart working to specification or drawing limits. We proceed as follows:

1   Draw an outline quality control chart, as shown in Figure 14.3. At this stage, our chart will show only the two left-hand axes for average and range, and a horizontal line at zero range.

2   Instruct the inspector to start plotting points on the blank chart. Thus, if the sample size is to be five taken once per hour, he will every hour:

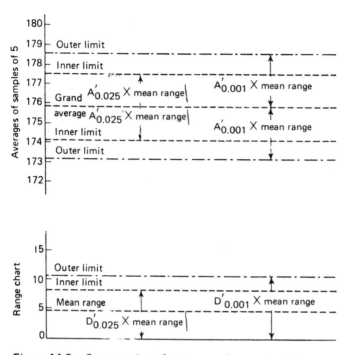

Figure 14.3 Construction of average and range charts for controlling·to process or machine capability

a Take a sample of five.
b Measure each piece, and calculate the sample average and the sample range.
c Plot the average and the range on the quality control chart.

3 When we have at least ten, and preferably twenty settled points on the chart, we are ready to set the limits. (As before, we reject any obviously unsettled points which are not typical of our process.)
a Average together all the sample averages to give a grand average, which we shall use as our estimate of the true average of the whole process. Draw a line on the average chart to represent this grand average. Thus, in Figure 14.3, the grand average is at 175.8 g.
b Work out the mean range by averaging together all the settled ranges.
c Multiply the mean range by the constant $A'_{0.025}$ below corresponding to the sample size.

Sample size	2	3	4	5	6	7	8
$A'_{0.025}$		1.23	0.67	0.48	0.38	0.32	0.27	0.24
$A'_{0.001}$		1.94	1.05	0.75	0.59	0.50	0.43	0.38

In Figure 14.3, start from the grand average and draw two inner control limits, each [(constant $A'_{0.025}$) × (mean range)] from it. Note, particularly, that for a process capability chart we start from the grand average and work outwards. (Compare this with a chart working to specification or drawing limits, in which we start from these limits and work inwards.)

d   Repeat step *(c)* exactly, except that we use [(constant $A'_{0.001}$) × (mean range)], and this gives us the two outer control limits.

4   Multiply the mean range by constant $D'_{0.025}$ and $D'_{0.001}$, respectively, and on the range chart set these values up from zero range to give the two range control limits, as shown in Figure 14.3:

Sample size	2	3	4	5	6	7	8
$D'_{0.025}$		2.81	2.17	1.93	1.81	1.72	1.66	1.62
$D'_{0.001}$		4.12	2.98	2.57	2.34	2.21	2.11	2.04

5   Summarising then, the position of the control limits for process capability quality control charts is:

1   Average chart

Inner control limits = (grand average) $\pm$ ($A'_{0.025}$ × mean range)
Outer control limits = (grand average) $\pm$ ($A'_{0.001}$ × mean range)

2   Range chart

Inner control limit = ($D'_{0.025}$ × mean range)
Outer control limit = ($D'_{0.001}$ × mean range)

14.5   An example of the calculation of process capability control limits

On a settled process, where the weight of each component must be controlled as accurately as possible, the inspector takes a sample of five from each batch made. Over ten successive batches, he obtained the following results in grammes, and he now wishes to calculate the position of the various control limits.

Batch	1	2	3	4	5	6	7	8	9	10
Weights	177	176	174	175	175	176	170	177	174	175
on	176	178	177	178	175	177	175	177	181	175
each	177	178	177	180	174	178	178	172	174	174
sample	178	180	176	172	173	178	177	176	176	175
of five	175	175	175	176	174	175	173	177	175	173
Total	883	887	879	881	871	884	873	879	880	872
Average	177	177	176	176	174	177	175	176	176	174
Range	3	5	3	8	2	3	8	5	7	2

Therefore, grand average = 1758/10 = 175.8
Mean range for a sample of 5 = 46/10 = 4.6

Average chart

Inner limits = grand average $\pm$ ($A'_{0.025}$ X mean range)
= 175.8 $\pm$ (0.38 X 4.6)
= 175.8 $\pm$ (1.75)
Draw limits at = 174.05 and at 177.55
Outer limits = grand average $\pm$ ($A'_{0.001}$ X mean range)
= 175.8 $\pm$ (0.59 X 4.6)
= 175.8 $\pm$ (2.72)
Draw limits at = · 173.08 and at 178.52

Range chart

Inner limit = ($D'_{0.025}$ X mean range) = (1.81 X 4.6) = 8.3
Outer limit = ($D'_{0.001}$ X mean range) = (2.34 X 4.6) = 10.8

The inspector, therefore, plots his process capability chart as shown in Figure 14.3 using the values calculated above. Notice that all the limit lines have come out to decimal values. Do not be tempted to round them off. It is useful to have limits which are 'between the lines', because then any actual sample which will not have much in the way of decimals will always plot, with certainty, either in or out of limit.

14.6 Taking samples and the sample size

When taking samples for process capability charts, we usually select them from among the last pieces made in order to get the latest 'news' about the state of the process. However, the general considerations discussed in Section 13.7 still apply.

Similarly, the choice of a sample size is exactly as set out in Section 13.8.

14.7 The frequency of sampling

In principle, the conditions upon which the frequency of taking samples should be based are the same as we discussed in Sections 13.9 to 13.13.

1 Processes which drift out of limit   Thus, if our process has a steady drift, we can estimate roughly how long it will take to drift out of limit and then inspect just before we expect this to happen. Difficulty may be experienced, however, if the drift is very marked, because process capability control limits attempt to hold the process as it was, without any drift. Hence, the process may constantly run out of limit. Where this is so, it may be necessary to widen the strict process capability limits to permit a run of reasonable length between resets. As usual, the problem is an economic one, and we have to decide whether the cost of frequent sampling and frequent process resets will be offset by the resultant reduction in quality variation.

2 Processes which go out of limit unpredictably   Where processes go out of limit at an unpredictable moment, the conditions given in Section 13.11 apply, at least in principle. Some difficulty, however, may be experienced in putting a value on the out-of-limit work produced and, in this case, some degree of judgement may be necessary in deciding how often to check. If the process is one in which even if everything goes well it is still touch and go whether the final specification quality is achieved at the end of the line, then we must play safe and sample fairly often. On the other hand, if our final quality is good enough to have something to spare, then we may be able to sample less often.

14.8 Interpretation of a process capability quality control chart

The interpretation of a process capability quality control chart is basically similar to the interpretation of one working to specification limits and, therefore, everything in Section 13.14 applies. In addition, we must remember the fundamental principles for setting up this type of chart which were as follows:

1   We observed the range within samples of say five, over ten to twenty samples. This gave us the mean variability *within samples* at this time.
2   We also observed the grand average at this time.
3   We then said that we wished to be warned of any change in either the average or range.

Now whether in fact a change in either average or range is significant in the practical sense depends very much on the process concerned, and we must ask ourselves:

1   Was the performance of the process at the time the limits were set good enough and typical enough for it to be used as a standard against which to compare future performance?
2   Is the process one in which we can reasonably expect the grand average to stay put? In many processes, it is difficult to prevent at least some changes in the grand average.

14.9   Review of control limits

We shall hope to use our process capability chart as a means of improving the process itself. For example, suppose our chart suddenly goes out of limit. We shall immediately investigate and, because we know exactly when the change occurred, we shall be able to relate it to any known change in the process. Suppose it exactly coincides with the use of a new batch of materiel. We shall investigate why that batch is different from other batches. Chemical analysis may show that it contains much more of a particular impurity than usual. We shall then have to do controlled tests to satisfy ourselves that it is the addition of this impurity which caused the trouble. If our tests confirm this, we shall have learned that this impurity is deadly and make sure that future batches of materiel are free from it. As all batches in the past contained a little of this impurity, the result will be an improvement in the overall quality from the process. The variability and, therefore, the range will reduce, and we shall be able to reset our control limits on both the average and range charts. Thus, in quality control terminology, a variable which was unassignable has now become assignable.

Therefore, from time to time, we recalculate the control limits to see whether an overall improvement has taken place. If it has, we shall find that the control limits on the average chart have moved in towards the grand average line, and that the range control limits are lower. We must, however, beware of issuing vague instructions to the inspector, for example 'to recalculate the control limits every three months', because it can happen that a process has got worse during this period. Thus, suppose the level of our undesirable impurity had gradually risen, then when the control limits were recalculated the average chart control limits would widen, and the range limits would be higher! As we have a process capability chart it follows that, if the process becomes less capable, the recalculated limits will relax to match its reduced standards. Therefore, we must tell our inspector that if, when he recalculates, the mean range proves to be greater than before, this must be reported for investigation. In general, we shall only accept wider limits if there is a compensating reason for them, for example if we are deliberately saving money by:

Buying cheaper, though lower quality materiel.

Employing a less skilled operator.

Using a less precise machine or other equipment.

14.10 Machine or process capability

There will be many occasions when we shall need to know what our processes and machines are capable of doing over a long run. For example, suppose that we make transistors. A customer may inquire for a special transistor with a higher output than usual, for which he is prepared to pay a greater than normal price. It is now essential to know what our processes are capable of doing for, if we can make these transistors economically, it will be a lucrative order to accept. However, if we cannot make them, it would be folly to pretend otherwise.

If we have process capability quality control charts in operation, we can get the information we want from them as follows:

1   Decide from the average chart the closest outer control limits which can be held over a long run. This may require some judgement but, in general, it is safer to base our deductions on what the process can do when well controlled, rather than on what it theoretically ought to do.

2   Now the outer control limits are based on the averages of samples. We must, therefore, multiply the distance between the two outer control limits on the average chart by the square root of the sample size. Thus, if the sample size is four, we multiply by two, and if it is five, we multiply by $\sqrt{5} = 2.236$, and so on.

Alternatively, we can do a special observational run to estimate the capability of a machine or process. One way of doing this would be:

1   Take about 50 pieces, just as they come off the machine or process, and record their measurements in strict order of manufacture.

2   Find the range of each successive group of five observations, i.e. observations 1 to 5 form the first group, 6 to 10 the second, and so on.
3   Calculate the mean range, and use the table in Section 12.6 to convert this to standard deviation.
4   Multiply this standard deviation by 6. This gives the tightest interval between the two drawing or specification limits which the process can hold, provided its grand average can be kept constant.
5   Now plot the original 50 observations as a graph, with the variable vertically and sequence of observations horizontally, and notice whether there is any significant drift, as shown in Figures 12.3 and 12.5. If there is, draw a best fit line (usually by eye) and estimate how much the average changes during the intended period between inspections.
6   Add the estimated drift of the average, as (5) above, to the inherent process variability, as (4), to get the overall process capability. Notice that the frequency of inspection and resetting of the process affects its overall capability. If we intend to inspect, say once per hour, but find that our calculated process variability is unacceptably large, we can halve the drift allowance by inspecting and resetting every half hour, although this will, of course, double our inspection and resetting costs. Conversely, if a larger variability is acceptable, we can reduce costs by increasing the time between inspection.
7   There is usually no way of predicting a sudden jump in the average as in Figures 12.2 and 12.4, and we have to deal with this as explained in Section 13.11.

14.11   Cusum charts

With a standard quality control chart, no action will normally be taken, so long as points plot within control limits. Thus a run of points, all above the grand average may not be noticed, because the position of each point is quite independent of those which preceded it. Sometimes this is unsatisfactory.

Suppose we are preparing a liquid chemical in which we wish the average content of a particular ingredient to be as near as possible to 10 g/litre. The liquid produced will be mixed in bulk before the next operation, so minor variations do not matter, so long as the *average* is kept at 10 g. For this we might decide to use a *cumulative sum chart*, or as it is usually called, a *cusum chart*. We start with a reference value, in this case the 10 g/litre, at which we wish to control the process, although in other applications it might be the average performance of the process established from past history. We sample test the process at intervals, and deduct the reference value from each observation. What is left, we then plot as a difference up or down from the last point. Thus suppose that our first 10 results are:

Observation = O	Reference value = RV	Difference = (O − RV)	Cumulative difference
10	10	0	0
11	10	+1	+1
9	10	−1	0
10	10	0	0
12	10	+2	+2
9	10	−1	+1
10	10	0	+1
8	10	−2	−1
10	10	0	−1
11	10	+1	0

Average 10

These results are plotted in section **AB** of Figure 14.4.

Suppose our observations continue like this.

Observation	Reference value	Difference	Cumulative difference
11	10	+1	+1
10	10	0	+1
12	10	+2	+3
11	10	+1	+4
10	10	0	+4
11	10	+1	+5
13	10	+3	+8
12	10	+2	+10
9	10	−1	+9
11	10	+1	+10

Average 11

When we plot these results in section BC of Figure 14.11, we get a *straight line* going *upwards*, and this indicates that the process has changed to a *new average* level which is *higher* than the reference value. A check shows that it is averaging 11 g/litre instead of 10. In section CD of Figure 14.4, further observations are plotted, in which the average is 12 g/litre.

192

Figure 14.4 Example of a cusum chart

Interpretation of a cusum chart is therefore as follows:

1 A horizontal line of points means that the process is holding an average value equal to the reference value.

2 A *straight* line upwards means that the process has changed to a new *steady* average level, which is above the reference value. The steeper the line, the greater the difference between the new average and the reference value. (Conversely if the straight line is downwards, the new average is below the reference value.)

3 If the line is *curved* upwards, the new average is above the reference, and still increasing. Similarly if it is curved downwards, the average is below the reference and still reducing.

4 Notice that the position of a point on the chart represents the cumulative past history of the process, since observations were started.

Thus there is no particular significance in whether the point is high up or low down on the paper. If points run out of the top of the chart, it is common practice to restart them again near the bottom. All that matters is the direction in which the points are heading. In our example, we must adjust the process so that they keep a horizontal course.

Use of a V mask

A number of methods are used to set limits to the permissible slope of the plotted points, the most popular of which is to use a V mask as shown in Figure 14.5. The mask is usually made of clear plastic so that points lying under it can still be seen. It is defined by the angle within the jaws of the V (usually denoted by 2θ) and a blanked off lead distance d. In use the mask is placed with its axis O—O—O horizontal, and with P over the last point plotted. If any of the plotted points is covered by the mask, the process average is deemed to have changed. If it is too high, then the plotted points will rise too steeply, and some of them will be hidden by the *lower* side of the mask BC. Conversely if the process average is too low, the plotted points will fall too steeply, so that some will be hidden by the *upper* limb AD. The two quantities, θ and d, are usually set using either a table or a nomogram, but in principle θ determines the maximum amount the process average can be above or below the reference value, and d sets the variability in successive samples about that average.

Advantages and disadvantages   The chief advantage of a cusum chart is that it is very sensitive to small changes in the process average in the region of the reference value. It will also show large changes in average, but conventional charts will do this just as well.

It is not very sensitive to changes in variability, but where (as is often the case) each plotted point is an average of several observations, a cusum chart can be used in conjunction with an ordinary range chart. Another drawback of the cusum chart is that operators find them difficult to interpret. Hence they tend to be charts for quality engineers.

14.12   Questions

1   A machine is set to produce a diameter of 9 mm nominal, and a sample of five pieces is taken every hour from amongst the last made.

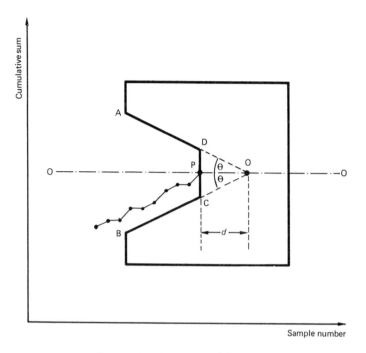

Figure 14.5 Use of a **V** mask

Over the first 10 samples the following results were obtained:

Sample No.	1	2	3	4	5	6	7	8	9	10
	9.05	9.05	9.04	9.04	9.06	9.06	9.04	9.06	9.05	9.03
	9.03	9.04	9.05	9.04	9.04	9.04	9.07	9.03	9.05	9.06
	9.03	9.06	9.04	9.04	9.05	9.05	9.06	9.03	9.05	9.04
	9.04	9.04	9.06	9.05	9.05	9.04	9.06	9.04	9.06	9.05
	9.06	9.05	9.04	9.04	9.06	9.04	9.05	9.05	9.05	9.03

1a Construct and plot appropriate average and range control charts, based on machine capability, and show clearly how the control limits were derived. *(15 marks)*

1b As an alternative to taking five pieces from amongst the last made, they could have been taken as a random sample from the whole of the last period's work. What considerations decide which should be used? *(5 marks)*

1c Under what circumstances is a chart controlling to process capability likely to be preferred to one controlling to drawing or specification limits, i.e. to a chart to modified limits? *(5 marks)*

2 A capstan lathe was set to produce a diameter with a nominal value of 12.05 mm. Samples of four pieces were taken from amongst the last made, at intervals of 15 minutes, with the following results:

Sample No.

1	2	3	4	5	6	7	8	9	10
12.05	12.06	12.05	12.06	12.08	12.08	12.10	12.09	12.10	12.10
12.06	12.06	12.06	12.07	12.07	12.09	12.09	12.08	12.09	12.11
12.05	12.05	12.07	12.08	12.08	12.09	12.07	12.10	12.11	12.12
12.04	12.05	12.07	12.06	12.07	12.07	12.09	12.11	12.11	12.11

2a Plot the above data on average and range quality control charts.
(7 marks)

2b Calculate and insert conventional control limits intended to control the machine to the best it is capable of achieving. *(7 marks)*

2c Explain why conventional control limits will not be satisfactory in this case, and hence suggest suitable control limits, assuming that patrol inspection takes place every hour. *(6 marks)*

2d A customer has enquired the tightest limits which this machine can hold. What would be your reply assuming that inspection continues at hourly intervals? *(5 marks)*

CHAPTER 15

QUALITY CONTROL OF ATTRIBUTES

15.1 The use of attributes

In Chapters 11 to 14, we considered variables, and we must now deal with quality control charts for attributes, that is for qualities which are not to be observed in figures. First, however, we must enlarge upon the advantages and disadvantages of each.

15.1.1 Advantages of variables

1   Actual figures usually tell us more about the process. Thus, suppose a diameter has limits of 6.50 to 6.60 mm and we decide to take a sample of one piece per hour. We might get the following:

Time	8 a.m.	9 a.m.	10 a.m.	11 a.m.	12 noon	1 p.m.	2 p.m.	3 p.m.	4 p.m.
Dia., mm	6.50	6.51	6.52	6.53	6.54	6.55	6.56	6.57	6.58

Clearly, this diameter is increasing 0.01 mm per hour, and we do not even need to plot a quality control chart in order to predict that it will reach the top limit of 6.60 mm at about 6.00 p.m., and that, unless we reset it, it will reach 6.61 mm by 7.00 p.m.

   If we check the same production run with a go/no-go gauge, we shall merely get the result 'OK' for all checks up to 6.00 p.m. Only at 7.00 p.m. will the go gauge fail to go on.

197

2   Variables usually require smaller samples than attributes. When we were discussing quality control charts for variables, we found that a sample of about five was usually sufficient. Because we had actual measurements we could estimate the average.and range of our process, and so learn quite a lot about its frequency distribution. If we check the same sample of five by attributes, we shall merely get the answer 'all OK' unless the process is already partially out of limit. In general, therefore, sample sizes for attributes have to be much larger than they do for variables and from a statistical point of view, therefore, variables are to be preferred to attributes.

15.1.2   Advantages of attributes

In spite of the statistical advantages of variables, attributes still play an important role in quality control:

1   Many qualities cannot be conveniently checked as variables, for example, appearance and the taste of many foods.

2   Even where we have a choice, attribute checks often have the advantage of being quicker, and of being satisfactorily done by less skilled inspectors. Direct reading test equipment may, however, modify this advantage where it is economically justified.

3   Where we are working to specification or drawing limits, and our machine or process is of the type which goes suddenly out of limit at some unpredictable time, then variables may have very little advantage over attributes. They cannot predict the moment of sudden change and, once this change has occurred, either method will detect it on the very next sample.

4   There are many cases where 100 per cent inspection is necessary. Thus, if we make electronic components, e.g. resistors, inductors, capacitors, or rectifiers, we shall probably decide that however good our production quality control they must all be tested before dispatch, simply because it is not fair to expect a customer to accept a faulty one. (In economic terms, this means that the cost of irate customers, in lost orders, exceeds the cost of 100 per cent inspection, which we shall probably do with automatic machines.) Now, our inspection may well be in attributes, on a pass or fail basis, but we shall not be short of information because our 'sample size' equals the whole of our production.

Section	Type ET 9 assembly														Supervisor				Mrs. K. Jones				
Date	March																						
	1	2	3	4	5		8	9	10	11	12		15	16	17	18	19		22	23	24	25	26	

Percentage of incorrect assemblies — scale: 10, 8, 6, 4, 2 (plotted points across dates)

% faulty Operator	1	2	3	4	5		8	9	10	11	12		15	16	17	18	19		22	23	24	25	26	
Miss G. Ewe	–	1	1	–	2	0·3	1	–	–	–	1	1	–	–	1	–	1	0·4	–	–	1	–	1	0·3
Mrs. V. Trune	5	3	–	4	9	3	–	7	3	4	2	2	7	6	–	–	2	3	2	–	–	5	4	2
Mrs. H. Watt	–	–	1	–	1	0·2	1	–	–	–	1	0·7	–	–	–	1	–	0·2	–	1	–	1	–	0·4
Miss D. Reeve													18	10	9	7	5	9	4	1	4	1	1	3

Number faulty — Assembly	1	2	3	4	5		8	9	10	11	12		15	16	17	18	19		22	23	24	25	26	
Wrong connection	–	–	–	–	–	0	–	–	–	–	–	0	–	–	–	–	–	0	–	–	–	–	–	0
Soldered joint	5	3	4	–	6	18	–	9	3	6	1	19	10	7	8	4	1	30	6	5	–	6	–	17
Wire missing	–	2	2	–	1	5	–	1	–	–	2	3	1	1	–	1	–	3	1	1	1	1	–	4
Wrong component	–	–	–	4	4	8	–	8	1	–	–	9	–	–	6	–	1	7	1	–	–	4	–	5
Loose component	1	–	–	1	–	2	–	–	–	3	1	4	8	5	2	–	1	16	–	1	2	–	3	6

Number faulty — Component	1	2	3	4	5		8	9	10	11	12		15	16	17	18	19		22	23	24	25	26	
Choke faulty	3	3	5	–	7	18	3	5	–	4	7	19	6	4	–	7	1	18	–	4	5	3	7	19
Transistor faulty	–	–	–	1	–	1	–	1	–	–	1	2	–	–	–	–	–	0	–	1	–	1	1	3
Capacitor faulty	–	–	–	–	–	0	–	–	–	1	–	1	–	–	–	–	–	0	–	–	–	1	–	1
Miscellaneous	–	–	–	–	–	0	–	–	–	–	–	0	–	–	–	–	–	0	–	–	–	–	–	0

Figure 15.1   Quality control chart for attributes for an assembly operation

5   A variables chart is for one particular quality. With attributes, several qualities can be combined. Thus, when we report that three of our samples are defective, two may be wrong on diameter and one on length.

We should, therefore, make a perfectly free choice between variables and attributes, depending on the practical needs of our type of production. If there is little difference, then we adopt variables, at least to start with, especially if it is our desire to improve the process. Attributes are often sufficient to maintain the quality standard on a process which we do not expect to be able to improve much further.

15.2   Quality control charts for attributes

Quality control charts for attributes have the advantage of being simple and, therefore, readily understood by operators. Figure 15.1 shows a typical example.

As with all charts, we design to suit the needs of the job in hand. Figure 15.1 shows the following:

1   This chart related to a section of some four girls, under a girl supervisor. Therefore, at the top we have the name of the section and the name of the girl supervisor. The latter is important, because it identifies the chart with the supervisor and so helps to encourage a personal interest in it.

2   At the top of the chart proper we have the date. As we are plotting the results of 100 per cent inspection for each day, the vertical columns bear the days of the week. At the end of the five working days of each week there is a column for the totals for that week.

3   Next we plot the percentage of incorrect assemblies each day. This shows the overall performance of the section, and encourages efforts to improve it.

4   Then we have the names of all the operators. This shows each of them how well she is doing, and keeps each well informed. Notice the line belonging to Miss D. Reeve. She was a new girl, and her performance the first day was not too good. The next day it improved, and by about the eighth day she was as good as the rest.

5   In the bottom part of the chart, we have an analysis of the various faults. Each figure now is the 'number of faults' and not the percentage.
a   Notice that it has been grouped into assembly faults, and component faults. This is important; the girls will be anxious that component faults are not 'booked against them.'
b   Notice, too, the way in which an attributes chart is able to cope with so many faults on one piece of paper. This is much more difficult with variables.

6   The weekly totals make it easy to see which particular faults cause most of the trouble, and these should be tackled first. (For further suggestions see Chapter 16.)

7   It is quite easy to get five or six weeks on one side of the chart and, if both sides are used, this means ten to twelve weeks per piece of paper per section, which is quite economical.

15.3   Sample size and frequency of sampling

As the attribute chart is particularly useful where 100 per cent inspection is being done in any case, the question of a sample size does not always arise. Where we have to sample, however, we must think in terms of much larger samples than we should use for variables and, curiously enough, the better the average quality the larger the sample size. Thus, suppose that about 10 per cent of our production is usually defective. Now that is one defective in ten, so that if we take a sample of, say, twenty we would expect on average to find two defectives in it. Suppose, however, we improve our quality so that only 1 per cent of our production is defective. Now that is only 1 defective in 100 and, therefore, a sample of twenty would be useless. It would only average one defective in every five samples. A sample of nearer 200 would be needed. As a general guide, we must take a sample which is large enough to give us a small number or percentage of defectives to plot.

Practical considerations usually decide the frequency of inspection. Often work is made in batches and, therefore, we take one sample per batch. If production is continuous, then we may treat each morning or afternoon as a batch, or make one's shift work into a batch, and so on. The principle of sampling as often as is reasonably practicable still holds. Indeed, one of the disadvantages of the type of chart shown in Figure 15.1 is that things can be wrong for a whole day, before the chart draws attention to it.

15.4 Control limits for attribute charts

Control limits can be set for attribute quality control charts along the same lines as for variables, but with the following differences:

1   Attribute charts control to process capability, since it clearly makes no sense to have specification limits saying for example, 'The percentage defective is to be between 7 and 9 per cent'. Thus, when we set our control limits we do, in effect, look to see what average percentage or number of defectives our process is making now, and then set control limits to ensure that this does not change without our knowledge.

2   We do not use a range chart. As our sample will give us a single result, i.e. the percentage or number faulty, range has no meaning.

We must decide whether to plot the number in the sample which is defective, or the percentage. If the sample size is always exactly the same, then we can plot the number defective, and so save the inspector from having to work out percentages. If the data for our chart come from 100 per cent inspection, it is unlikely that the number inspected will always be the same, and percentage will be the best choice. The method of setting the limits is slightly different in each case, as explained below.

15.5 Control limits for number defective

1 The inspector starts taking the stipulated sample size.
2 He plots his results on a chart which as yet has no limits.
3 When he has ten to twenty typical points, he works out the average number of defectives per sample. He then draws a line on his chart showing the average number of defectives per sample (see Figure 15.2).
4 Suppose the sample size is n and the average number of defectives per sample is c.
   He estimates the standard deviation L, where

$$L = \sqrt{\left\{ c[1 - (c/n)] \right\}}$$

Figure 15.2 Construction of a quality control chart for number defective

202

5   Using his average line as a datum line, he now marks off $2L$ upwards and also downwards to give the inner control limits, and $3L$ upwards and downwards to give the outer control limits (see Figure 15.2).

Example of control limits for number defective

Suppose that the average number defective, c, is 20 and the sample size, n, is 100 for each point plotted, then

$$L = \sqrt{\{c[1 - (c/n)]\}}$$
$$= \sqrt{\{20[1 - (20/100)]\}}$$
$$= 4$$

Therefore we set the two inner limits:

    $20 + (2 \times 4) = 28$ defectives
    $20 - (2 \times 4) = 12$ defectives

and we set the two outer limits

    $20 + (3 \times 4) = 32$ defectives
    $20 - (3 \times 4) = 8$ defectives

We will discuss the meaning of these control limits in Section 15.7.

15.6   Control limits for percentage defective

1   The inspector again starts checking the stipulated sample size and plots his results on a chart without limits, this time as a percentage of sample size.

2   When he has 10-20 typical points, he works out the average percentage defective. Notice that unless all the samples are of the same size, he must not average all his percentages together. He must first add up the *total number* defective, divide this by the total of all the samples added together, and multiply by 100. This is illustrated in the example below.

3   He draws a line on the chart showing the *average percentage* of defectives per sample.

4   Suppose the average percentage of defectives per sample is $\bar{p}$ and the average sample size n. He estimates the standard deviation M, where

$$M = \sqrt{[\bar{p}(100 - \bar{p})/n]}$$

5   Using his average percentage of defectives per sample ($\bar{p}$) as a datum line, he now draws his two inner control limits a distance $2M$ upwards and $2M$ downwards, and his two outer control limits a distance $3M$ upwards and $3M$ downwards. This is shown in Figure 15.3.

Figure 15.3   Construction of a quality control chart for percentage defective

6   Notice that the formula for M contains the sample size n. This means that, strictly speaking, if the number inspected changes the control limits must also be adjusted. This is clearly inconvenient in practice and, therefore, unless the variation is more than, say, 25 per cent, we usually base our limits on a fixed average value of n.

An example of control limits for percentage defective

Suppose that the inspector's results on ten typical samples are:

Sample number	1	2	3	4	5	6	7	8	9	10
Number defective	10	12	8	9	11	12	8	10	11	9
Number inspected	90	110	90	100	110	110	80	120	90	100
Percentage defective	11.1	10.9	8.9	9.0	10.0	10.9	10.0	8.3	12.2	9.0

Therefore, average percentage defective is:

$\bar{p}$ = Total defective/Total inspected
    = 100/1000 = 10%

Since $n = 100$, we have

M = $\sqrt{[\bar{p}(100 - \bar{p})/n]}$
    = $\sqrt{[10(100 - 10)/100]}$
    = 3

Therefore we set the inner limits at

10 + (2 × 3) = 16%
10 − (2 × 3) = 4%

and the outer limits at

10 + (3 × 3) = 19%
10 − (3 × 3) = 1%

15.7   The meaning of the control limits

The control limits we have just set show us the present capability of the process. Thus, in the example shown in Figure 15.3 the average percentage of defectives is 10 per cent, and the two inner limits are at 4 and 16 per cent. This means that although 10 per cent is the value we expect, because of the 'luck of the draw' when we take samples, etc., we could easily get any value from 4 to 16 per cent. Thus, if one day we get a single value of, say, 15 per cent we should not immediately conclude that disaster is befalling our process. Most likely it is merely that our inspector happened to take a worse than average sample. Of course, if we get two or three points in a row all at 15 per cent, then we should rightly be very suspicious; almost certainly our process has really got worse. Similarly, if we get a single value of say 5 per cent, we should not be jubilant at the sudden improvement. This, too, is probably only a sampling fluctuation. Thus, control limits make it possible to distinguish between chance sampling variations and real changes in the process.

The meaning of the inner and outer control limits is similar but not identical to that which we set for charts for variables in Sections 14.2 and 14.3. The probability of being outside the inner limits, just because a much worse than average sample is drawn, is not exactly 1 in 40, nor is the corresponding probability of being beyond the outer limits exactly 1 in 1000. If we turn back to Figure 4.1 we can see that for attributes the frequency distribution curve is not symmetrical and, therefore, it is non-Normal. Thus the probabilities of being outside the inner and outer control limits are not exactly 1 in 40 and 1 in 1000, respectively, but for practical purposes we can think of the probabilities as being roughly this.

15.8 The lower control limits

It is at first sight surprising to find that we have lower limits for charts for number or percentage defective. Obviously, if the process suddenly makes a lot *more* defectives than usual we want to know about it, but why should we be concerned if it suddenly makes less than usual? Surely this is all to the good?

There are several reasons why we may still want to be informed.

1   We must first check that the inspection is still going as planned. The *apparent* number or percentage of defectives will drop if either:
a   A new inspector is put on who, not being fully experienced, misses some of the defectives he should be finding. If we thereby allow some defective work to go out to our customers the result could be serious and costly.
b   Inspection has got behind production. We have already said that attribute charts are particularly useful for utilising information from 100 per cent inspection, which may have to be done anyway regardless of whether a chart is plotted. Now, if due to ill-

ness, etc., the inspection staff is depleted, it may well be that the remaining men temporarily fail to keep up with production. In that case, the number of defectives found will be less than usual, not because we have made less, but because the rest of the defectives have not yet been found. They are in the work which has been made but not yet inspected.

2   If our inspection is all right, then maybe our process really is temporarily better, in which case there must be some temporary change which caused it. If only we can find out what it is maybe we can make that change permanent, and so achieve a permanent reduction in the number or percentage of defectives. To have any real chance of finding this change in conditions, however, we need the lower control limits, so that we are informed quickly when it occurs. For example, I remember a case in which the proportion of defectives from a process suddenly dropped substantially below the lower control limits. Immediate investigation revealed that one of the raw materials being used was appreciably wet, and that this was due to carelessness in bringing that batch from the stores to the production shop on a wet day. Furthermore, scientific tests established that this particular operation was indeed improved if a certain amount of water was added to the ingredients. In future, then, we stipulated that:
a   The ingredients must be dry.
b   A controlled amount of water would be added during the production operation.

15.9   Applications and precautions in using attribute control limits

In our example in Section 15.6, we set control limits for a process which was at present averaging 10 per cent defectives. Now, because our control limits are based on process capability, our chart will not raise any alarm so long as this average stays at 10 per cent. In many cases, this may be a bad thing. Thus, our process may be a new one. Lots of processes start off with 10 per cent or more defectives, but we do not intend that they should remain like that. Our objective will be to reduce the percentage of defectives progressively to a much more acceptable figure. However, the control limits may act against us, because there is a danger that they will create the impression on the shop floor that '10 per cent is good enough' and, therefore, there will be little incentive for improvement. The lower control limits are particularly dangerous in this respect, unless their meaning has been fully explained to everybody.

In such a case, it may be better to set a 'target' upper limit, that is a number or percentage below which the shop is to try to keep. Thus, if the average percentage is now 10 per cent defective, we might set a target limit of 10 per cent. At first sight this might look a very easy target to achieve, but this is not necessarily so. Remember that if none of the inspection points is to be above 10 per cent, then 10 per cent is approximately equivalent to the upper, inner control limit. To achieve this, the average percentage of defectives can only be a little over 5 per cent, assuming that the sample size is still 100.

For example for $\bar{p} = 5\%$ and a sample size, n, of 100, the position of the upper inner limit is

$\bar{p} + 2\sqrt{[\bar{p}(100 - \bar{p})/n]}$
$= 5 + 2\sqrt{[5(100 - 5)/100]}$
$= 9.4\%$ approximately

If we decide to set a target limit, we must try to make it:
1   Stiff enough to be worth striving for, but
2   Reasonable enough to be attainable with effort.
We must make target limits quite clear to the shop floor. They must realise that the limits are targets which they may not be able to achieve immediately.

From the above, it follows that ordinary capability control limits for attributes are mostly of use on established, settled processes which have already been improved as much as seems likely to be possible. Thus, we can then use them:
1   To detect sudden or gradual rises in the proportion of defectives.
2   To keep track of several types of defective, all on one chart as Figure 15.1. Where one particular type of defective dominates, we can consider a variables chart if this is possible.

15.10   Questions

1a   Outline the circumstances in which a control chart for defectives would probably be preferred to one for variables.   *(7 marks)*

1b   A department making 500 ties per day does 100 per cent visual inspection, and finds that over a typical period of 20 working days, the numbers of ties rejected are respectively as follows:

13 10 18 12 12 9 11 13 11 16 13 10 14 15 10 9 17 12 12 13

Without drawing the charts themselves, calculate the position of the

inner and outer control limits for both the upper and lower positions
for

    (i)   a percentage defective chart   *(6 marks)*
    (ii)   a number defective chart   *(6 marks)*

1c   What are the merits of using each type of chart in *(i)* and *(ii)* above?
                                             (6 marks)

Author's note.   The above question does not ask for the charts to be
plotted, because it would then take more than the allowed time
to complete. However the reader may like to plot it out for his own
satisfaction.

    A further question involving defective charts is given at the end of
Chapter 16.

CHAPTER 16

CORRECTION OF QUALITY DEFICIENCIES

16.1 Sometimes the best-made plans go awry

If our quality planning and execution are perfect, then we shall have no
scrap and no corrective operations. However, we shall not always achieve
perfection and, therefore, we must provide in our system for the correction of such quality shortcomings as may occur.

Thus, sometimes a batch gets right to the end of the production line
and, just when it is due to go out, the final inspector finds a reason why
it must be rejected. When this happens, the immediate panic is usually
to correct that batch and dispatch it. After all, it is now overdue, and
the customer is rapidly getting anxious because he has not received it.
This is right and proper; such corrections must usually be done as a
matter of urgency.

In our anxiety to get that batch out, however, we often forget that
unless we correct the *cause* of that quality deficiency, the next time we
make another batch of that type the chances are that the same thing
will happen again and we shall have another batch of urgent corrections on our hands.

16.2 Sifting the evidence

Before we can come to any conclusions about what is wrong, we must
carefully and systematically analyse and study the evidence. If we have
a planned quality control system in operation, then we shall have

quality control charts, etc., available to assist our investigation. However, even if we are just starting planned quality control, our investigations will still follow similar lines except that we shall not have so much information readily available to us. Although any investigation must be adapted to suit the type of production concerned and our experience with it, the following is fairly typical of the steps we shall expect to take.

16.3 Has the work been fairly rejected?

To answer this question we must begin by making sure that the quality standard demanded is clearly defined in practical terms. All variables must have tolerances, and attributes must have suitable comparative standards (Sections 3.3 to 3.8).

16.3.1 Rejection by our own inspectors

Where work has been rejected by our own inspectors, we can ask them to demonstrate its shortcomings. Inexperienced inspectors, faulty test equipment, etc., may cause satisfactory work to be rejected, and we must make sure that the fault is real, before we spend a lot of time tracing it. If it is, then we must be quite clear how the work or process falls short of the minimum standard required.

16.3.2 Rejection by our customers

Rejections by customers are liable to be more serious, because of their damaging effect on our company's reputation. An immediate apology and a promise of investigation is desirable in the interests of good relations, even if it subsequently transpires that our quality is all right, and that it is our customer who is wrong.

If we are quite clear what our customer is complaining about, then we can proceed with the investigation. If not, we may have to pay him a visit and/or arrange for some of the rejected work to be returned to us. It is not uncommon for this first contact to reveal the basic cause of the trouble. For example:

1   Our customer's idea of the quality standard may be different from our own. Who is right is a matter for commercial negotiation. Remember, however, that our selling price will have been based on our conception of the quality standard and that, if the standard is changed,

our price may also require adjustment. Clearly from the factory point of view, if our production quality control system has produced the quality standard for which it was asked, it is no good blaming it if that standard proves to be incorrect. The fault may still, of course, lie in that part of our quality assurance which is within the orbit of our salesmen and designers.

2 Our customer's measuring equipment may be different from our own, and we shall have to co-operate in comparing the accuracy and precision of both sets of equipment. (See Section 3.5.)

If it transpires that both the quality standard and its method of measurement are satisfactory, then we are left with two major questions to answer:

a   How did it happen that incorrect quality was produced in the first place, since our quality control system should have prevented this?

b   Given that the product quality was wrong, how was it possible for it to get through our quality control system undetected, with the result that it was sent out to the customer?

16.4 Assistance from the quality control charts

We must identify what went wrong and correct it. Almost any sort of record is useful at this stage, but it is an occasion when the quality control chart is particularly valuable. From the type of fault concerned, we shall be able to deduce which operations or areas of the production line must be responsible, and so we immediately call for the relevant quality control charts. Even if some months have elapsed since manufacture, and this is common with customer rejections, the charts will still yield the vital information. Thus, they will tell us:

1   Was the quality which was wrong included in the quality schedule or on the quality control chart, as suggested in Sections 8.10 and 8.11? If we did not schedule it for control then we cannot be surprised if it received no particular attention.

2   If control was scheduled, does the chart show that the operator, inspector, etc., claim to have carried out the specified checks? The chart will tell us which operator and inspector are concerned.

3   If the checks were carried out, were any quality difficulties recorded, and if so what action was taken to overcome them? If no difficulties were recorded, then clearly either the control system was not being operated properly or the system itself is not foolproof.

16.5 Locating the cause of trouble

The source of our trouble must be somewhere in stages 2 and 3
of our quality control system, as given in Sections 1.3 to 1.6. Thus, if
we are honest, we shall be obliged to answer 'No' to at least one of the
following questions:

1   Was the method of manufacture satisfactory for the quality
     standard demanded? Did it comply with all the points we dis-
     cussed in Sections 8.1 to 8.8?
2   Was the tooling and equipment adequate to achieve the quality
     standard? (Section 8.8.)
3   Was the materiel satisfactory? If not, then we have a triple
     question:
     a   Why was unsatisfactory materiel used for manufacture?
     b   If the raw materiel or components were bought, how did
          they get through our incoming materiel inspection system
          as described in Chapters 6 and 7?
     c   If the materiel or components were made in our own
          factory, what went wrong with the quality control system
          etc.? How did it happen that they: *(i)* made them wrongly,
          (ii) released them to another department?
4   Were our operators sufficiently trained? Did they know the quality
     standard and the method by which they were to achieve it? It is
     unfortunately common to find that things went wrong because
     the operator was never clearly told what was required of him.
5   Was our shop floor quality control properly planned and executed?

16.6 Dealing with the 'culprits'

It is no use crying over spilt milk. Scrap which has been made cannot
be unmade, and our actions must be directed towards seeing that we do
not make another lot of scrap tomorrow. We must try to avoid dressing
people down, and if we decide that this must be done, we must do it
primarily with an eye to securing their co-operation in future. Unless
we do this, we achieve nothing whatever.

16.7 Analysis of scrap and rework — the Pareto curve

We can get further information by analysing the scrap or rework itself.
A good quality control chart will have been designed to be largely self-
analysing. Thus, in the example in Figure 15.1, it is very easy to see the
chief types of fault, etc., being incurred. Where such a chart is not

213

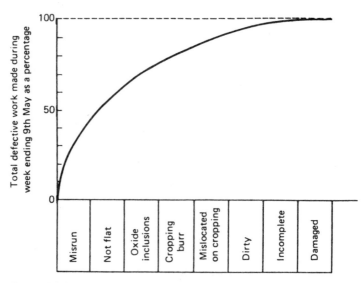

Figure 16.1 Example of a Pareto curve for a diecast shop

available, then we can make a direct analysis. Indeed, the following is particularly useful when we are making a first survey of a department, which as yet has no planned quality control.

The fundamental principle is simple. We take a load of defective work just as produced and sort it out into piles, depending on the type of fault concerned. In practice we usually do our sorting on paper, using inspection reports, etc. Figure 16.1 shows how this can be done.

This example is for the defective work made during a particular week by a diecast shop working on a long run of one part number. Vertically, we draw a percentage scale, where 100 per cent means all the defective work made during this period. Horizontally, we list the reasons why the work was defective, starting with the most numerous type and then going down in strict descending order. Thus, Figure 16.1 was plotted from the information in the table.

Reason defective	Total defective (%)	Cumulative Total (%)
Misrun	29	29
Not flat	25	54
Oxide inclusions	16	70
Cropping burr	10	80
Mislocated on cropping	9	89
Dirty	6	95
Incomplete	4	99
Damaged	1	100

214

Thus, 'misrun' was the worst single cause, at 29 per cent followed by 'not flat' at 25 per cent and 'oxide inclusions' at 16 per cent. We have now taken in a total of 70 per cent of our defective work in only three categories. Clearly, if we wish to reduce the proportion of defective work we must have a drive against 'misrun', followed by 'not flat' and 'oxide inclusions'. It would be a waste of time to try to eliminate 'incomplete' and 'damaged', because these only account for 5 per cent of the defective work between them. The practical man will also notice that most of the defective work is coming from the diecasting operation itself, and comparatively little from the subsequent cropping operation.

The graph in Figure 16.1 is called a Pareto curve, after the Italian economist who used it for studying the wealth of Italy. It has a very general application. We almost always find that most of the defective work comes from a small fraction of the total possible causes, in the same way that most of the crimes in Britain are committed by a small fraction of the population. The Pareto curve is sometimes called an 80/20 curve, because we often find that some 80 per cent of the defective work comes from only 20 per cent of the causes.

The Pareto curve can be drawn in various ways to suit the problem. For example:

1   If all of the defective work is the same part number, it is usually convenient to plot in percentage of defective pieces as in Figure 16.1. If, however, a variety of products is included in the analysis, it is usually best to plot vertically the value in money that is lost due to the defective work. Otherwise, fifty small nuts at 3p each will count more than one complicated part worth several hundred pounds.

2   If we have a short-run shop, working on a variety of part numbers, then horizontally we can make an analysis by part number as well as an analysis by types of defective work. It is not unusual to find that one part number makes a large proportion of the total scrap value. Indeed, this will tend to occur if three conditions are fulfilled:

a   The part concerned is made in largish quantities, compared with other production in the shop.
b   It tends to run with a high scrap percentage.
c   It is a valuable part, so that every time one is scrapped the money loss is large.

16.8   The measles chart

The measles chart is a variation of the Pareto curve, and is useful if the location of the fault in the work is important. Figure 16.2 shows a sketch

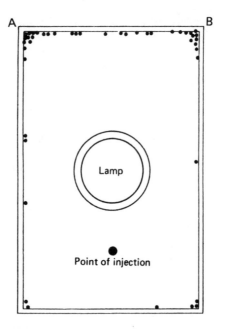

Figure 16.2 Example of a measles chart

of a special sealed lamp in which trouble was experienced with leaks at the top, where it was sealed by an injection moulding operation. We, therefore, gave the inspector the factory drawing of the top together with a red pencil, and instructed him that every time he found a leak he was to put a red dot on the drawing, to show where it occurred.

His results are reproduced in Figure 16.2, and they show that most of the leaks occurred in the two corners A and B, which are farthest from the point of injection. We were, therefore, able to cure the trouble by altering the process conditions of injection, e.g. temperature.

Thus, a measles chart can be used for any type of production which has a layout drawing, and particularly for electronic apparatus with a circuit diagram.

16.9 Analysis of manufacturing factors contributing to defective work

Sometimes we have no doubt which particular defect is causing most of the rejected work, but we still have to identify which section of the manufacturing process is at fault. For example, suppose we have a heat treatment process where a big proportion of the work finishes up either too hard (over top limit) or too soft (under bottom limit). With the help of the heat treatment engineer, we can set out the things which *might* contribute to our trouble. At this stage we try to include everything which *might* be concerned, and are very careful not to reject any possibility without a fair investigation.

This may be just a straight list, it may take the form of a family tree, or a popular method is to make a *fishbone* or *Ishikawa* diagram of it. An example of a fishbone diagram is shown in Figure 16.3, for the heat-treatment problem above. The central horizontal line sets out the overall objective of the process, in this case the satisfactory heat treatment of forgings. The main branches up and down from this centre line set out all the main sections of the operation within which the cause of the trouble could conceivably lie, e.g. materiel, equipment, operation, etc. Subsidiary branches then break each section down, and further even more subsidiary branches are inserted as required. Now we look at our evidence. The fact that work is sometimes too hard and sometimes too soft shows that, overall, we have a variability problem. Our investigation might proceed like this:

1   We satisfy ourselves that the hardness checks are being done properly. If there is more than one inspector we can compare results to see if they are much the same. Obviously, if heat treatment conditions are adjusted on the basis of inspection results, incompetent inspection could cause chaos.

2   We investigate whether the wide variability we are suffering is eliminated if we examine the results from:
a   One part number at a time. In this case, each part number probably requires its own heat treatment conditions, and a common treatment for all part numbers is unsatisfactory.
b   One furnace load at a time. If the variability within a furnace load is reasonably satisfactory, then our problem must be due to changes in *average* conditions from one load to another, for example:
   (i)   The furnace temperature controller allows the temperature to drift. If the controller has a recorder, this is easily

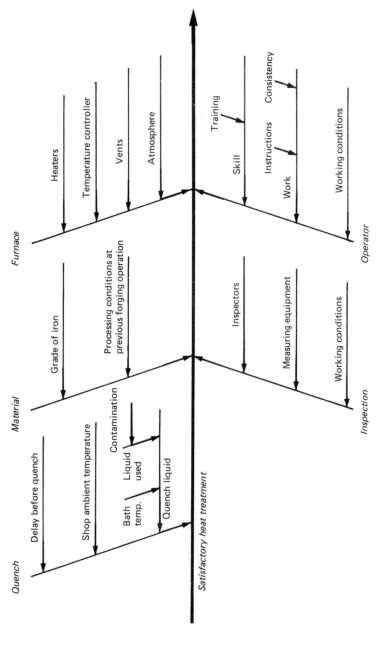

Figure 16.3 Example of a fishbone or Ishikawa diagram

218

checked, but otherwise we may have to make direct oberva-
tions of it.

(ii)   The time in the furnace or the quench routine is varying.

3   If variability is great even within one furnace load consisting of one
part number only, then we shall suspect the temperature distribution
within the furnace. Perhaps a bank of heaters has failed or a vent is
blocked, etc.

4   Having analysed the variability into its obvious categories, it will be
well worth our while to plot frequency distribution curves, and compare
their shape with those given in Sections 11.3 and 11.4.

The approach to any particular problem must clearly depend upon
the type of production concerned, but the above gives a fairly typical
method.

16.10   Organising for corrections

We must provide a routine for the correction of quality deficiencies,
otherwise no effective action is likely to be taken. Thus:

1   We must define what we mean by a quality deficiency which
justifies corrective action. This will depend upon the type of work, etc.,
but the following are examples:

a   'Any part making more than 7 per cent scrap.'
b   'Any machine which runs out of limit at a rate exceeding 15 times
         per 100 hours.'

2   The term 'quality deficiency' will sound pompous to the shop
floor, so we shall need something more down-to-earth. The word
'Squawk' is useful. It creates the right mental image of someone calling
urgently for the trouble to be put right.

3   We must arrange for squawks to be identified quickly. Where variables charts are used, we may ask the operators and inspectors to collect
all charts which have been used into a single container, so that the
quality engineer can analyse them for squawks.

4   Once identified, we must see that all available information about a
squawk is immediately fed to the person detailed to take action. For
example, it may be fed to the section supervisor or the planning
engineer, etc. The person so detailed must be responsible for seeing

that action is always taken, even if a minority of squawks is not within his sphere of responsibility. In such cases, he must coordinate effective action with the person who is responsible.

5   Unless the department concerned is small, we shall need an organised feedback showing what action has been taken, otherwise we shall soon find that those concerned 'just haven't had a chance to do anything about squawks' for a month or so!' Sometimes, an even more complicated system is required. For instance, where a method is unsatisfactory, the planning engineer may design or modify a jig, but this will achieve nothing unless we ensure that the jig is made and tested.

6   This brings us to the problem of setting the squawk value. For example, why did we say 7 per cent scrap in (1a) above, rather than any other value. Strictly speaking, a quality fault is worth correcting if what will be saved by doing so exceeds the cost of correction. In practice, we must also consider our corrective capacity. If the supervisors, engineers, etc., in a department can only deal effectively with two squawks per day, it is no good setting a squawk limit which throws up an average of four, because in attempting to deal with all four they are liable to effectively complete very few. Therefore, the squawk limit must be set so that the rate at which they are thrown up roughly equals the rate at which they can be corrected.

16.11   Questions

1   In a glass-making factory the numbers of defects per batch of 100 pieces of glass over a representative period were sub-divided as follows:

Batch No.	1	2	3	4	5	6	7	8	9	10	11	12	13	14	15	16	17	18	19
Glass plucks	1	0	2	1	3	0	1	1	2	0	0	1	2	1	1	0	0	1	2
Under-polymerised	0	0	1	0	1	0	0	1	1	0	0	1	0	1	0	2	0	1	0
Inclusions	3	3	2	3	3	4	2	3	4	3	2	3	3	5	2	4	3	1	3
Handling scratches	0	0	0	0	1	0	0	0	0	1	1	0	0	0	0	1	0	1	0
Miscellaneous	0	0	1	0	0	0	1	0	0	0	0	1	0	0	1	0	1	0	0

1a   Draw a quality control chart for the total number of defects per batch, complete with inner and outer control limits, and plot the above data on it.   (17 marks)

1b Draw a Pareto curve for the whole of the data, analysing it by defect. *(8 marks)*

2a Explain, in general terms, the principles involved in setting about locating and correcting the causes of quality deficiencies on a production line. *(12 marks)*

2b Describe how these principles have been or could be applied to a production line or service industry with which you are familiar.
(13 marks)

PART FOUR

THE DESIGN, ORGANISATION AND INTRODUCTION OF A QUALITY CONTROL SYSTEM

CHAPTER 17

LAUNCHING QUALITY CONTROL

17.1 Company organisation for quality

In Chapter 1, we agreed that everybody in a company has some contribution to make to quality and that, therefore, 'quality is everybody's business'. Unfortunately, if responsibility for quality is so wide, there is a real risk that in practice it will be nobody's business. To avoid this, overall responsibility for coordinating the company quality effort must be given to somebody, but the question is to whom.

As quality concerns everybody, the only person who is logically responsible for all quality is the very top man, for example the managing director, but he can seldom spare the necessary time. Therefore, responsibility for quality is usually delegated, and again we ask 'To whom should responsibility go?' There is no single answer to this and probably the perfect solution is yet to be found. In practice, the quality organisation of most companies is along the lines of one of the following.

17.1.1 Chief inspector type

Responsibility for quality co-ordination is delegated to a chief inspector, who controls the inspection organisation. His approval is necessary before anything is dispatched from the factory to the customer, and often he must also approve work before it can leave one department for another. His authority over the production departments is usually indirect. He cannot stop them from producing defective work, but he can stop them from dispatching it to another department or to the customer. Often, he will be called quality manager rather than chief inspector, and if he lives up to his name, he will do everything he can to assist the production departments to make right first time.

17.1.2 Advisory type

The quality manager may have a purely advisory role. He will help any department, including inspection, to solve its quality problems. He thus has what in management theory would be called a functional role, similar to that of production engineer, the safety officer, etc., and, like them, he usually needs some degree of authority to be successful. Thus, if a safety officer 'advises' the use of a particular guard, the department concerned is normally expected to act on this advice. Similarly, for this system to be successful, departments must be prepared to accept the advice of the quality manager.

17.1.3 Full authority for quality

In some companies, the quality manager is a very important person. He may be a director, and he has far-reaching powers to control quality. This type of quality organisation is discussed further in Chapter 30.

17.2 The quality role of top management

Whatever the quality organisation, it is essential that top management should back the quality effort, and that they should be seen to back it. There is always a risk that, having appointed a quality manager, top management will assume that quality is now taken care of and that they can forget all about it.

17.3 Putting management in the picture

The introduction of quality control is both hard work and very time consuming and, therefore, in general it can only be done one department at a time. Wherever we decide to start, we must first explain our objectives to the people concerned.

We begin with the managers or equivalent top line of supervision. It is best if the managing director or similar very senior man does this, so that the managers realise that quality control has his backing. Typical of what he may say will be that:

1   The board of directors has decided to introduce quality control, and they request the manager's help in doing this.
2   The quality manager will be responsible for co-ordinating the effort.
3   In each department a careful investigation will first be made, and proposals will then be fully discussed with the managers concerned and their approval obtained before anything in that department is changed.
4   The first department will be. . . .

As some of the managers may be very hazy about what quality control is, it may be useful to show them one of the films obtainable from The Central Film Library, Government Buildings, Bromyard Avenue, Acton, London W3. The managers will be expected through the normal channels of communication to inform the lower levels of supervision, etc. This will be supplemented by a works notice, etc., and where appropriate, use may be made of the company magazine.

17.4   The shop representatives

The shop representatives, e.g. the shop stewards, must also be told in much the same way as the managers were and, in doing this, use might well be made of the joint production committee or in some cases of the works committee. Shop representatives will wish to be assured that quality control will not affect earnings. This assurance can be given with confidence, because a reduction in scrap, etc., if it has any effect at all on the earnings of pieceworkers, is likely to slightly increase them.

Detailed proposals are usually best discussed with the individual shop representatives concerned rather than with the general factory representatives, and they must be given every opportunity and encouragement to comment and make suggestions. They will not, of course, be formally asked to approve the proposals, but if it should happen that they obviously disapprove then we shall be well advised to try to understand why before going ahead.

17.5   Deciding where to start

The choice of the first department to receive quality control is often a difficult one, for clearly it is vital for the first project to be a success. Sometimes it seems as though every department has thought up reasons why it should not be first! In such cases, it may be best to start with incoming materiel since, usually, almost everyone will agree that they need improvement. Alternatively, there may be a department which is obviously in quality troubles, and knows it. Such a department may not yet be convinced that quality control will help but it may, nevertheless, be quite prepared to let the quality engineers 'have a go'. (A department which to the quality manager is obviously in trouble with its quality, but which has not itself realised this, may, however, be quite a different proposition to tackle.)

17.6 Starting quality control in a department

Having decided on the department, we first request an interview with the head of that department at a time which is convenient to him. At this, we shall:

1   Request his approval and co-operation. If for any reason this is not forthcoming, it will probably be better to start somewhere else. If we have top management's backing, it is unlikely that we shall encounter a direct refusal. However we might, for example, be told that in the next six weeks there will be panic to complete an urgent contract, and that it would be better to get this out of the way before starting quality control.

2   Assure him that at this stage we shall only observe and collect information. We promise to discuss proposals fully with him before attempting to alter or disturb anything.

3   Make a careful note of any suggestions he makes.

4   Ask him to tell all his supervisors and shop representatives what is afoot, requesting them to co-operate.

CHAPTER 18

COLLECTING AND ANALYSING QUALITY CONTROL INFORMATION

18.1 Collecting information

We now begin a careful collection and analysis of every bit of information which might help. As at this stage it will be difficult to foresee exactly what might be useful, we shall gratefully collect almost anything which is offered. Most information will come from one of the following sources:

1   From conversations with the staff concerned.
2   From departmental records.
3   By direct observation.
4   From quality control and allied literature.

In practice, we do not work down the above points stage by stage, in that order. Sources of information are interlocked, and the order in which it is collected tends to be partly a matter of convenience and partly decided by the apparent importance of the information.

1 Convenience   Some operations may only be carried out at a specified time and so, if we wish to observe them, we must attend at that time. Again, a person we want to see may not always be available.

2 Importance   Sometimes, quite early, it becomes apparent that certain information is going to be vital. For example, in a department where nearly all the production centres round one large piece of equipment it may be obvious, almost from the start, that a detailed determination of the capabilities of that machine will provide crucial information.

As the necessary observational runs, etc., will take some time, the sooner they are put in hand the better.

For example, in the manufacture of some refractory materiel, the initial blending and mixing, etc., of the materiel is followed by a lengthy heat treatment in huge furnaces. Clearly, information about the temperature variation in different parts of the furnace is going to be important, and initial checks might be put in hand right away. These may be followed by more extensive checks, depending upon the results.

18.2 Conversations with the staff concerned

We must talk to each person concerned, at a time and place convenient to him or her. It is impossible to state in general terms exactly who these people will be, but they are likely to include:

1   All direct supervision staff.
2   Engineers and other technical people.
3   ˙ Inspection staff.
4   Possibly maintenance staff, and those who purchase and store materiel, etc.

It is important to:

1   See that no one is left out.
2   Talk to people in strict order of status in the company, for example the head of the department before the foreman, and the foreman before the assistant foremen, and so on.

As we must both find a convenient time and see people in the correct order, these conversations may spread over an appreciable period and we can collect other information in between them.

1   We shall take a notebook to write down any ideas and suggestions which are made. If we can possibly make use of these, we shall, because if we adopt suggestions from the staff members in the department, they will have an interest in making sure that their suggestions work, and therefore, a stake in ensuring that the whole quality control system works.

2   We shall try to make friends with each person, and try to convince him that quality control is there to help him.

3   We shall ask questions appropriate to the person concerned. Thus, we shall ask the supervisor about the sequence of operations and the correct procedure at each stage. We shall ask the inspection foreman for details of checks carried out by his staff, numbers of each type of defective found, and so on. Do not be too narrow with these questions, how-

ever, or try to confine them too rigidly to that person's role. Because the members of a department must work together, they will overlap their knowledge. Make a point, where appropriate, of asking the same questions of several people to see whether we get identical answers. Often, although the questions are the same, the answers vary appreciably and then it is instructive to try to understand why there should be a difference. This may arise from differences in outlook.

For example, suppose that the department prepare a mix to which a percentage of water is added. We ask the production foreman what this percentage should be and he says 15 per cent, while the engineer says 10 per cent and the inspection foreman only 5 per cent. We must clearly find out why these differences occur, and we must also take into account any information given in the specification. Our investigations might reveal that:

a 15 per cent water makes the mix easy to work, and the production foreman prefers it because it helps to keep up the rate of production.

b 5 per cent gives a product with the best final quality, and hence the inspection foreman's preference. Unfortunately, during the various production operations, this yields components which are very brittle and, therefore, easily broken.

c 10 per cent water gives a material which is easiest to handle on a subsequent operation in another department. The same engineer controls both operations but the foremen are different, and hence the difference in outlook.

Before we come to any startling conclusions about the above, we must go and see for ourselves what water the operators really put in. We may well find that in spite of the references to precise percentages the operators merely tip in about half a bucket, and then add a bit more if they think it needs it! Probably they will err on the generous side because, like the production foreman, they will know that more water makes the materiel easier to work.

We shall have to set a water content which is as near as possible to 5 per cent, consistent with satisfactory working and subsequent processing properties. The way to set about this general type of problem is detailed in Section 21.2, sub-section (2).

4 Ask about the organisation of the department. Our new quality control system must not only be right technically, it must also be tailormade to fit the existing organisation and routines. It must dovetail in with any projects done by the methods engineer, O & M staff, etc. Notice whether any difficulties in human relations are thrown up. Thus, a situation like the following is not uncommon:

a The production foreman says, 'We do our best to produce good quality, and then the inspectors do their best to reject as much as possible. Half the time, I can't see anything wrong and we never get any information from the inspectors.'

b   The inspection foreman says, 'The general quality produced is well below what is required. We bend over backwards to pass as much as possible, so much so that one day the customer is going to complain and then I shall get the blame and have to tighten up. We used to send the production foreman detailed reports of all rejects, but he never looked at them. Three years ago, when the output increased, I found I couldn't spare an inspector any more to prepare reports that were never read.'

Clearly, we shall have to bring these two together again with our new quality control system. It will also be prudent to design a system which does not require more co-operation from them than is absolutely necessary.

5   Find out how the departmental cost system works, and what information is available.

18.3   The quality standard in practice

Very early, we must consider the impact of the first stage of quality control, as discussed in Section 1.4, and we must ask ourselves:

1   Do we know clearly what quality standard we have to make?
2   How do we check that we have in fact achieved the quality standard demanded?

In the example in paragraph 4 of Section 18.2, it is obvious that the production foreman and the inspection foreman have different ideas about the quality standard which is demanded. We shall have to consider:

1   What is the correct quality standard?
a   What do the relevant specifications and drawings say?
b   Where these do not make the quality standards clear, who is responsible for clarifying them? This may be a job for the quality control department liaising with the designer, or maybe either the production engineer or the inspection foreman can do it.
c   There may be relevant British Standard Specifications which would help.
d   Visual quality standards may be required (see Section 3.7).

2   Is the quality standard demanded higher than can be achieved with the operators, materiel and equipment available? If our capability runs

as Sections 12.1, 14.10 and 18.6 show this to be the case, then we must face up to the situation, and either:

a   The department must be re-equipped with more accurate machines, tools, etc., operators retrained, better materiel bought, etc., to raise the quality standard to which it is capable of working; or
b   The designers must be told that they must not call for a higher quality than the department is capable of producing.

The decision is often a difficult one, but no good can come of failing to be realistic and leaving the people concerned to get by as best they can.

While clarifying the quality standard we must make sure that we have a satisfactory method of measurement, otherwise the department will never be sure whether they have got their quality right or not.

18.4   Departmental records

Every department has some records and, fairly early, it pays to investigate these to see what information is already available. Among them, we may find the following:

1   *Inspection records*   These usually show how much defective work has been found for each type of product, and often they also show what the fault was in each case. The defective work may be related to production batches, furnace loads, batches of materiel, machines, etc.
2   *Ordering particulars*   We shall need to know the quantities in which each type of product is made. Are we dealing with short or long runs? How is work loaded on to the department, and what warning does it get of what it has to make?
3   *Existing paperwork*   Collect together copies of every form used. Sometimes these can be adapted for quality control, and this saves introducing more paper.
4   *Cost records*   Cost information, if accurate, is most valuable since our quality control system must be designed with the object of saving as much money as possible.
5   *Personal records and sketches*   Often the staff in a department have already thought about their quality problems, and may have sketched out something which they never completed.
6   *Method cards*   Where methods have been set down get hold of copies of them. Find out what the method engineer believes to be the best approach.

18.5 Direct observation

There is no substitute for direct observation, and we must see for ourselves what the problems are. In every case, we must compare what is done with:

1   What the foreman says is done.

2   What the specification, drawing and method card, etc., says.

Even then, we may not get the whole truth because the operator may change his pattern of work while we are watching. I remember a case in which castings had to be put into the bottom of a pit 2 m deep for special tests, and a hoist was provided for this purpose. When I went to see this job, however:

1   The operator laboriously carried each casting down the steps, one at a time, and then returned up the steps for the next.

2   The condition of the hoist, covered in dust, told me that it was never used and, when I asked the operator about it, he said that it was too slow to be convenient.

I accepted that the manually operated hoist would be slow, but I was still puzzled. Surely, I thought, it must be quicker and less tiring than carrying every casting down the steps. Later I found out the reason. The carrying of castings down the steps was only done because I was watching. When no one was looking, it was the practice to stand at the top of the pit and drop them in! As the castings were being checked for cracks, presumably any which cracked as a result of their fall were merely reported as defective!

In the course of our observations, we must get to know the operators and ask them for their suggestions. As we said in Section 9.5, most of them are very knowledgeable about their own operations.

18.6 Observational runs

Our direct observations are almost certain to include some formal observational runs with the object of establishing the capability and characteristics of a process or machine. In principle, these will be as discussed in Section 14.10, but done on a broader basis such as the following:

1   Choose a typical machine doing a typical run.

2   Decide on the qualities to be checked, and these again should be typical of the production concerned. If possible they should be variables which can be checked quickly and easily.

3   Decide on the frequency of checks. Ideally, every piece made should

be checked, but at the same time we should be able to keep up with the machine or process, as otherwise we may miss something important. Hence, it may be necessary to limit checks to one piece in two or three, etc.

4   Where a machine has several heads or channels of output, then the output of each must be kept separately and plotted separately, since the quality from one head may be quite different from that from the others.

5   Take care to see that the observational run in no way disturbs the output of the department. Thus, any existing patrol inspector should continue his normal checks, etc.

6   Start the observational run at the beginning of the shift, or perhaps at the beginning of a typical production run.

7   Try to measure and plot results as the run proceeds.

8   An observational run provides an opportunity to collect a lot of additional information. For example:
a   Notice whether the machine or process drifts as it warms up or as chemical baths become spent, etc.
b   Record the time and duration of every hold-up, why it was caused, and what was done to correct it.
c   Record all process changes, new batches of materiel, tool adjustments, etc.
d   Notice how often the inspector comes round, how many he checks, and what action he takes on his results.
e   Notice how often work is cleared from the machine or process.
f   We keep our eyes open. We shall be in the department for some hours, not specifically looking at the operators. They will, therefore, probably be more relaxed and behave more nearly as they always do. Note anything which might help to design the new quality system.

9   An observational run should not, in general, last less than a whole morning and may be much longer. Often, it is best to start the run with no definite plans about its duration, and then to continue as long as useful information is being collected. Notice whether the quality changes when the process is shut down for the lunch break, etc.

10   Work out the machine process capability, as described in Section 14.10, but also list all the other information which comes to light. As a

result of the observational run, it should be possible to decide which of the six patterns of variation given in Section 12.1 is appropriate.

11 Repeat the observational run, at least in part, for what the shop say is 'the worst machine in the shop' and also for 'the best machine'. We must know the worst, before we attempt to design the new quality control system.

18.7 Quality control and other literature

A lot of information can be obtained from quality control and other literature. We must, however, be careful not to be carried away by technically involved ideas. Remember that the foreman, etc., will not be familiar with complicated quality control theories, and sooner or later we shall have to explain our proposals to him.

If we are just starting quality control, this book will probably cover all our needs for some time and we should beware of launching into more elaborate techniques.

18.8 Analysis must be impartial

As we gather information, we shall begin to analyse it. This analysis must be systematically carried out, however, and we must resist the temptation to jump to conclusions. Thus, an inspector may show us a couple of dozen scrap pieces, with the remark, 'It's Frank Edwards; he's always making them like that.' Before we blacklist Frank Edwards, however, we must make quite sure that this really is the whole story. We may subsequently find out that:

1   The location stops on Frank Edwards's machine are so worn that they are useless; or that
2   This particular type of work is very difficult to do, and is always given to Frank because he is the best man in the shop, although even he makes an appreciable proportion of scrap.

18.9 Patterns of variation

The object of our analysis is to make the patterns of variation clear, and generally to understand the problem for which we must prescribe a remedy. We must progress from merely knowing how much of each type of scrap we make, to being able to compare the scrap rates from one machine to another, and from one operator to another, and so on.

Much of the work will probably prove to be straightforward and logical analysis of the information, and to help us we have:

1 The whole of Chapter 16 on quality deficiencies, and in particular:
   a Pareto curves.
   b Measles charts.
2 Frequency distribution curves as discussed in Chapter 11.

Analysis of information does not follow its collection in two clear steps. Analysis invariably reveals gaps in our knowledge and, therefore, the need for more information. This has to be collected and further analysed, and this process must be repeated until the problem is fully understood.

18.10 Need for action in other disciplines

Our analysis is primarily aimed at understanding the quality needs of the department. It is very common, however, to find that other needs come to light. For example:

1 The method may prove to be unsatisfactory, in which case method study must be systematically employed in order to effect an improvement, as discussed in Chapter 8.
2 Extensive operator training may be required, as considered in Chapter 9.
3 Plant maintenance may need improvement.
4 Production control may be the prime source of difficulty.
5 It is just possible that we may uncover the need for a more complicated technique like operational research.

Each of these needs must be negotiated with the specialists concerned, and an appropriate improvement made.

CHAPTER 19

THE FOUR FUNDAMENTAL TYPES OF QUALITY CONTROL SYSTEM

19.1 Starting to design the new quality control system

When our analysis is nearing completion it will be time to think about the design of our new quality control system, and we shall aim for a system which:

Will do exactly what is required.

Is so simple and practical, it looks as though it could only have taken five minutes to think up.

It will be based on the five stages of quality control which we set out in Section 1.10. Thus, whatever our type of production, we must make provision for:

1   Defining the quality standard in clear, practical terms.
2   Planning for satisfactory quality.
  a   The method of manufacture (Chapter 8).
  b   The equipment (Section 8.8).
  c   The materiel (Chapters 4 to 7).
  d   The selection and training of operators (Chapter 9).
  e   Inspection and shop floor quality control (Chapter 8).
3   Manufacturing right first time as far as is reasonably possible (Chapters 9 to 15).
4   Correction of quality deficiencies (Chapter 16).
5   Long-term quality control.

These reduce to four steps which we can check as we design our system:

1   *Start right*   Clearly, if production does not start right it is un-
     likely to be right at any stage. This is why we have put so much
     emphasis on:

     a   Defining the quality standard.

     b   Planning for satisfactory quality.

2   *Keep right*   Having started correctly, we must see that produc-
     tion keeps correct and that, if the quality shows signs of going
     outside specification or drawing limit, adjustments are immediately
     made to bring it back again. This is the role of shop floor quality
     control. It is necessary because, in general, we cannot ensure at
     the quality planning stage that the job cannot go wrong during
     production. The better we do our quality planning, the less shop
     floor quality control we shall need.

3   *Finish right*   If we really keep the quality right throughout the
     production run it is bound to finish right. Our concern here,
     therefore, will be primarily directed at the quality of the tooling,
     since this may require attention before the next run is com-
     menced.

4   *Final inspection*   Final inspection is not so much part of the
     quality control system proper as a means by which we prove that
     our quality control system is working properly. If, on final
     inspection, everything is satisfactory it speaks well for our quality
     control.

19.2   The four basic types of quality control system

Quality control provides us with a large number of different techniques,
the most useful of which have been described in Parts 2 and 3 of this
book. In designing a quality control system, we must select those
which are suitable for the production line in question and then blend
them into a unified, practical whole. Few of these techniques are universally applicable. Each tends to have a certain range or class of work
for which it is particularly suited. Developing this idea further, I have
found that it is possible to classify almost any type of work as belonging to one of four basic groups. We shall define these as follows, and
then discuss them in detail in the next four chapters.

Type A   Each small stage of production can be easily checked as soon
as it is made. Most machine work comes into this class.

Type B   Interdependent production stages, where the product can only be checked at infrequent intervals. This class includes much of what we often loosely call the process industries.

Type C   Assemblies.

Type D   Service undertakings.

19.3   Effect of mechanisation and automation

There is no clear distinction between manual production, mechanisation and automation. At one end of the scale we have craft-type production, where only hand tools and a fair amount of labour are used, and at the other extreme we have completely automatic equipment, which works entirely unaided, with computers to monitor quality and correct processing conditions as required. Within these two extremes, many hybrid arrangements are both possible and entirely practical. Thus an assembly flow line may have some stages mechanised and others done by operators.

In each of the next four chapters, we shall consider first manual and single-machine production, where quality is controlled largely by the operator, and then mechanisation and automation, where quality is dictated and possibly controlled by the machine. Where work is done by craftsmen using hand tools, the rate of production is likely to be slow, and although the general quality standard may be high, it will suffer from unpredictable human variations. The watchful eye of the operator will however be ever-present. A piece of wood with a knot in it, or a screw without a thread, will be rejected, and no attempt made to use it.

Mechanisation means that we give the physical work to the machine. Because a machine does not suffer from human vagaries, the quality produced usually becomes much more consistent, but not necessarily consistently right; it may be consistently wrong! The following are examples:

1   If a cutting tool moves out of position, all subsequent production may be out of drawing limit.
2   A machine will attempt to use a screw without a thread, thereby damaging the assembly, and possibly itself as well. Hence it is most important that the materiels are of consistently satisfactory quality.

Automation implies that some degree of control is built into the machine. Ideally it has sensing devices which monitor all the process parameters, and then adjust them as necessary. Usually a computer of some sort is at the heart of the decision-making process. Often this is in the form of a large central multipurpose computer, and all equipment requiring control is 'on-line' to it. Indeed, the central computer does not need to be in the same factory, because telephone links can be used. However there is a distinct modern trend towards dedicated computers. These are smaller computers designed specifically to do one job, or maybe a limited range of related jobs. We can see examples of this in some numerically controlled machines, and in specialised items of test equipment used in the electronics industry.

CHAPTER 20

DESIGNING A QUALITY CONTROL SYSTEM

TYPE A: WHERE EACH SMALL STAGE OF PRODUCTION CAN BE EASILY CHECKED AS SOON AS IT IS PERFORMED

20.1 The scope of Type A

Where we can easily check each small stage of production as soon as it is made, this is usually the most convenient basis for our quality control system. Thus, if we turn up a diameter we can immediately check it with a micrometer; if we want to know whether a steel sheet is 120 ± 1 mm, we can use a rule, and if we want to know whether medicinal pellets are the correct weight we can weigh them, etc. The following is typical of this class of work:

1   Most machine work, e.g. automatic and semi-automatic lathes, capstan and turret lathes, etc., milling machines, drills, etc.
2   Sheet metal work, and fabrication generally.
3   Diecasting.
4   Forging and hot pressing.
5   Manufacture of many plastics components.
6   Dressmaking, knitting, etc.
7   Any operation even in a process industry where the quality can be immediately checked, e.g. as a weight.

Consider Figure 20.1 where the row of symbols at the top represents the output of some machine or other operation in this class. Thus, it begins by making a run of pieces denoted by a circle. Then follows a 'one-off' denoted by a triangle, and this is clearly the shortest 'short run' which is possible. Next, we have a long run of the piece donated by a square, and this could in principle be very long since only the limitations of the

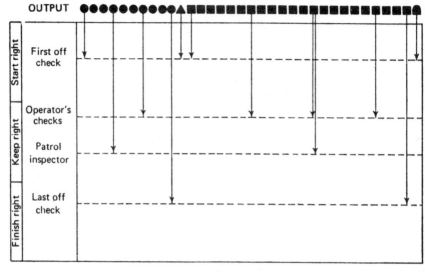

Type A   easy to check each small stage of manufacture

Figure 20.1   Quality control of a Type A process

diagram make us stop after 22 pieces, and set up the piece indicated by a half moon. Consider the design of our quality control system, along the lines of the basic stages of quality control outlined in Section 19.1.

20.2   Start right

1   Define and clarify the quality standard
a   All variables must have tolerances (Section 3.4).
b   All attributes must have practical quality limits, such as visual quality standards (Sections 3.7 and 3.8).

2   Plan for satisfactory quality
a   Make use of method study in order to ensure satisfactory methods, devised so that it is as easy as possible for the operator to carry them out correctly, and as difficult as possible for him to do them incorrectly (Chapter 8).
b   Make sure that all tooling and equipment is adequate to achieve the quality standard demanded (Section 8.8).
c   Ensure a supply of satisfactory raw materiel (Chapter 7).
d   Select and train suitable operators and inspectors (Chapter 9).

243

e   Prepare a quality schedule, in principle as described in Sections 8.10 and 8.11, and in detail in Section 20.3 below.

3   The first-off check   Insist on a correct 'first-off' check before the production run is allowed to proceed (Section 8.12). The 'first-off' inspector must remember that the object of this is not so much to check the first piece made, as to make sure that everything is satisfactory for the first period's run. In Figure 20.1 the arrows on the 'first-off' check line show which pieces will receive this check.

20.3   Keep right

In so far as the quality of our production can go wrong, we must provide checks to detect this quickly so that the machines, etc., can be reset before any, or hardly any, out-of-limit work has been made.

1   The quality schedule will state what checks must be applied during production and these may or may not be exactly the same as those for the 'first-off' checks. This will depend upon:
a   How likely each quality is to go wrong.
b   What it costs when it does go wrong.
We may be able to get some information about this from:
a   Our Pareto curves (Section 16.7) which will tell us which types of defective work are most commonly made.
b   Frequency distribution curves (Chapter 11) which will show which qualities are only just within the capability of the machine, and so are the most likely to get out of limit.
c   Our knowledge of the process. Thus, the diameter on an automatic lathe may change quite suddenly by quite a large amount, but the diameter of a punched hole is unlikely to change appreciably. If our method is such that the quality is unlikely to go wrong, then we do not need to check it so often.

2   Next we must decide how often checks must be made. This is basically a question of economics, and is fully discussed in Sections 13.9 to 13.13. In addition, it depends partly on the pattern of behaviour of our machine, and we shall know this from our observational runs (Sections 12.1 and 18.6).

3   The question of who is to do these checks is bound up with how difficult they are and how long they take. Consider first how much the operator can reasonably be expected to do.
a   If he can check every piece while the machine is working on the

next, then it will probably be prudent to ask him to utilise his idle time in this way (Section (9.7). If his checks will hold up production, then we must limit them severely. In Figure 20.1 the operator has been told to check every sixth piece, as shown on the line marked 'operator checks'.

b   Checks which the operator cannot conveniently do must be done by someone else. Often this person is called a patrol inspector, but in some cases it may be the setter or the supervisor. Consider the staff in the department concerned and ask, 'Who is the best man or woman to do it?' and not, 'What is he or she called?' In Figure 20.1, the inspector takes periodic samples. Notice that the piece checked may or may not be one which the operator has already checked. This is purely a matter of chance.

4   The choice of sample size is basically as discussed in Section 13.8. Thus, Figure 20.1 shows a sample of one, but clearly this will not always be the case. Operator checks will tend to be a sample of one because, in general, we shall better to inspect more often (and so catch our machine quicker when it goes out of limit) rather than check more at each inspection. Furthermore, operators will be less likely to have time to average samples for control limits which is desirable if we are to make best use of a sample exceeding one. Where we use a patrol inspector, there will probably be a limit to the frequency with which he can conveniently visit the machine, but he is more likely to be able to undertake the averaging of his results, etc., at each visit. Hence, there is a stronger case for a sample exceeding one if the pattern of variation of the machine makes this desirable.

5   The routine of keeping each period's production separate, until the check at the end of that period has proved satisfactory, is most desirable (Section 8.14).

6   We must provide some method of ensuring that the operator actually does the checks he is paid to do. One simple way to do this is to ask the operator to mark the pieces which he checks. According to the type of work, this may be done with crayon, chalk or by inserting paper or plastics markers, etc. The routine then is that, when a patrol inspector finds something wrong with a piece which he checks, he checks the last piece which the operator claims to have checked and has declared all right. If this piece is found to be all right, then presumably the machine has only just gone wrong and the out-of-limit work in the last few pieces can easily be isolated. If the last piece checked by the operator is also wrong, then the operator is not doing his checks properly and must be corrected. The patrol inspector must go backwards through the

marked pieces, in order to locate where the change in quality occurred and so isolate all the out-of-limit work.

20.4 Finish right

It is usually desirable for a production run to conclude with a patrol inspection, both to check that the run itself has finished satisfactorily and also to check the state of the tools. If these need resharpening, recutting, etc., then this should be done *before* they are returned to stores (Section 8.16).

20.5 Final 100 per cent inspection

Some contracts, particularly defence and similar government contracts, specify that 100 per cent final inspection must be applied. If we have a free choice, however, we shall try to make such final inspection unnecessary. It is nearly always possible to devise the production quality control routine so that nearly all the work which gets through the system as satisfactory is in fact all right. Unsatisfactory pieces, therefore, should only get through in any quantity when something happens which is not provided for in the routine, such as the occasional operator mistake. Act firmly where defective work gets through, because somebody has failed to work the quality control routine correctly.

Where components made in, say, a machine shop go next to an assembly shop within our own company, 100 per cent inspection is unlikely to be justified. Usually, it will be cheaper for the assemblers to throw out the occasional bad piece. There will be exceptions to this rule, for example in aircraft work, where safety is at stake. But, in general, if we think we need 100 per cent inspection it probably means that the quality control system itself is not sufficiently efficient, and we must have another look at it.

Where the output of a department is going directly to a customer, then customer reaction to any unsatisfactory work it contains must be considered. Remember, however, that the cost of any 100 per cent inspection must either come out of our profits, or from an increased price to the customer. Try, therefore, to achieve an acceptable quality level by improving the quality control system proper, and only resort to 100 per cent inspection when this proves to be impossible. Even when the customer specifies 100 per cent inspection, try to achieve an initial quality of production such that very little is rejected by this final inspection.

20.6 Mechanisation and automation

Where equipment is mechanised or automated, the same principles for designing a quality control system apply, but the emphasis changes.

Start Right   Correct initial set up is now of vital importance. Plugs, tapes, etc., used in NC or CNC machines must be right, or the whole run will be out of limit.

Keep Right   If manual patrol inspection is to be applied, then the sample size and frequency can in principle be determined from Sections 13.8 to 13.12. Typically the sample size will be $n = 1$ per outlet, but where a large volume of expensive production is concerned, the economic interval between inspections may be impossibly short, e.g. 5 sec. This indicates a mismatch between mechanised production and manual patrol inspection. When mechanisation of a production line is contemplated, it is important that we also consider quality control, which should be built into the machine. It should check its quality as it goes along, and if this is unsatisfactory, it should at least shut itself down, and give warning that it has done so. Ideally it should correct itself and continue production.

(Problems on the design of a quality control system are given at the end of Chapter 23.)

CHAPTER 21

DESIGNING A QUALITY CONTROL SYSTEM

TYPE B: INTERDEPENDENT PRODUCTION STAGES, WHERE THE PRODUCT CAN ONLY BE CHECKED AT INFREQUENT INTERVALS

21.1 The scope of Type B

There are many processes where the product can only be checked at infrequent intervals, so that a quality control system of the type discussed in the previous chapter becomes impracticable. Examples of this type are described below:

1 Many food processes   Thus, in making bread, we must obtain our materials, prepare and mix them, etc., and bake, before we can take a bite to find out whether our loaf is all right. Even then our check is destructive, so 100 per cent inspection for taste is out of the question.

2 Many chemical and physical processes   In the manufacture of transistors, for example, it is not possible to check the functioning of the transistor as such until after it has been made. If it is then wrong, there is often little that can be done about it.

Similarly, in the manufacture of motor-car tyres, the raw rubber must be masticated, blended, calendered and then the tyre must be assembled and heat treated before the tyre itself can be checked.

3 Some engineering processes   Examples of this type are:

a   Foundry work.

b   Plating, painting and other forms of metal finishing.

c   Processes with a lengthy time cycle, as sometimes occurs in heat treatment, the manufacture of refractories, etc.

Take foundry work as being typical of the family of processes which comprise this group. When we make a casting, there are roughly nine operations which must be completed before we can check whether the casting itself is good. They are:

1   Make the pattern.
2   Prepare the sand.
3   Prepare and melt the metal.
4   Make the mould.
5   Close the mould.
6   Pour the metal.
7   Cool.
8   Knock out.
9   Clean up and fettle.

Only when all of these have been completed can we check whether our casting is good or not, and as this sequence may take two or three days, if checks then show that our castings are bad we may have a great deal of unsatisfactory work already in our long pipeline, i.e. possibly two or three days' production. Checks at the end of the production line are, therefore, of little use as the basis of our quality control system.

With this type of production, it is usually best to argue that, if everything is correctly made with satisfactory materiel and equipment, then all production must be good. This argument is somewhat idealistic, of course, but it forms the basis of our quality control system, which again goes in four steps.

21.2   Start right

1   Define and clarify the quality standard

a   All variables must have tolerances (Section 3.4).

b   All attributes must have practical limits, such as visual, audible or taste quality standards, etc. (Sections 3.7 and 3.8).

2   Define and plan the method of manufacture   Since we propose to base our control system on method, it follows that our method must be defined with considerable care. At every stage of the process, we must set down precisely what is to be done, expressing as many parameters as possible in figures complete with tolerances. For example:

a   Distribute 48 ± 1 g of powder A evenly on a nickel plate 300 mm square.

b   Cure at $240 \pm 3°C$ for 180 ± 5 seconds.

Some processes may appear to contain an element of 'black art' or 'mystery'. The supervisor, operators and even perhaps the engineer will tell us that the process cannot be controlled by ordinary scientific means, because the quality varies all the time, and only experience with the process can help in deciding what to do, and even that is not always satisfactory.

Now it is a well-established scientific fact that, if we repeat the same operations, on exactly the same quality and quantity of materiel, we shall get exactly the same result every time. How then does it happen that these 'black art processes' are relatively common? The reason must be that in these departments they *do not* always carry out exactly the same operations on exactly the same quality and quantity of materiel, and hence they do not always get the same result. Additional variations may then be caused by arbitrary adjustments made by the 'experts' in order to regain control.

We must not be demoralised by assertions that formal quality control has no chance. We must diligently set out every detail of the method, and the probability is that this will be most revealing. We ask as many people in the department as possible to tell us what the method is, and compare their answers. We shall almost certainly find that they differ, because each person will have his own opinion based on his own particular experience. For example:

Mr. White says, 'I put on 50 g to make quite sure that there are no thin patches, but the temperature must be $250°C$.'

Mr. Black says, '45 g is enough, otherwise it cracks, and a temperature of $230°$ is plenty.'

As quality engineers, unless we happen to know which of these opinions is right, we shall have to fix the two parameters arbitrarily to start with, and then make sure that everyone observes them. Thus, we might set the weight of powder at 48 ± 1 g, and the press temperature at $240 \pm 3°C$. We shall go right through the whole process setting every parameter, and giving it a tolerance based on our knowledge of the process capability. This may not immediately yield the best method, but at least we know what the method is, and we can control it. Thus, if 48 g then proves to be too high, we can reduce it to say 46 g. Previously when everyone put on different weights, we had no effective control at all and no possibility of finding out what the best weight was.

We must not be put off because we are told that something is not critical. For example, 'We just throw in a handful; it's not critical.' Provide a measure for everyone to use. It may only be an old cup, but at least we have some idea what volume is put in. No parameter should be left uncontrolled, however loudly the department protest that it is not important.

3 Provide satisfactory equipment   Again we must make sure that the equipment provided is adequate to achieve the quality standard required (Section 8.8). With processes, we often have a chance to provide automatic controls. Thus a temperature of $240° \pm 3°C$ will require control equipment, and if it is not economic to buy it, then it is no use our pretending that we are controlling to that accuracy.

4 Materiel   Materiel for a process often presents its own peculiar problems. Where relevant, we shall apply the routines described in Chapter 7 but, in addition, we may have uniformity problems especially if we are dealing with natural materiel. Thus, if we buy flour, its quality may vary according to where the wheat was grown, natural rubber may vary from plantation to plantation, perhaps even from tree to tree, if we are able to investigate that closely. Even inorganic materiel is not free from this problem. The impurities in copper, selenium, tellurium, etc., even after they have been purified, still vary according to the location of the mine from which the ore was obtained.

In such cases, we may decide to homogenise, that is to mix several batches thoroughly together to obtain a large batch of uniform quality. Sometimes a degree of blending may be included. We decide that we will keep a particular impurity constant at a certain level, e.g. 0.1 ± 0.02 per cent, and so we check the impurity content of all incoming batches, and then blend them together in the right proportions to achieve our agreed quality level of impurity.

In a foundry, the quality of the sand used for moulds depends in part on its spectrum, that is on the proportions of large and small particles which it contains. Now sand from different quarries will tend to have different spectra. Therefore, it is common practice to check the spectrum of each load of sand when it arrives, and then to blend it with other sands in just the right proportions to achieve a constant spectrum over a reasonably long period.

5 Operators   We must obtain and train suitable operators, as discussed in Chapter 9.

6 First-off checks on the method   First-off checks will still be necessary every time a machine is prepared or an operator gets ready for a fresh run. We may not be able to check the product, but we can still check the method, equipment and set-up, etc. For example:
a   Has the correct equipment been correctly set up?
b   Are temperatures, weights, concentrations, speeds and feeds, etc.,

all correct?

c   Is the correct materiel being used?

d   Is the operator carrying out the correct method, in the correct sequence?

To ensure that the operator knows what the correct method is, we must break down the standard method which we prepared in (2) above, into key points as Section 9.3.

21.3 Keep right

Now we must ensure that our method is observed right to the end of each production run. One way to do this is to use the equivalent of a patrol inspector, except that we shall probably call him a quality control assistant. He will make periodic visits to the operators and machines to check that the process parameters and operations are correct, for example:

1   That the curing temperature is still $240 \pm 3°C$.

2   That the operator spreads the correct weight of powder evenly over the plate, etc.

We can still give each operator a quality control chart, but this time it will list the key points of the method, and the quality control assistant will enter on each visit whether or not they are being observed, by a tick or a cross. Parameters which are in figures, such as temperature, can be plotted as a variables chart with specification limits, even though it is not always possible to use control limits.

Even on a process, there are usually some points where a quality control chart can be based on a direct check of the quality of the product. Thus, in the foundry, when the sand has been prepared, a sample can be checked for moisture and clay content, etc., and used as a basis for controlling sand quality.

21.4 Finish right

A last-off check on the method used for the run usually has little value, unless it is possible to check the condition of the equipment in preparation for the next run.

21.5 Final inspection

As before, we try to make final 100 per cent inspection unnecessary. If we decide to do it, its purpose will probably be one of the following:

1   To prevent defective production from reaching the next operation, or maybe the customer, and in some cases because the customer has insisted that it shall be done.

2   To confirm that the quality control system proper is working satisfactorily and to give the alarm if it is not. We shall be very careful, however, that we do not attempt to use final inspection as the quality control system in its own right.

21.6   Mechanisation and automation

Much of Section 20.6 applies. If the process has been mechanised to increase throughput, without regard to quality control, an inbalance between the two is likely, and the patrol inspector may be unable to keep up. Mechanisation must include corresponding improvements to the quality control system.

Some processes have a number of interrelated parameters which must be controlled. Continuous optimisation between them is needed, and this calls for a computer. Sometimes this is done by putting the plant on-line to a central computer; sometimes it has its own dedicated computer. The computer may also control complicated tests on the final product. As mechanisation and automation increase, the operator has an ever-decreasing effect on quality. Ultimately, an operator in the true sense is almost eliminated. His or her job becomes that of plant minder, with little or nothing to do until the control equipment indicates unsatisfactory processing conditions. The operator must then locate the fault and correct it.

(Problems on the design of a quality control system are given at the end of Chapter 23.)

CHAPTER 22

DESIGNING A QUALITY
CONTROL SYSTEM

TYPE C: ASSEMBLIES

22.1 The scope of Type C

Under assemblies we include every case where components, large or small, are fitted or fixed together. Thus, in principle, we range from, say, the assembly of a nut to a bolt at one extreme to the assembly of, say, a diesel locomotive or an aircraft at the other. The principles of our quality control system will be the same even though its intensity and complexity may vary considerably.

22.2 Analysis of incorrect assemblies

At the start of a quality control project on an assembly line, a Pareto curve of rejected assemblies is often most revealing (Section 16.7). Assembly takes place after various components have been made and, in some cases, the components themselves are fairly complex. Thus, it is not uncommon for a Pareto curve to reveal that most of the causes of rejection originate *outside* the assembly department. The following example of a light electrical assembly line illustrates this point:

Reason for rejection	Percentage of all rejections	Cumulative total (%)
Faulty transformer	35	35
Faulty choke	24	59
Component not available	20	79
Wiring faults	12	91
Soldering faults	6	97
Miscellaneous	3	100

On this line, a high percentage of assemblies were being rejected on final test so that, at first sight, it looked as though the assembly operators were very unsatisfactory. However, the above Pareto curve paints a very different picture. Notice that 35 per cent of the rejections were due to faulty transformers, and a further 24 per cent to faulty chokes. Neither of these is anything to do with the assemblers. Furthermore, both transformers and chokes were made in the same component supply department, hence underlining the need for better quality control there. Next, we have 20 per cent rejections because a component is not available and, therefore, the assembler cannot put it in. These were faults originating in the production control department, and it illustrates how quality control will often draw attention to problems originating outside its popularly recognised sphere (although there is no reason why we should not do quality control of production control or, indeed, any office work).

Thus, in this example, 79 per cent of the faults originated outside the assembly department, and the quality engineers concluded that they must tackle these first, before dealing with the 21 per cent which originated from within it.

22.3   Design of assemblies

In Section 3.1 we discussed the designer's general contribution to quality control. In assembly work, however, the designer has additional scope because he can design so that as far as possible the components will only go together the correct way. For example:
1   Components which must go a particular way round should not be designed so that they will go equally well either way.
2   Small differences should be introduced so that similar components cannot be interchanged.

22.4   Start right

1   Define and clarify the quality standard   All variables must have

255

tolerances (Section 3.4), and all attributes must have practical limits, such as visual or audible quality standards (Sections 3.7 and 3.8). Thus, we may have to define what we mean by a 'satisfactory soldered joint' or a 'moderately tight nut'. The latter we may be able to define by means of a torque spanner.

2 Plan a satisfactory method Assembly work is a particularly happy hunting ground for the methods engineer, for there are considerable savings to be made. There are also opportunities to work with the designer, to ensure that assemblies will only go together the correct way. Jigs, etc., can often be designed so that they will only accept components if they are inserted into it in the correct way (Sections 8.3, 8.4 and 8.5).

3 Plan the equipment Some assembly lines use relatively little equipment, and therefore, it is very easy to forget that satisfactory equipment is an essential part of our quality control system (Section 8.8).

4 Plan materiel As our example in Section 22.2 showed, the materiel used may prove to be the vital key to trouble-free assembly.

1   *Materiel purchased* from outside suppliers will need incoming materiels quality control (Chapter 7).
2   *Where materiel is manufactured* within our own company, it may be wise to improve the quality control in the supply departments, before tackling the assembly.

5 Select and train operators In most assembly work, there is considerable scope for the operators to go wrong. In particular, we must see that they are trained in any basic skills required, such as soldering, stripping wires, the principles of fitting, etc. Next, we must provide each of them with a method card showing the steps and key points of each type of assembly to be made (Chapter 9).

6 First-off checks On assembly work, as much as on machine work, there is scope for a 'first-off' check. If the first assembly of a particular batch or run is incorrect, it is very likely that the rest will also be wrong.

22.5   Keep right

In so far as we have been *unable* to ensure that our assemblies cannot go wrong, so we shall have to do assembly shop floor quality control. Therefore, periodic checks will be required by the operator, inspector, supervisor, etc. Our position is probably a little like that discussed in Chapter 21 for processes in that, although we can check that each component is correctly assembled, we cannot usually check until an assembly is completed whether or not it actually functions as intended. Thus, we have to argue that, if every assembly is correctly made, with correct components, to a correct design, then every assembly must work when completed, and so we need a control system as outlined in Section 21.2.

A quality control chart, either per operator or per production section or department, may be useful so that both operators and supervisors know how well or otherwise they are doing. Much, but by no means all, assembly work is concerned with attributes, and Figure 15.1 shows a typical chart for such a section.

The sequence in which assembly operations are done often affects the probability of mistakes, as the example in Section 8.5 illustrates.

22.6   Final inspection

In many cases, assembly is the final manufacturing operation before dispatch to the customer and, therefore, 100 per cent test and inspection is commonly applied. Its object may be to:

1   Comply with a customer's contract (this is often the case with government defence contracts, etc.).
2   Prevent a faulty assembly from reaching the customer. (A customer buying, say, a record player will not have stipulated by contract that 100 per cent final inspection and test must be applied, but he will nevertheless expect it to work satisfactorily, and it will reflect on the manufacturer if it fails to do so.)
3   Adjust transformer taps, resistors, carburetter settings, etc., to obtain best performance.

As always, we should regard this final test and inspection as *proof* of our quality control system, rather than as the system itself. Anything which has gone wrong anywhere during manufacture will, we hope, be discovered on final test. The information which we get will, therefore, be most valuable. A Pareto analysis, probably grouped initially in the departments in which the faults originated, will show us where further quality control effort is required. Our aim must always be to have a minimum of rejections on final inspection.

22.7   Mechanised and automated assembly

Sometimes only one or two stages of an assembly flow line are mechanised; the rest is done by operators. At the other extreme, the whole assembly can be made and checked by the machine. It is particularly important to ensure that all components are satisfactory, unless the machine will check what it uses. Ideally it should also check every stage of assembly as it goes along and correct itself, or at least give warning, if anything goes wrong. Either a central or a dedicated computer can be useful in carrying out a complicated sequence of tests. It can supply a printout of every parameter, although it is more likely that it will be programmed to print out only parameters that are out of limit.

(Problems on the design of a quality control system are given at the end of Chapter 23.)

CHAPTER 23

DESIGNING A QUALITY
CONTROL SYSTEM
TYPE D: SERVICE UNDERTAKING

23.1   Examples of a service undertaking

In this chapter we are concerned with organisations which provide a
service, rather than manufacture a product, and the following are
examples:
>Wholesale and retail distributors.
>The Post Office.
>Transport undertakings such as British Rail, bus companies and
>>airlines.
>Educational establishments.
>Medical services.
>The armed forces.
>Government Departments.
>Maintenance organisations, both those which exist solely for this
>>purpose, such as car repair garages, and those which are part
>>of a factory organisation.
>Clerical work.

When manufacturing, we carry out a prescribed performance in
order to obtain a satisfactory end product. We can regard a service as
one where the prescribed performance is an end in itself, and there is
no end product. Then we can apply the quality control principles we
have already discussed.

23.2   Define the service required

A manufacturing organisation must begin by surveying the market to
find out what its customers require, and its designers must then reduce
this to a fully defined quality standard, in the form of a manufacturing

specification. In the same way, a service undertaking must start with a survey of the needs of their market. From all the information which is available, they must produce a clear specification of operational requirements. For example:

1   A retail organisation needs to decide where shops will be established, what range of goods they will sell, and in what quantity.
2   A bus company needs to know what routes will be covered, and what passenger density is anticipated.
3   The armed forces must work from an overall statement of defence needs, to a detailed specification of what, where, when and how much.
4   A college must define as precisely as possible what it means by a student who is adequately educated and trained to be, say, a quality engineer.

23.3 Plan to provide the required service

This will broadly follow the five basic sub-stages which we discussed in Chapter 1.

1 Plan the method   We must decide as precisely as possible how our organisation will work. For example:

a   A retail organisation must decide how it will organise and lay out a shop, what storerooms it wants, and with what conditions, etc.
b   A bus company must consider how routes can be economically dovetailed together, so that buses and their crews are not idle, yet there is always a bus at the time and place required.

2 Obtain equipment   Next we must obtain the equipment which we require, for example:

a   A retail organisation must obtain suitable counters, shelving, scales, refrigeration equipment, delivery vans, etc.
b   A bus company must obtain buses, and ensure that they are reliable. No doubt they will need a maintenance organisation, which will require a service quality control system in its own right.
c   A water company must decide on pumping equipment, and an electricity board on alternators, etc.

3 Obtain materiel   We must obtain an adequate supply of satisfactory materiel, but the magnitude of the task will vary enormously with the type of undertaking. Thus:

a   To a wholesale or retail organisation, the purchase of saleable goods with the required quality, quantity, price and delivery, is so important that it may well be the most important single task they have to perform.

b To a bus company, the purchase of diesel fuel is a relatively small problem, which can be calculated fairly precisely.

c The purchase of, say, shells for the army presents a problem which is peculiar to the armed forces. Apart from practice and trial firings, the army probably hope that they will never need to use them, yet in an emergency, adequate supplies must be available, and the soldiers must be able to rely on them to function correctly.

d Electricity and gas boards must ensure that they have adequate supplies of the correct grades of fuel. Notice that part of their materiel is the final output of another service undertaking, the National Coal Board.

4 *Select and train personnel* Service undertakings have in principle the same problems as do manufacturing organisations, in selecting and training suitable staff. Indeed many people work for both at different times in their lives.

5 *Plan the operational quality control* Throughout we shall plan so that, as far as possible, the service must be performed as intended. Where we cannot be certain that this will happen, we shall have to provide additional safeguards, probably in the form of spot checks, equivalent to the patrol checks of industry.

23.4 Perform the service correctly to plan

At last we are ready to perform our service to the specified quality standard. The better our planning has been done, the less the trouble we shall have in carrying it out. Our problems may however be aggravated by having our staff scattered, as is the case with maintenance men and vehicle drivers. Again we consider the three phases.

1 *Start right for example*

a A shop window display can be checked to see that it is correctly priced and described. Under the Trade Descriptions Act, incorrect descriptions may result in legal action.

b A bus inspector can ensure that buses leave the garage on time, displaying correct destination boards.

c The output of an alternator can be checked when it is started up.

2 *Keep right* We must now ensure that our service keeps to its plan, e.g.:

a   A bus inspector can board buses at random times, to check that they are running to timetable, and that tickets have been correctly issued.

b   College students are set tests from time to time, to check that their education is proceeding as planned.

c   Shop supervisors can make snap observations on the way their staff serve customers.

Sometimes other checks can be included, for example:

a   The output of an alternator can be continuously recorded and controlled by mechanical means.

b   The time a bus passes a point can be recorded by instructing the conductor to insert a card in an automatic clock recorder.

3   Finish right   In many cases a customer receives a service in person, so that it is not possible to do a 'final inspection before despatch'. If a haircut has been incompetently done, probably nothing can be done until the hair has grown again. We can still however use information from a final check to plan for better quality in future, even if alas we have a dissatisfied customer now. For example:

a   We can check the time a train arrives at its destination.

b   We can check a repair job on, say, a car, before handing it back to the customer.

23.5   Correct the cause of any quality shortcomings in our service

In addition to all the information we have already discussed, we are sure to have a feedback from our customers in the form of complaints, comments, etc. It is clearly important to see that these are dealt with quickly and courteously, but in addition it is most important to learn from our mistakes. We must do our best to improve the basic planning and execution of our service, so that shortcomings in our service do not recur.

23.5   Questions

1   Discuss practical ways of tackling quality control for *two* of the following:

        a   A food processing line.
        b   An electronic assembly shop.
        c   Clerical work.
        d   A foundry.
        e   A transport undertaking.   *(25 marks)*

2 Describe a suitable quality control system for *two* of the following:

  a A plastics workshop making small components: most of the machines have operators working on short to medium runs, but some are mechanised, and only require the operator to load them occasionally with raw powder, and remove finished work; the latter are on long runs.

  b A workshop making wooden 'adventure' toys for schools, e.g. climbing frames.

  c A small workshop cutting and sewing ladies' dresses.

  d A department heat treating small components. *(25 marks)*

3 Select any *two* of the following, and outline a suitable quality control system for *each*. (Candidates should state any further assumptions they make to define practical operating conditions.)

  a A section of a machine shop containing 24 automatic lathes, in which runs are fairly long.

  b A small company which contracts to clean the windows of other industrial concerns.

  c The manufacture of printed circuit boards on to which components are assembled and wired, but which are not incorporated into equipment at that stage.

  d A small foundry making non-ferrous castings up to about 4 kg. *(25 marks)*

Author's note: Each of the above questions asks for only two systems to be designed because more could not be completed in 30 minutes. The reader however might care to attempt them all.

CHAPTER 24

QUALITY CONTROL OF SHORT RUNS

24.1 The approach to short runs

If the reader has to deal with short runs, then he should read this chapter in conjunction with Chapter 20, 21, 22 or 23 as appropriate. Basically, there are two main ways in which we can deal with short-run production:

1　We can control the features which are common to every run.
2　Where each type of product repeats from time to time, we may be able to plan its quality control system once and for all, and then use it every time a batch of that product is made.

24.2 Controlling on the features that are common to every run

Quality control is not as difficult as it may appear to apply to short-run production. The important thing to realise is that any one department only does one class of work. This is bound to be so, because machines and equipment are always built to do a given limited range of work, and operators only have a limited range of skills. Thus, when the foreman tells us that, 'All our runs are different; we never get two things alike,' we need not take him too literally. Consider, for instance, the following examples which are deliberately exaggerated in order to make the point:

1　In a short-run sheet metal shop, every job has roughly the same operations, for example to:
   a　Cut sheet to size.
   b　Punch holes and slots, etc.
   c　Bend to shape.
   d　Weld, etc.

2   In many electronic circuit assembly departments, the sequence of operations is roughly to:
   a   Insert components in printed circuit board.
   b   Solder.
   c   Test.
If we give some thought to the particular short-run shop for which we wish to design a quality control system, we shall soon discover the features which are common to every production run, and we can then use them as the basis of our new system. Broadly, there are two ways in which we can do this.

1   We can use a number or a percentage defective chart   The first possibility, which is almost always applicable, is to use a number or a percentage defective chart, plotting one point for a day's work, a morning's work or even an hour's work, depending on the rate of production. Thus, a chart of the type shown in Figure 15.1 is completely independent of run length. Where the average number or percentage of defectives is roughly constant, regardless of the actual part number being made, it is even possible to use control limits.

2   We can control on the method   A defectives chart has of course the objection that it waits for faulty work to be made before calling attention to it. We may be able to overcome this by basing our control system on the method, as we did in Section 21.2. This again is not dependent on run length.

24.3   Having an individual quality plan for each product

Where each individual type of product repeats from time to time, it is possible to have an individual quality plan for each. For example, in most machine shops, each part number has a method card or maybe a planning route card showing the method which is to be followed each time that part number is made. In the same way, we can provide an individual quality control chart and quality schedule, etc., for each part number.

Thus, the short-run department is given a complete set of quality control charts, one for each part number. The routine is that whenever a part number is set up, the inspector gets the chart for that part number out of the file and puts it in the holder on the machine. This tells the setter what checks will be applied, which are specially important, and shows him what troubles were incurred the last time that part number was made. When the run is finished, the chart goes back into the file and another is put up in the holder. Even a one-off gives no trouble; the chart can always be got out quicker than the machine or process can be set up.

With this system, we can control on variables as well as on attributes. In a few cases, we may even be able to use control limits for variables. We set the control limits on the first run, and then use them for subsequent runs. Some care is necessary, however, because if in the meantime the machine wears appreciably, the control limits will no longer be appropriate for the next run.

In general, control limits for variables are difficult to apply to short runs because the run tends to be finished before we can complete the routine, given in Sections 13.2 and 14.4, for setting the control limits. We can, however, use pre-control charts as discussed in Section 13.17.

24.4 Question

Discuss the difficulties involved in controlling the quality of short run or batch production, and hence suggest how a satisfactory quality control system can be devised. (Your answer may be related to a production line with which you are familiar.)

CHAPTER 25

THE DESIGN OF A
QUALITY CONTROL CHART

25.1   Chart sizes

Whatever our type of production it will not be long before we need a
quality control chart of some sort and, although there is nothing
difficult about its preparation, it does need to be approached in the
right way.

We shall not want our charts to be all shapes and sizes, so we must
start by choosing one or maybe two sizes which we shall use as
standards. As charts spend more of their time in the file than they do
out on the job, they must fit economically into our storage arrangements. Therefore, find out the largest size which will just fit into the
files which you will be using. Other considerations permitting, there is
a lot to be said for making the charts to one of the international paper
sizes. Thus, a convenient size for charts which are to take one or two
variables, along with some attributes, is:

Size A3 11¾in. × 16½in. or 297 mm × 420 mm

Where, however, only a few attributes are required, especially if runs
are short, we may use a much smaller chart, such as:

Size A6 4⅛in. × 5⅞in. or 105 mm × 148 mm

25.2 The chart holder

When the chart is in use, it must be readily visible to all who should use its information. As the operator often has the greatest need, such charts must be strategically placed on the machine or process where the operator cannot help seeing them. Therefore, for protection, the chart will need a simple holder with the following features:

1   A solid back to provide a rest for on-the-spot entries.
2   Provision for hooking the chart on to the machine or process once entries are complete.
3   It should be painted in a distinctive bright colour so that it is easy to see. If that colour is uniform throughout the factory, it soon becomes associated with quality control.
4   Each holder should bear the words, 'Quality Control Chart', as a form of publicity.
5   Where the work is dirty, or machines are likely to spray oil about, the holder will need a piece of clear Perspex in front to keep the chart clean. If this is designed to slide to the right, then a right-handed person can use the Perspex as a hand rest while making entries, so keeping dirty marks off the chart.
6   Sometimes it is possible to put slots in the Perspex, so that entries can be made without removing it.

If charts are out in the thick of production, it is inevitable that occasionally one will come to grief. This need cause us no undue concern. It is better for them to die usefully on 'active service' than to idle their days away in an inspector's drawer.

25.3 Standard chart layouts

Although we can use any design of quality control chart we choose, the chances are that many and possibly all our needs will be met by one of the three designs illustrated in Figures 25.1 - 25.3 which we can regard as standard.

In Figure 25.1, the basic chart consists almost entirely of graph paper, and this is intended to be used where the qualities concerned are all to be plotted as variables. Notice that every alternative vertical line is printed a little heavier, and extended upwards to make 'boxes' at the top, for further information. The X of each point is plotted on the light vertical lines in between.

Where the qualities to be checked are a mixture of variables and attributes, then the paper shown in Figure 25.2 is useful.

The design shown in Figure 25.3 is for use where only attributes have to be recorded. Notice that where not too many qualities are to be

The chart contains the following labels along its left edge:

PART or PROCESS No. | ORDER No
INSPECTOR
DATE
TIME / BATCH No

DESCRIPTION

MEASUREMENT

No. TESTED PER

METHOD OF TEST

M/C TYPE & No.

MATERIAL

REMARKS

OPERATOR

SETTER

CHART No.

DEPT

Figure 25.1 Paper for an 'all variables' chart

Figure 25.2 Paper for a mixture of variables and attributes

PART NO.
ORDER NO.
INSPECTOR
DESCRIPTION
DATE
TIME
ISSUE NO. | I | INSPECTORS CHECKS
OPERATION | R | RE-SETS
| | PREVIOUS M/C ERROR
SECTION
M/C TYPE | MTLS & CASTING FAULTS
PLANT NO.
MTL
SETTER
OPERATOR(S)
INSPECTOR
CHECKS
PER HRS
CODE
A = ACCEPTED
C = CORRECTED
R = RETURNED
S = SCRAP
REMARKS
MAKE ANY
COMMENTS
OVERLE AF
H | 100% INSPECTION
A | RESULTS
P
L
TOTAL QTY.
TOTAL REJECTS
OPERATORS CHECKS *
OPERATOR
CHECKS
PER HRS
TIME
COMPILED BY
IR. OFF INSPECTION STAMP

Figure 25.3 Paper for an 'all attributes' chart

plotted it is possible to divide the chart horizontally across the middle, and so get two complete lines of information on one side. The charts from which these illustrations were made were about A3 in size.

25.4 Information on a quality control chart

Although we can and indeed should put any information on the chart which might be useful, the following is typical.

25.4.1   On the left-hand side of the chart

1   The part number or process number, and its name or description for example:
ABQ 314   Pump Body
2   The name of the operator, setter, supervisor, etc., and the name of the department or section.
This helps to make these people feel part of the system, as well as permitting later analysis of each individual operator's performance. It is common practice on clock cards to put the name devoid of 'Mr'. In quality control, never fail to be courteous, so on a man's chart we write 'Mr V. E. Foster'.
3   The number to be inspected, and the frequency of inspection.
4   Leave space so that the method of inspection can be recorded where necessary.
5   Provide for any other information. Written notes from the operator, inspector, setter, etc., are often most valuable. Sometimes, instead of putting this information down the left-hand side, it is more convenient to put it along the top.

25.4.2   At the top of the chart

Here we put information which may change in the course of a production run, for instance:
The order number.
The inspector's initials.
The date.
The time of inspection or, alternatively, the batch number.
Where the operator's name may change, as when there is both a day and a night shift, then the operator's name should also appear at the top.

25.5   Special quality control charts

From time to time, jobs will come along with special requirements and we shall find it desirable to design a special chart for them. In general, it is as well to keep to the same size of paper, otherwise we shall upset our filing arrangements. However, we can include additional information. For example:

1   We can include the results of any final inspection.
2   Where there are subsidiary operations, successful completion of these can be recorded. For example, after forging, it may be useful to record the completion of grinding, heat treatment, etc.

25.6   The preparation and duplication of quality control charts

In preparing quality control charts, we must use paper sparingly. We do not want to be accused of littering the factory with tons of paper. Charts of the type illustrated in Figures 25.1 - 25.3 will take 50 to 60 entries, in one row, on one side of the paper. If we can get two rows of information per side, this makes 100 to 120 entries. By using sufficiently thick paper or thin card both sides of the chart can be used, and we have a possible maximum of 200 to 240 entries per piece of chart paper. Thus, if checks are made once per hour, one piece of chart paper lasts about six weeks on day shift, or three weeks if there is also a night shift.

The information to go on to each chart comes from the quality schedule, as discussed in Sections 8.10 and 8.11, and the labour of transferring this information on to each new sheet is not very great in most cases. However, it is better to avoid even this by getting a supply of standard charts as shown in Figures 25.1 - 25.3 and using them as originals. The checks relevant to a specific process, operation or part number, etc., are then entered on this original, and photocopies are made from it as required for use on the shop floor. This method has several advantages:

1   It eliminates the work of drawing duplicates.
2   It avoids mistakes. If the original is correct, all the prints are bound to be correct.
3   The original can frequently be used as the quality schedule, so eliminating that as well.

25.7   Charts for new quality control systems

When we devise a new quality control system, we may not be able to hit upon the best chart design immediately. Furthermore, operators, inspectors, supervisors, etc., may, on seeing our proposals, make suggestions which should be included. Again, jobs which at first sight require a special chart often settle eventually to a standard pattern. Hence, we should not rush into print with our first proposals.

An easy way to overcome this is to have a supply of completely blank paper, the size of the standard chart. When we require a new chart, we draw our proposals as an original and run off a few copies at a time, as required. If we wish to modify the design, we merely redraw the original. Only when we are sure of our design do we go into print.

25.8   Points concerning the operating routine

Try to establish a standard operating routine which as far as is applicable can be used throughout the factory. Inevitably, supervisors, operators and inspectors sometimes get moved from one department to another, and it helps if they still recognise the quality control system as a familiar and useful friend. For example:

1   The limit at which a machine or process is to be stopped and reset could always be drawn with a solid red line. (Where duplicated charts are used, as discussed in Section 25.6, then this will have to be a solid black line.)
2   Out-of-limit points should always be ringed in red.
3   The action taken when points are out-of-limit and all machine resets, process adjustments, new batches of materiel, etc., are always recorded. This information often proves to be the most valuable part of the chart.

CHAPTER 26

INSTALLING THE NEW
QUALITY CONTROL SYSTEM

26.1 Preparing to sell the new system

We have now investigated the quality problems of our department,
analysed the information we collected and designed our new quality
control system. Next, we have to sell our ideas to the personnel concerned, and install the new system. It sounds simple, and yet it is no
exaggeration to say that this will probably take us as long as all the rest
put together.

We begin by preparing examples of any charts or forms we propose
to use, and then fill them in with typical information preferably drawn
from existing records. We shall need to do this in any case, to satisfy
ourselves that the design is entirely convenient. We also collect together
anything else which will help us sell our system.

26.2 Explaining our proposals

We have not said anything about being in the department concerned
since Chapter 18, and this may seem rather a long time. It is in fact bad
for the department to be left too long, because interest wanes and the
cynical conclude that the problem has beaten us! It seldom happens,
however, because from time to time we almost always have to return to
gather more information. If not, we should deliberately show ourselves, to keep the interest alive.

Now that we are ready to proceed, however, we return and request an interview with the head of department, at a time convenient to him. At this we shall:

1 Explain our proposals carefully, emphasising the ways in which they will help them.

2 Ask for his criticisms and suggestions.

3 Seek his approval to try the proposals out on a small scale, for example on one machine or one section, etc. The agreement is that we will show by demonstration that the new system works and, if for any reason it does not, we shall take it out again. This is a fair agreement. If the new system does not work, it would be stupid to retain it. Needless to say, however, we shall take very good care to see that it does work!

Our request for criticisms and suggestions needs some comment. Having spent some hours designing our new system, our natural reaction will be to feel reluctant to alter it, unless the suggestions made are obviously better. Yet, in fact, we must go along with the express object of incorporating every suggestion we possibly can, in order to make as many people as possible feel that they have a stake in making the new quality control system succeed. Only if a suggestion is obviously inferior shall we reject it, and even then we shall carefully explain why. If we are doubtful about a suggestion, then we make a note of it and promise to consider it carefully, and return with our opinion.

When we have convinced the head of department, we must do the same with each grade of supervision, in strict order of seniority, not forgetting production engineers, inspection foremen, etc. We shall talk to exactly the same people mentioned in Section 18.2, in exactly the same order. This time it will take a little longer, for proposals must be discussed in detail and charts, etc., redrawn as required. Sometimes, we may even have to go back up the line to the more senior people again, to get approval for a major change which has been suggested.

In due course, we shall reach the shop stewards or other shop representatives. Our approach to them is much the same as that adopted for top supervision. The only difference is that we do not have to ask formally for their approval to go ahead. In theory, we inform them. However, we must still listen to their criticisms and adopt their suggestions with exactly the same care. If they are worried about our proposals, we must try to understand why and attempt to allay their fears. It is difficult to get a quality control system to function well if either the supervision, shop stewards or the man on the shop floor is against it.

Next, we explain it to the operators who will be concerned with the first pilot run. Selection of those to be 'first' requires careful consideration but usually, by the time we have done observational runs, we have a pretty good idea who is likely to be co-operative and to enjoy trying out something new. If anybody says of our proposals, 'It won't jolly well work', we must resist the temptation to reply that 'it jolly well will', because this creates an impasse! The correct reply is, 'Why, Fred, what's the snag?' and then, 'Would you explain it to me?' and perhaps 'Would you show me?' Finally, if we still have doubts we ask, 'Can I try it for myself?' People seldom protest about proposals just to cause trouble, but often the snag they have foreseen is a minor one and we shall have no difficulty in overcoming it. Large or small, however, it is our job to find a satisfactory solution.

Avoid technical terms when talking to the shop floor, but on no account talk down to them. Do not present the proposals in too serious a vein. A few quips help, but not at their expense. Do not hide any snags in the proposals. On the contrary ask for help; someone familiar with the work can often think of a way to get over them.

26.3   The pilot quality control system

When at the last the selling is complete we fix a day, the sooner the better now, to launch the pilot scheme. This is the most critical moment of all, particularly if it is the first scheme in our company. Everyone will be watching to see if our quality control really does work. If it had to be taken out again and modified, the loss of prestige would be considerable and selling a second time doubly difficult. If preparations have been carefully made, however, there is no need to fear this but we must be on our guard to see that all goes smoothly.

Everything must be ready and we must be there, whatever the hour in the morning. If possible, start the new scheme off without disturbing the old, because this gives the shop confidence. Equally, if practicable, we do every job in the new system ourself and then show and teach the operators. There is nothing like trying proposals out on ourself, to see if they work, and if they do we are then in a strong position to discuss snags with other people.

Keep everybody, but particularly the operators, well in the picture. Discuss progress with them, and praise their efforts. Show particular eagerness to solve any snags which may arise, whether they are caused by our oversight or not. Always refer to it as 'your quality control system' and never as 'ours'. After it has been installed, it will be theirs permanently.

If the operators are interested, they will work with us often solving snags for themselves. If not, they may delight in thinking up snags for us to solve. It is quite usual for the original proposals to suffer some modification during the pilot stage, and to be all the better for it.

26.4 Enlargement and consolidation

We shall visit the new quality control system at least twice a day during the early stages, and be prepared to stay for longer periods whenever necessary. Soon we hope that the pilot scheme will have settled in well enough for us to request the head of department to withdraw the old quality control system in favour of the new, and to allow us to spread the innovation.

If the department is large this will take some time. On each occasion that a few more operators are added, the new system must be carefully explained to them, and the addition to the system must be carefully watched over, much as the pilot scheme was.

Meanwhile, the original pilot scheme will still require attention. For years perhaps, the department have operated their old system of quality control. Now, to begin with, they will regard the new system as a 'try out'. Even after they are satisfied that it works, it may be some weeks or months before they regard the new system as the accepted one, in the sense that they would not go back to the old even if they had a chance. Throughout the whole of this period. the new system needs very careful, fatherly care. It can easily falter and die.

Therefore, we must visit each part of the new system regularly. When a group of operators is first put on to the system, they must be visited twice a day with continuous attention where necessary. In a day or so, this will become once per day and after two or three weeks, twice a week. This reduction in the frequency of visits goes on until eventually the system is inspected once per month. I would suggest that you continue to visit every system once per month, permanently.

Once the system has settled in, make sure that its equipment is of a permanent nature. Thus, as a try out, we may have used:

Makeshift forms and charts.

Odd bits of wire to put up chart holders.

Gauges, etc., borrowed from another department.
All such points must receive attention.

26.5 Calculate the savings

When the quality control system is complete it is important to calculate the savings made. Top management should want to know what these savings are, and we must in any case tell them. This is part of the task of selling quality control to management.

The calculation is not always easy. We always know the cost of defective work, etc., after quality control has been put in, but often little information exists about what it was before. Many accounting systems do not easily separate quality costs from other costs. Thus, any accurate calculation may be difficult. Fortunately, however, the savings from quality control are nearly always large compared with the cost of putting it in and operating it, and there is, therefore, usually no difficulty in showing that a very satisfactory saving has been made, even if its exact magnitude is in doubt.

26.6 Question

1 It has been decided to install a formal quality control system in a production department which has previously relied on a few inspectors working on an accept or reject basis.

1a Explain briefly what information should be collected, and how this information should be analysed, in order to decide on the appropriate quality control techniques to be used.   *(12 marks)*

1b Suggest how a suitable quality control system could be designed, and the points to be watched in getting it successfully installed.
                    (13 marks)

CHAPTER 27

THE DESIGN OF EXPERIMENTS

27.1 Introduction

At any time during the planning, installation or day-to-day maintenance of a quality control system, a quality engineer may wish to carry out experiments, in order to improve his understanding of the processes concerned. Sometimes these can be done under laboratory conditions, but many must be done on the production plant itself.

27.2 Significance tests

Suppose we have a production process which produces an average of 70 kg of satisfactory output, from each batch of materiel fed into it. One day one of our assistants says that by making certain alterations to the processing conditions, he has been able to produce a satisfactory yield of 80 kg. Should we congratulate him, or tell him kindly that his discovery is of little value? Our answer will depend upon how that process normally behaves.

1   If the process is very consistent at 70 kg, seldon varying by more than 1 or 2 kg up or down, then a single batch of 80 kg is quite remarkable, because it has never happened before.

2   On the other hand, if the process varies considerably about its average of 70, so that outputs of both 60 and 80 are quite common, then there is nothing unusual about one batch of 80 kg. If of course the new process *averages* 80 kg over a lot of batches, that would certainly be noteworthy, but this will require more results to establish. At the moment the new process is not proven.

We can now restate our problem in more scientific terms. If we have sufficient past records, we can plot the output of our usual process as a frequency distribution curve, along the lines explained in Section 11.6, and the result might be as shown in Figure 27.1. Curve (2) corresponds to (2) in our discussion above. Although the mean is 70 kg, the standard deviation about that mean is large at 10 kg. If the curve is approximately Normal, we can apply the percentages given in Figure 11.17. Notice that the output of 80 kg which has been|claimed is exactly 1 standard deviation above the mean, and Figure 11.17 shows that the chances of being 1 standard deviation or more above the mean are (13.6 + 2.2 + 0.1) = 15.9 per cent. Now 15.9 in 100 is roughly 1 in 6, meaning that the old process achieves 80 kg on 1 batch in 6. Hence there is nothing very significant about it happening once on the new process.

With curve (1) in Figure 27.1 the position is quite different, because the standard deviation is only 3 kg, so that there is only a chance of about 1 in 1,000 of getting an output of even 79 kg from the old process. Therefore if our new process has achieved 80 even once, this is no accident. The new process must really be better than the old.

We can now set out our argument in general terms, so that we can apply it to any similar case.

1   We begin by assuming that the new process is no better than the old. This is called a *null hypothesis*. We then consider whether there is sufficient evidence to show that this hypothesis must be wrong.

Weight of satisfactory output in kilogrammes per batch

Figure 27.1   Assessing the improvement offered by a new process

2   We estimate the probability that the new result is due to chance
variations, in a process that is really no better. If we find that it is
quite likely that the new results are due to chance, then we say
that the result is *not significant*, i.e. it is unproven. It is consistent with our null hypothesis. If the result is very unlikely to
be due to chance, we say it is highly significant, because the new
process is almost certainly better than the old. The descriptions
usually assigned to probability values are as follows:

Probability = α = 0.10 or more, not significant without more
evidence
α = 0.05 probably significant
α = 0.01 significant
α = 0.001 highly significant

Notice that whereas a low probability means that the new process is
almost certainly better than the old, a high probability does not
necessarily mean that the new process is no better. It merely means that
there is not yet enough evidence to decide.

We can of course collect further information by doing additional
tests with the new process. Thus suppose we make n batches to the new
process, and they *average* 80 kg. This is mathematically analogous to
the situation shown in Figure 12.8 for the heights of men, and to be
fair to our new process, we must compare this average with the frequency distribution curve, which we should get by plotting averages of
samples of n from the old process. This would have a shorter base and
steeper sides, and in accordance with Eq. (12.1) its standard deviation
would be given by:

$$\sigma_n = \sigma / \sqrt{n}$$

If we now let $\bar{X}$ be the mean value of the old process and $\bar{x}$ the
observed mean value of the new process, then the number of
standard deviations, z, by which $\bar{X}$ is displaced from $\bar{x}$ is given by

$$z = |\bar{X} - \bar{x}| / \sigma_n$$
$$= \sqrt{n} \, |\bar{X} - \bar{x}| / \sigma \qquad (27.1)$$

(The vertical lines in $|\bar{X} - \bar{x}|$ mean 'take the smaller from the
larger'.)

If the standard deviation of our old process is well established from a lot
of observations, we can use Eq. (27.1) directly:

Thus for our example
$$\bar{x} = 80, \ \bar{X} = 70 \ \text{and} \ \sigma = 10$$
and if $n = 5$ observations averaged together, we get
$$z = \sqrt{5}(80 - 70)/10 = 2.24$$

We now consult tables, such as *Statistical Tables for Science, Engineering Management and Business Studies*, by J. Murdoch and J.A. Barnes, in which we shall find the areas in the tail of a Normal distribution. These are of course the figures in Figure 11.17 in more detail. This gives us that:

$$\alpha = 0.0125$$

Comparing this with our standards of significance, we conclude that our result is almost low enough to be called significant (0.01) and is certainly much better than probably significant (0.05). Thus there is a good chance that our new process really is better than the old one.

27.3 Student's t

The foregoing assumed that we knew the standard deviation of our old process fairly accurately. Where this is not so, we have to estimate it from the observations we make. To do this we use Eq. (11.1):

$$\hat{\sigma} = \left\{ \left[\Sigma(\bar{x}_i - \bar{x})^2 \right] / (n - 1) \right\}^{\frac{1}{2}}$$

We rewrite Eq. (27.1) as follows:

$$t = \sqrt{n} \ |\bar{X} - \bar{x}| / \hat{\sigma} \tag{27.2}$$

This is known as Student's t test, Student being the pen name of its originator. Because we have only an estimate of the standard deviation, we must now use a table giving the percentage points of the t distribution. (Murdoch and Barnes' tables contain this.) This table requires the number of degrees of freedom, which as far as we are concerned is $\nu = (n - 1)$. Thus if in our example, our value of 10 for the standard deviation is only an estimate from our sample of 5, we have:

$$\bar{x} = 80$$
$$\bar{X} = 70$$
$$\hat{\sigma} = 10 \qquad \text{whence from Student } t \text{ tables we get:}$$
$$t = 2.24 \qquad \alpha = \text{a little less than } 0.05$$
$$\nu = (5 - 1) = 4$$

283

Hence our observations show that the new process is probably significant, but we cannot be as certain as we were when we knew precisely what the standard deviation was.

Student's t is called a *significance test,* and we can use it whenever we want to find out whether a sample whose mean is $\bar{x}$, could have come from a frequency distribution whose mean is $\bar{X}$, and whose standard deviation is estimated to be $\hat{\sigma}$.

27.4 Correlation

Suppose we suspect that the percentage of a particular materiel which we add to a product affects its final electrical resistance. This has not mattered in the past, but now a customer requires consignments in which this resistance has been controlled to defined specification limits. We therefore need to determine corresponding limits for the percentage of added materiel.

We decide to do an experiment in which we deliberately treat batches with different percentages of the additive, and measure the resulting electrical resistance. We have thus got two variables, the percentage of the additive and the resistance, and to check the relation between them, we shall probably plot a graph of our results. This might look like any of the plots shown in Figure 27.2. If our graph is similar to *(a)*, we shall conclude that there is good *correlation* between the additive and the resistance. It is a linear relation, which we can estimate roughly by drawing a ruler line as shown. Ideally all experimental points should lie exactly on the line, but in practice this seldom happens.

Indeed we should be lucky to get a result as good as *(a)*. More likely we would get result *(b)* where the correlation is not nearly so good, and it is difficult to decide which position of the line fits best.

If we were very unlucky, we might get *(c)* which shows no correlation at all. This does not necessarily mean that the additive and resistance are completely unrelated. It may be that uncontrolled variables in the process swamp any relationship. It would however, mean that we could not use the percentage additive in order to control the resistance, until we had got the stray variables under better control.

27.5 The principle of least squares

In many cases a line fitted by eye is adequate for practical purposes, but it is possible to calculate a 'best fit' line, based on what is known as the *principle of least squares.*

When we worked out a standard deviation in Section 11.5, we sub-

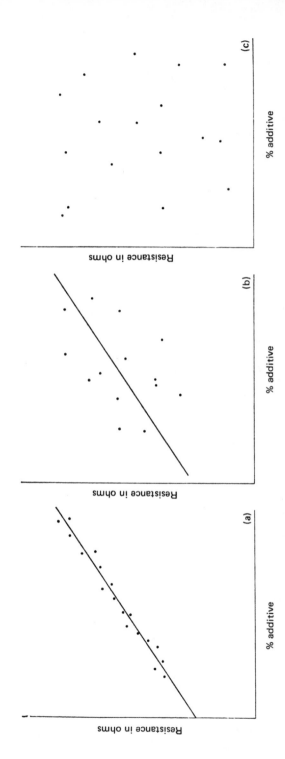

Figure 27.2 Examples of: (a) good correlation; (b) partial correlation; (c) no correlation

tracted the mean value from each observation in turn. Now it would obviously be possible to do this calculation with any other number, instead of the mean. However by its nature, the mean is always in the middle of the observations, and this would not be quite true of any other number, especially if it was nowhere near the mean. As a consequence the differences $(x - \text{chosen number})^2$ would tend to be larger, and so therefore would the final answer.

We now apply this principle to the problem of choosing the best fit line. Suppose that we have tested five different percentages of the additive, and obtained the following results.

% additive	0.1	0.2	0.3	0.4	0.5
Resistance in ohms	7.3	10.5	12.2	15.3	18.5

We can plot this data on a graph as shown in Figure 27.3. The points do not form a perfect straight line, but they leave us in no doubt that they have a linear relationship. Now any straight line can be represented by an equation of the form:

$$y = mx + c \qquad (27.3)$$

In our problem x is the percentage of additive and y is the resistance, whilst m and c are constants.

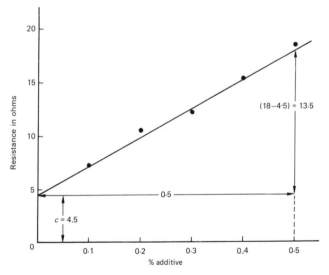

Figure 27.3 Fitting a straight line to experimental data

286

If we put $x = 0$ we get $y = c$, and therefore c is the value of y for which x is zero. If in Figure 27.3 we fit a line by eye, we can see that c must be roughly 4.5. Now m represents the slope of the line, and the figure shows us that:

$$m = \frac{18 - 4.5}{0.5} = 27 \text{ approximately}$$

Therefore our rough estimate for the equation for this relation is:

$$y = 27x + 4.5 \tag{27.4}$$

Of the five sets of observations which we have, only the 0.4 per cent addition giving 15.3 ohms happens to lie exactly on this line. If we insert any other pair of observations into the equation, it will not balance exactly. Thus for the first pair, we have:

Observed resistance	7.3
Calculated resistance = $27x + 4.5 = (27)(0.1) + 4.5$ =	7.2
Discrepancy =	0.1

If we work out the discrepancies for each pair in turn, we get:

0.1, 0.6, 0.4, 0, 0.5

Now the principle of least squares says that the best fit line is the one for which the sum of the squares of these discrepancies is a minimum. For our example, this gives:

0.01 + 0.36 + 0.16 + 0 + 0.25 = 0.78

However these discrepancies relate to a line which we fitted by eye, and there is almost certainly another line which will give a better fit, and therefore a lower total of these squares. There are a number of ways of finding the best fit line, but the following is the most straightforward.

1   Prepare a table as follows:

x (% additive)	y (Resistance)	xy	x^2
0.1	7.3	0.73	0.01
0.2	10.5	2.10	0.04
0.3	12.2	3.66	0.09
0.4	15.3	6.12	0.16
0.5	18.5	9.25	0.25

Totals $\Sigma(x) = 1.5$ $\Sigma(y) = 63.8$ $\Sigma(xy) = 21.86$ $\Sigma(x^2) = 0.55$

Σ means 'summation of' and in this case merely implies that we must total each column.

2　　Insert these totals in the following simultaneous equations:

$$(\Sigma x^2)m + (\Sigma x)c - (\Sigma xy) = 0$$
$$(\Sigma x)m + nc - (\Sigma y) = 0$$

Therefore,

$$0.55m + 1.5c - 21.86 = 0$$
$$1.5m + 5c - 63.8 = 0$$

Solving these equations for m and c gives:

$$m = 27.2 \qquad c = 4.6$$

3　　Hence our best fit line is:

$$y = 27.2x + 4.6$$

It requires a knowledge of calculus to prove that the equation deduced by the above method does in fact give the lowest possible total to the sum of the discrepancies squared. The reader not so equipped may however like to check that the total for the best fit line is lower than for our line fitted by eye. (It is in fact 0.648 against 0.78.)

Notice that the least squares calculation can easily be carried out on any set of pairs of observations, regardless of whether or not they form anything approaching a straight line. It will still give a best fit line for a case like that shown in line *(c)* of Figure 27.2, even though there is no useful relationship at all. Hence we should only use this method where it is reasonably evident that a straight line relation exists. (There are methods of checking the degree of correlation, and readers who are interested should consult a standard book on statistics.)

27.6　Sources of experimental error

When we carried out the experiment in the last section, we hoped that all the variations which we observed in the electrical resistance were caused by deliberate changes which we had made to the quantity of additive. In practice this is never strictly true. However careful we are there will always be uncontrolled sources of variation, and we can easily guess what some of these might be. For example:

1　　Variations in the quality of consignments of the materiel.
2　　Variations in the way batches were processed. These will be partly due to the plant, and partly due to the operators.
3　　Errors in estimating the resistance produced, and in weighing the additive.

We can get some idea of the magnitude of these variations by treating a succession of batches with the same quantity of additive, and observing how the resistance varies. If the variation is very little, we conclude that there are no large uncontrolled variables. If however the variations in resistance are comparable with those which we observed when we were deliberately varying the additive, then we can only proceed if we can separate the uncontrolled variables from those which we deliberately caused. Where uncontrolled variables occur completely at random, we can reduce their effect by *replication*. This means that at each percentage of additive, we make a number of tests, and average the results together. We are in fact eliminating errors of precision as we discussed in Section 3.5, but we shall not be able to eliminate inaccuracies in this way. Thus suppose that the consignments on which we carried out our experiment already contained 0.1 per cent of the additive, instead of being free of it as we assumed. Then all our results would tend to be the equivalent of 0.1 per cent too high, and no amount of replication would eliminate this error.

Suppose now that a consignment of materiel as received from the supplier is just sufficient to make five batches for our process. We decide to allocate a single consignment for our tests, using the top 1/5th for the batch at 0.1 per cent, the next 1/5th for that at 0.2 per cent, and so on. This however would leave us wide open to errors. Perhaps the top has been contaminated in transit, and the materiel gets progressively purer towards the bottom. If the contamination affects the reaction, it could be that the differences in resistance which we observed were not due to changes in the additive at all, but to changes in the contamination.

Errors of this type are called *systematic errors*, and we shall try to eliminate them by:

1   Eliminating all extraneous sources of variation.
2   Randomising those which remain.

By *randomisation* we mean that we shall try to ensure that all remaining sources of variation have an equal chance of affecting all of our observations in the same random way, so that they can be reduced to an acceptable magnitude by replication. In our example, we might begin by homogenising, that is thoroughly mixing, the consignments immediately before test. We shall then carry out our tests in random order. This can easily be done with playing cards. If we allocate say the ace, 2, 3, 4 and 5 of diamonds to denote the five percentages of additive, and the same of spades to denote the part of the consignment, then we can thoroughly mix each group of cards, and draw them in random order. The diamonds will tell us the order in which the different percentages are to be applied, and the spades the part of the consignment to use. We could equally use random number tables, and in more complicated tests, this is the easiest way.

289

27.7 Factorial design

As we originally did it, our test involved only one observation at each percentage of additive, but in practice we would probably make several. If we decide on five tests at each percentage, we should need five consignments of materiel. If we can we shall mix all five thoroughly together, and then use random numbers to decide the order of the tests. If this is not practicable, then we shall make sure that each of the five batches treated at one percentage have come from different parts of a different consignment, and that they are treated in random order. This is called a *factorial design*, and when done as described, it is said to be *balanced*. The following is an example. (We have used letters so that the design is quite general for any similar experiment.)

			Batch Number		
Part of consignment to be used	1	2	3	4	5
Section 1	A	E	D	C	B
Section 2	E	C	A	B	D
Section 3	C	A	B	D	E
Section 4	B	D	E	A	C
Section 5	D	B	C	E	A

27.8 Questions

1a Explain the statistical basis of Student's *t* test. *(10 marks)*

1b A press makes plastic components which are known to have a mean weight of 121.1 g. A test is run using a new materiel and 10 components are weighed as follows:

120, 121, 119, 120, 120, 122, 121, 118, 120, 119 g.

(i) Estimate the standard deviation of the process when working with the new materiel, showing every step of the working. *(7 marks)*

(ii) Assuming that variability has not been changed by the use of the new materiel, and that the frequency distribution is approximately Normal, use a suitable significance test to determine whether the new process uses less materiel per component than the standard process. (All steps in the calculation must be shown.) *(8 marks)*

2a Explain the principle of 'least squares'. *(12 marks)*

2b   Use this principle to deduce the best straight line equation relating the following two variables x and y:

x	-4	-3	-2	-1	0	1	2	3	4	5	6
y	-31	-29	-27	-24	-19	-17	-13	-12	-7	-6	-3

(13 marks)

3a   What is meant by 'randomisation of the variables' in an experiment? Explain in general terms how this is done.   *(12 marks)*

3b   A manufacturer has a new type of car in production and now wishes to determine how many kilometres it will do to a litre of petrol, in order to compare this with predictions.
- *(i)*   Outline how such an experiment might be devised and executed.
- *(ii)*   How might the results be presented?

CHAPTER 28

AN OUTLINE OF RELIABILITY

28.1 Definition of reliability

Our products must not only work correctly when first manufactured, they must continue to do so for as long as our customers reasonably expect. Hence we must see that they are reliable. Suppose we have a new television set, and we want to know whether it will work reliably for say five years, under normal domestic conditions. There is only one certain way to find out, and that is to work it for five years under these conditions. If at the end of this time it is still working satisfactorily, then it was a reliable set. The trouble is that we have had to wait five years for the result, and anyway the set is now largely worn out.

Hence in practice we cannot be certain in advance about the reliability of any particular item, and we have to use probabilities. If for example experience shows that 95 per cent of our television sets are reliable under the conditions stated, then we say that they have a reliability of 95 per cent or 0.95. As explained in Section 4.7, probabilities are usually expressed by the numbers from 0 to 1.0, so that a reliability of 1.0 means certain to work as intended, and reliability 0 means absolutely certain not to work as intended. We can now define reliability as follows.

Reliability is the probability that an item will perform as required, under stated conditions, for a stated period of time.

Notice that the reliability quoted applies to 'stated conditions'. If our television set was to be used in a club instead of a home, then it would probably receive rougher treatment, and we could not expect it to last so long. We must also state what maintenance will be required, to achieve the reliability we quote.

If we put a large number of similar items on life test, and observe when each fails, we can write:

$$\text{Reliability at any time } t = R(t) = \frac{\text{No. surviving at instant } t}{\text{No. at start when } t = 0}$$

$$(28.1)$$

28.2 Failure rate

When an item is no longer capable of performing its required function, we say that it has failed. We must however be clear what its required function is. Thus a racing car intended to reach 300 km/hr will be considered to have failed if it only reaches 250, whereas a family car might be considered very satisfactory if it would do 150 km/hr.

Suppose we are able to put 10,000 of a particular part on life test. We note when each part fails, and replace it on test with a good one. After the test has run for many hours, we analyse the results, and find that on average seven parts have failed for each 100 hours, and that this figure appears to be quite constant. This however related to 10,000 parts, and so in order to express a meaningful failure rate, we relate it to one part and one hour:

$$\text{Average failure rate} = \frac{7}{100 \times 10,000} = 0.000007 \text{ per hour}$$

Because failure rates are often very small, it is common, especially in the electronics industry, to express them as probability of failure per million hours:

$$\text{Average failure rate} = 7 \text{ per million hours}$$

Failure rates are often constant, but they can vary and in theory have a different value for each instant of time. Hence we can write, for a very large number on test:

$$\text{Instantaneous failure rate} = z(t) = \frac{\text{No. failing per hour at instant } t}{\text{No. still surviving at instant } t}$$

Where the instantaneous failure rate is either constant or is averaged over a convenient period of time, the symbol λ is usually used instead of $z(t)$. Notice that we still refer to the number failing *per hour*, even when dealing with an instant in time, in the same way as we might refer to a car reaching 150 km/hr, 'just for an instant'.

28.3 The failure probability density function

In our example, we decided to replace any part which failed, so that there were always 10,000 on test. If we had not done this, the number on test would have gradually reduced, and hence the number of failures per hour would have reduced, even though the failure rate remained constant. Hence we can write:

$$
\begin{bmatrix} \text{Observed number of fail-} \\ \text{ures per hour, at instant } t \\ \text{(out of 10,000)} \end{bmatrix} = \begin{bmatrix} \text{Number surviving} \\ \text{at instant } t \end{bmatrix} \times \begin{bmatrix} \text{Instantaneous} \\ \text{failure rate} \end{bmatrix}
$$

Again expressing this in terms of one part on test, we have:

$$
\begin{bmatrix} \text{Observed number of fail-} \\ \text{ures per hour, at instant } t \\ \text{per part on test} \end{bmatrix} = \begin{bmatrix} \dfrac{\text{Number surviving}}{\text{at instant } t} \\ \dfrac{}{\text{Number at start}} \\ \text{when } t = 0 \end{bmatrix} \times \begin{bmatrix} \text{Instantaneous} \\ \text{failure rate} \end{bmatrix}
$$

$$
= R(t) \qquad \times \quad z(t) \qquad (28.2)
$$

The expression in Eq. (28.2) is called the *failure probability density function*, and given the symbol $f(t)$. Therefore

$$
\begin{array}{l} \text{Failure probability} \\ \text{density function} \end{array} = f(t) = R(t) \times z(t) \qquad (28.3)
$$

28.4 The mean time between failures

If an item has a constant failure rate of 0.001 per hour, we shall expect it to fail and have to be replaced on average every 1000 hours. This would therefore be called the *mean time between failures* or MTBF, and given the symbol θ. Notice that the MTBF is the reciprocal of the failure rate. Thus in our example:

$$
\text{MTBF} = \theta = \frac{1}{\lambda} = \frac{1}{0.001} = 1000 \text{ hours} \qquad (28.4)
$$

Where it is not practical to replace an item which has failed, we refer to the *mean time to failure* or MTTF.

28.5 The bath-tub curve

Suppose we have a large number of parts, which we are able to put on a life test together. We observe, but do not replace failures, and plot a graph of failure rate against time, as shown in Figure 28.1. Because of its shape, this is called the *bath-tub curve*, and it divides into three sections:

1 The early failure period In the first few hundred or so hours of test, the failure rate may be relatively high. Possible causes are:

a Manufacturing faults which were not detected in the factory. This may indicate deficiencies in our factory quality control system.
b The design may be deficient. This is most likely when a new and relatively untried design is concerned.
c Where we are concerned with failures in the customers' hands, they may be due to misuse or inexperience.

2 The constant failure rate period Once parts with inherent weaknesses have failed and been replaced, it is common, especially for electronic parts, to find that the failure rate settles down to a constant and quite a low value for a considerable time. This is therefore called the constant failure rate period.

3 The wear out failure period Since nothing lasts for ever, there will come a time when the bath-tub curve begins to rise again, probably at an ever-increasing rate. This is therefore called the wear out failure period. If our products are to be reliable for the whole of their planned

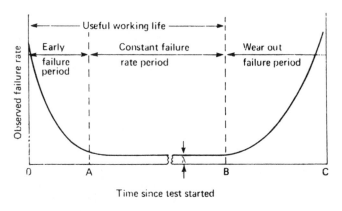

Figure 28.1   The bath-tub curve

working life, wear out must not begin until after it has finished. Sometimes when technical improvements are likely in the near future, it is economic to plan for a short working life, at a correspondingly reduced manufacturing cost, so that the equipment can then be replaced by a more up-to-date one. This is called *planned obsolescence*. It may also be used in the fashion trade, to encourage customers to buy new designs, rather than make old ones do.

28.6 Calculation of reliability when the failure rate is constant

Where the failure rate is constant, we can calculate the reliability after any time t from

$$\text{Reliability} = R(t) = e^{(-\lambda t)} \tag{28.5}$$

Thus suppose that the failure rate is 0.00002 per hour, and we wish to know the reliability after 10,000 hours of operation. Then

$$R(t) = e^{[-(0.00002) \times (10,000)]} = e^{[-0.2]}$$

Now 'e' stands for exponential, which we look up in tables such *Statistical Tables for Science, Engineering Management and Business Studies* by J. Murdoch and J. A. Barnes, and find that

$$R(t) = 0.8187 = 0.82 \text{ or } 82\% \text{ approximately}$$

28.7 Design for reliability

For an equipment to be reliable, it must be faithfully manufactured to a design which is itself inherently reliable. There are many techniques which assist the designer, and the following are some of the most important.

1 Use reliable parts, derated as necessary Since any equipment is made up of parts, it is essential that they should be reliable. The techniques which we discussed in Chapters 6 and 7 for controlling the quality of purchased materiel are most useful for ensuring that only reliable parts are accepted.

The reliability of individual parts can often be improved by *derating* them. Thus we may decide that resistors with a nominal rating of 1 watt shall be used in our equipment at 0.5 watt, in order to lengthen their life.

2 Use as few parts as possible An equipment will only function as intended if all its vital parts work properly. The more parts there are, the greater the risk that there will be one which fails, so causing the whole equipment to fail. We can illustrate this quite simply.

Suppose we have an equipment in which all the parts have a reliability of 0.90 or 90 per cent, and that every part is vital, in the sense that if one fails, the whole equipment fails. If our equipment only contained one vital part, then:

Reliability of equipment = 0.90

If there are 2 vital parts, then since both must work, we use the multiplication rule, explained in Section 4.8. From this

Reliability of equipment = (0.90 $\times$ 0.90) = 0.81

Continuing this argument, we get:

For 3 parts, reliability = $(0.90)^3$ = 0.73
For 4 parts, reliability = $(0.90)^4$ = 0.66
For 5 parts, reliability = $(0.90)^5$ = 0.59
For 10 parts, reliability = $(0.90)^{10}$ = 0.35

Our equipment reliability is now dropping rapidly. Fortunately however parts are usually much more reliable than 0.90, but as none of them are perfect, the fewer we use, the better. When parts or other items in an equipment are such that if one fails, the whole fails, they are said to be *in series*.

3 Redundancy Even though we use the most reliable parts available, and keep their numbers to a minimum, we may still find that the reliability of one unit in the equipment is insufficient to achieve the overall reliability demanded. Where cost and weight considerations permit, we may decide to include two or more of that particular unit, arranged so that the whole equipment will continue to work, so long as at least one of these units survives. This technique is called *redundancy,* and the units are said to be *in parallel.*

The reliability of a block of units in parallel can most easily be deduced by considering the probability of overall failure. Suppose that one unit of an equipment has a reliability of only 0.88, and that this cannot be economically improved in time to meet delivery requirements. The designers decide therefore to insert a block of three parallel units into the equipment. We can calculate the overall reliability of this block as follows:

Probability 1 unit fails = $(1.00 - 0.88) = 0.12$

Since the block will function if any one or more units is working, complete block failure will only occur if all 3 units fail. This requires the multiplication rule discussed in Section 4.8.

Probability all 3 identical units fail = $0.12 \times 0.12 \times 0.12 = 0.001728$

Therefore,

Reliability of block $\quad = (1.00 - 0.001728) = 0.998272$
$$= 0.998 \text{ say}$$

In the above example, all three units were energised for the whole time the equipment was working. This is called *active redundancy*. Sometimes it is convenient to keep a unit in reserve, and only start it up when the first unit fails. This is call *standby redundancy*. An example of this is the standby generator which a hospital keeps, so that it can light the operating theatre if the mains supply should fail during an operation.

Sometimes, although some failures are permissible, more than one unit must function to keep the equipment working. This is called *partial redundancy*. A simple example of active partial redundancy is the spokes of a bicycle wheel. One or two spokes can fail, but so long as the broken ends are removed, the cycle is still rideable, but clearly we cannot ride it with only one spoke! As an example of standby partial redundancy we can take a car, where we have a spare wheel which we can bring into service if one of the four road wheels fails. However for the car to function, at least four of the five wheels must be in working order.

28.8   Reliability prediction

Suppose a customer asks us to design and make a special piece of equipment, with a guaranteed reliability. It would obviously be foolish to push ahead with design and manufacture, trusting to luck that when the equipment was finally installed, it would have the reliability demanded. Months later we should find out that we had failed.

It is essential therefore to predict the final reliability right from the first conception of the design, and then at every stage we:

1   Recalculate the prediction, using additional information as it becomes available.

2   Modify the design as necessary.

The first prediction, before the design proper has started, is likely to be the most inaccurate, and then at every stage our accuracy improves, until

when the equipment finally goes into service, we discover its true reliability. At the start we shall be relying mostly on past experience, but it
is unusual for a company to undertake to make a complex piece of
equipment of a type which is very different from anything it has previously made. Nearly always there is a background of experience on
which we can draw.

We divide the equipment into identifiable sections. Thus suppose we
have to produce a special tunnel oven for a new type of cereal. We
break this down into:

1   The oven itself with reliability = R_o.
2   The conveyor mechanism with reliability = R_c.
3   The temperature control equipment with reliability = R_t.

The overall equipment reliability might be specified directly in reliability,
or as a failure rate or an MTBF. Suppose that a reliability of not less
than 0.85 is demanded. Now the sections of the equipment are effectively in series, because if one of them fails, the whole equipment will fail.
We can therefore write:

$$R_o \times R_c \times R_t = \text{ not less than 0.85} \qquad (28.6)$$

Suppose we made an oven like this last year, and its reliability was at
least 0.99. We also made a conveyor mechanism which was similar,
except for being a bit longer. Its reliability was about 0.97. It is the
control equipment that worries us, because it contains 6 identical instruments each controlling the temperature of one section of the oven,
and all the cereals will be scrap, if any one of them fails. We can now
allocate a target reliability to the control equipment, using Eq. (28.6):

$$0.99 \times 0.97 \times R_t = \text{ not less than 0.85}$$
$$R_t = \text{ not less than 0.885}$$

But the six instruments of the temperature controllers are also in series,
so if r is the reliability of one section, we have:

$$R_t = r \times r \times r \times r \times r \times r = \text{ not less than 0.885}$$
$$r = \text{ not less than 0.98}$$

Our development engineers must now devise an instrument for one
section of the oven, with a reliability of at least 0.98, or alternatively
we may call in one of the firms who specialise in this sort of work. If
we should find that 0.98 is not easily obtainable, it is still open to us to
improve the reliability of either the oven itself or the conveyor.

Where the reliability is quoted as a failure rate, this is divided directly
between the sections. Thus if we are permitted five failures per million

hours, we could provisionally allocate say one to the oven, one to the conveyor and three to the control equipment.

28.9 Reliability life tests

Much of the reliability information which we require for prediction must come from specially designed tests.

1 Life tests Most reliability tests are basically life tests, in which the items concerned are operated as nearly as possible as the customer will use them. Tests are usually continued until some or all of the items have failed, and their times to failure recorded.

2 Accelerated life tests Many parts have a very long life, e.g. an MTBF exceeding 10 years is not uncommon, and hence an ordinary life test would take an unacceptably long time. Accelerated life tests are therefore often used, and these take two main forms:

a   When operation in practice is intermittent, it may be possible to make it continuous for the purposes of the test. A home film projector, for example, will only be used occasionally by its owner, but in the factory it could be run continuously thereby compressing many years of use into an acceptable number of hours.

b   Electronic parts in particular are often continuously loaded in normal use, and so in order to accelerate the test, we have to increase this load, and probably the ambient temperature as well. Thus what is normally a 1 watt resistor might be operated at 2 or 3 watts, at an elevated temperature. The chief difficulty with this type of test is to correlate results with practical use. Thus a statement that a component has a mean life of 200 hours under some specified accelerated test, tells us little unless we know the equivalent number of hours of normal use.

3 Environmental tests Often our real interest is not to see whether the items concerned will work in a clean temperature-controlled laboratory, but whether they will be satisfactory in the conditions under which our customers will operate them. Hence we may do environmental tests, in which we simulate conditions of temperature, humidity, vibration, shock, mud, dirt, sand, sea water and so on.

28.10 Reliability acceptance tests

There are two main types of reliability test:
1. Reliability acceptance tests, which we shall discuss here.
2. Reliability measurements, which we shall consider in the next section.

In theory, reliability acceptance tests are analogous to sampling inspection of incoming batches of materiel.

1. We take a random sample of the items to be tested.
a. They may be actually drawn from a batch, but often they are advance samples, before bulk supplies are ordered.
b. Cost usually prohibits tests on large equipments, and so we are mostly concerned with parts and small assemblies.

2. The items are usually tested for a preset time, but the test may be stopped if the allowed number of failures is exceeded (this is c in quality control terms).

3. Acceptance tests are based on an operating characteristic, and the theory in Chapters 4 and 5 applies to them. A reliability engineer will talk about 'demonstrating a certain reliability (say 0.95) at a certain level of confidence (say 90 per cent)'. The reliability to be demonstrated is related to the lot tolerance percentage defective of Section 5.3. Thus if a fraction 0.95 are reliable, then $(1.0 - 0.95) = 0.05$ must be unreliable, and this corresponds exactly to an LTPD of 5 per cent. The confidence level is effectively $(1.0 - \text{consumer's risk})$, so that in our example the consumer's risk is to be $(1.0 - 0.9) = 0.10$ or 10 per cent.

4. The batch or supply of items will be accepted if at the end of the preset time the number of failures observed does not exceed the number allowed by the sampling plan.

28.11 Reliability measurements

Acceptance tests are concerned with demonstrating that the reliability of the items is satisfactory for some purpose. In general they do not provide enough information to give any adequate estimate of the actual reliability or MTBF. For this we must use a reliability measurements test. This is similar in principle, but normally lasts longer. It is, for example, essential to continue until some failures have occurred. When the test is stopped, we estimate the MTBF from:

$$\text{Estimated MTBF} = \frac{\text{Total time all items survived on test,}}{\text{Total number of failures}}$$

Thus if ten items were put on test for 1000 hours, and three failed at 300, 672 and 806 hours whilst the remaining seven were still working at the end, we should calculate:

$$\text{Estimated MTBF} = \frac{300 + 672 + 806 + (7 \times 1000)}{3}$$

$$= 2926 \text{ hours}$$

Because our sample size is small, the above might not be a very accurate estimate of the MTBF. If the reliability is required, we convert the MTBF to failure rate and insert it in Eq. (28.5).

28.12 Questions

1a Draw a typical bath-tub curve and name both its axes and its *three* main sections. *(6 marks)*

1b Fifteen similar components are put on life test and failures observed to occur at the following times, measured in hours from the start of the test:

20, 100, 130, 220, 270, 330, 470, 670, 870, 980

The test finished after 1000 hours with five components still surviving. Assuming that the failure rate is constant, estimate for the components

    (i)   the mean time to failure (MTTF). (Treat as **MTBF**).
                                                              (5 marks)
    (ii)   the failure rate. *(4 marks)*
    (iii) their reliability after 100 hours in operation. *(5 marks)*

1c A small assembly contains six of the above components connected in series. Estimate its reliability for an operating life of 50 hours.
(5 marks)

2a Define the term 'reliability'. *(3 marks)*

2b A system consists of three units whose reliabilities are, respectively,

0.95, 0.90 and 0.80. What is the reliability of the system if these units are connected in series? *(3 marks)*

2c Explain briefly the basis of reliability prediction. *(19 marks)*

CHAPTER 29

THE USE OF COMPUTERS IN QUALITY CONTROL

29.1 Introduction

A computer is able to do simple calculations extremely quickly. To enable it to do complex calculations it must be provided with a detailed set of step-by-step instructions, so that what it really does is a long succession of simple steps. These instructions are called the *program,* and their preparation is a skilled and time-consuming task. If there is the smallest mistake in the program, the computer will either say it does not understand, or it will give a wrong answer. It has no ability to deduce what the correct instruction should be.

Computer manufacturers provide many ready-made programs for commonly required calculations. Where no program exists, it is only likely to be economic to prepare one if that calculation is going to be required many times, working on different numerical data.

29.2 Pocket and desk calculators

Pocket and desk calculators are readily available, and many have in-built programs, called functions, so that commonly required calculations can be done at the touch of a button. Those most useful to the quality engineer include mean, standard deviation, natural logarithms and exponentials, powers of numbers (especially squares and square roots) and factorials. Even shop floor inspectors can be provided with simple calculators for working out averages and mean ranges for quality control charts, or acceptance sampling by variables.

29.3 Analysis of data

Where large quantities of data have to be analysed, a central or local computer will be useful, and the following are examples.

1 Scrap and other defective work

This can be analysed, Pareto-style, into type of defect, cause, part number, machine used, batch number, operator, inspector, department responsible, etc. Provided data are available, the analysis can be in terms of money rather than numbers defective.

2 Customer returns

Failures in the customers' hands can equally be analysed into type of equipment, the type of part which has failed, the cause of failure, the age of the equipment, how much it had been used, and the type of work on which it had been engaged, etc. If code numbers permit the manufacturing conditions to be identified, as is the case with Defence contracts, then analysis can proceed as in (1) above into department responsible, machine, materiel, batch, operator, etc. It may also be possible to analyse customer use into faulty operation, faulty storage, faulty installation, bad maintenance, etc. Better instruction manuals will help customers to avoid these failures.

29.4 In-process uses of computers

These have already been explained in Sections 19.3, 20.6, 21.6 and 22.7.

29.5 Computer control of complex tasks

Many equipments, especially those which are fundamentally electronic, need a complex succession of tests to ensure that they function correctly and are properly adjusted for optimum performance. If this is done manually it is time-consuming, and any test which is not essential is likely to be omitted. Suitably programmed, the computer can carry out these tests as quickly as the equipment can take them. It can then print out a complete set of results, or merely report those parameters which are out of limit.

29.6   Design and analysis of experiments

The computer can easily generate random numbers for the design of an experiment, for the taking of truly random samples from a batch, etc. It can also be used for analysing experimental results. Thus it can find the line of best fit, not only for the linear case discussed in Section 27.5, but also where a higher-order curve must be fitted.

29.7   Control of purchased supplies

Again we can use the computer to generate random numbers for batch sampling, where this is worthwhile. It can analyse information from incoming inspection, suppliers' test reports, laboratory analyses, etc. It can also work out vendor ratings, and keep them up-to-date on an ongoing basis.

29.8   Reliability testing

As we saw in Sections 28.10 and 28.11, reliability tests tend to be complicated, and there is often a lot of data best analysed by computer. For economic reasons, tests are usually made on parts and units, rather than on complete equipments, and the computer can then be used to work out the overall reliability of the assemblies and equipments built from them. This technique is known as *testing by parts*.

At the design stage, reliability predictions are often made from published data, such as that given in the American MIL-STD-HBK-217. Amongst other things, this gives failure rates for many types of component, mostly electronic, together with allowances to be made when they are working under arduous conditions, such as exposed on the deck of a ship. The equipment reliability can then be predicted if the arrangement of these parts in series or parallel (Section 28.7) is known. A computer can store all these data, so that if it is given a list of parts to be used, their arrangement and the working environment it cannot only predict the overall failure rate, but it can draw attention to the sections of the equipment where failure is most likely to occur.

29.9   The computer in design

As designs become more complex, so it becomes almost essential to use a computer for the necessary calculations. This is particularly so where the problem is primarily one of optimisation. Out of perhaps thousands of combinations of the relevant parameters, the best combination must be chosen. The designer might hit upon a reasonable set of conditions, but in many cases only the computer can find the best with certainty.

29.10 Question

Explain the uses and limitations of a computer when assisting in the control of quality.   *(25 marks)*

CHAPTER 30

QUALITY ASSURANCE

30.1 The changing quality scene

In recent years the thinking of quality managers has tended to be modified by external influences, such as the following:

1 Customer pressure Customers in general have become increasingly discerning about the quality they buy. Purchasers of capital equipment, especially the armed forces, have put a great deal of pressure on manufacturing industry, in order to obtain better and guaranteed quality and reliability. Domestic consumers have equally become more critical. This stems partly from the influence of the Consumers' Association, and partly from greater expectations with ever-rising prices.

2 Industrial relations Meanwhile relations between employers and the trade unions are passing through a difficult phase, so that operator co-operation for quality is not always easy to achieve.

Both of the above have made it increasingly necessary to have a strong quality organisation, which can both ensure that the customer receives the quality and reliability for which he has paid, and influence quality in all departments in the company. Hence what was once the inspection department has emerged as the quality assurance department, with much wider powers and responsibilities. These include:

a New design control.
b Purchased materiel quality control.

c   Quality assurance of production.
d   Trouble shooting and industrial experimentation.
e   Liaison with reliability engineers.
We shall now consider these in more detail.

30.2 New design quality control

As we saw in Section 3.1, quality control divides into two main sections namely quality of design and quality of conformance. However quality engineers have tended to devote themselves almost exclusively to quality of conformance, and to overlook the fact that they can offer considerable assistance to the designer. They can provide data about machine and process capability, and about the ease or otherwise with which different qualities can be assessed. They can assist with problems of mating tolerances and selective assembly. Their role is essentially one of co-ordination rather than interference, although they may well have sufficient power to ensure that designs whose quality is unsatisfactory, cannot be passed for manufacture.

30.3 Purchased materiel quality control

Incoming inspection of materiel along the lines discussed in Chapters 4, 5, 6 and 7 has long been used by many companies, but at least two factors have tended to modify this concept.

1   Companies have become increasingly concerned about the cost of incoming inspection.
2   There is a tendency to minimise materiel stocks, in order to free as much working capital as possible, and incoming inspection becomes a farce if a rejected batch cannot be returned, because to do so would shut down the purchaser's own production line.

Companies in a strong enough position have therefore tended to put much more pressure on their suppliers, to ensure that what they send is correct to the specification before they dispatch it. Anyone who pays a fair price is clearly entitled to expect this.

Hence various techniques have been developed:

1 Specification control   If we expect a supplier's goods to be consistently satisfactory, we must ensure they are correctly ordered to a clear and practical specification.

2 Vendor rating   As we saw in Section 7.6, the performance of each supplier and materiel can be assessed on quality, price and delivery.

More and more we find that the quality assurance department are empowered to instruct the purchasing department about where particular goods may or may not be bought.

3 Vendor appraisal Many companies inspect their suppliers' premises before placing an order. They thus satisfy themselves that the suppliers' quality control systems are adequate to achieve the quality standards demanded.

30.4 Production quality assurance

Our object here is to ensure that production quality control is adequate, and that a satisfactory final quality is produced. Sample checks, usually called quality audits, are carried out at various stages of production, and the quality assurance department is empowered to demand that:
1   Production which they declare to be unsatisfactory is not passed to the next operation.
2   Machines and processes are capable of achieving the quality demanded. This may take the form of an instruction that a particular machine may not be used until specified maintenance work has been done upon it.

30.5 Industrial experimentation and trouble shooting

As we saw in Chapter 27, the quality engineer should be well qualified to assist with industrial experiments to improve the performance, quality or yield of a process. He can similarly help with trouble shooting, to restore a process to normal after a fault has developed.

30.6 Quality and reliability

The quality assurance department must maintain particularly close links with the reliability engineers. There is often a lot to be said for combining quality and reliability into one department.

30.7 Ministry of Defence quality requirements

In 1972 the Ministry of Defence Procurement Executive announced a new system of quality assurance which they proposed to adopt for all their purchased materiel. It was to be based on a system used by NATO, for which a series of Allied Quality Assurance Publications (AQAPs) already existed. The Ministry therefore issued a corresponding set of Defence Standards, the most important of which are numbered 05-21, 05-24 and 05-29.

In them the Ministry accept that it is their responsibility as purchasers to ensure that all their quality and reliability requirements are clearly and completely satisfied. They will also stipulate what quality assurance they require. The contractor, i.e. the company which undertakes to supply the materiel concerned, is then left freer than previously to organise his work. He must ensure that:

1   His products or services achieve the quality and reliability demanded.
2   He offers 'objective evidence' that his control has been adequate.

This system differs from those previously used in the following respects:

1   All Ministry Directorates now have the same system, thereby eliminating overlaps and inconsistencies between them.
2   The visiting or resident inspectors have been replaced by quality assurance representatives (QARs), who have a liaison-type role, dealing with queries and ensuring that the relative Defence Standard, etc., is being observed. They are not primarily concerned with checking out the final product since this is now the contractor's responsibility.
3   The contractor is required to provide sufficient management organisation and records to show that the quality and reliability which is demanded has actually been achieved. Mere 'lip service' is not acceptable. This is a far-reaching innovation.
4   The contractor is responsible for the quality of all materiels he purchases or obtains by sub-contract, and this is true even if the sub-contractor is himself registered under the Defence Standards.

A contractor who wishes to tender for Ministry work can apply for approval under a number of categories. He will first be sent forms DEFCON 1 to complete and return. These enable the prospective contractor to do a rough self-assessment on his chances of getting approval. If he thinks he complies he will then be visited by several Ministry personnel, who typically may spend two or three days on their assessment. The main categories under which approval may be given are as follows.

DEF-STAN 05-21 — Quality Control System Requirements for Industry

This, together with its guide 05-22, is used where a complex product is defined by the Ministry primarily in terms of its performance and reliability, and the contractor is responsible for design, manufacture, etc., right through to installation and field trials. To obtain registration to tender for this type of work, a contractor must comply with the following:

1   A quality manager or equivalent must be appointed with sufficient authority to ensure that all Ministry requirements are met. He must report solely to top management, and should have no allegiance to either design or manufacture.

2   Prescribed procedures, usually in the form of a quality manual, must be prepared, giving details of the whole of the company's quality organisation and arrangements. These must be reviewed periodically and updated as necessary.

3   Designers' responsibilities must be clearly defined. As early as possible in each contract, they must review its requirements in order to ensure that they will be met. Manufacturing drawings and specifications must specify requirements completely, and tolerances must be as wide as possible, consistent with achieving the required quality and reliability. The issue and recall of drawings must be properly controlled.

4   The contractor is responsible for the quality and reliability of all materiel he obtains, and each consignment must have a purchasing specification. Goods inwards inspection or its equivalent must monitor all incoming consignments and ensure that they are satisfactory.

5   Written work instructions must be provided throughout, not only for manufacture itself, but also for handling, transporting, installing, etc.

6   Inspection and test must be carried out as necessary throughout manufacture.
    a   All test and inspection equipment must be calibrated in accordance with DEF-STAN 05-26.
    b   Records of all checks must be kept.
    c   At each stage work must be properly segregated by *materiel status* into *(i)* awaiting inspection, *(ii)* checked and found satisfactory, *(iii)* checked and found unsatisfactory.

7   Effective corrective action must be taken immediately unsatisfactory work occurs or may occur.

8   A complete set of records of the above must be kept until their disposal is authorised by the Ministry.

9   Liaison with the contractor is kept by Ministry Quality Assurance Representatives, who must be allowed to inspect records, carry out checks, and enter any department where Ministry work is being done.

10 In addition to the general requirements above, each contract must have its own quality plan or equivalent. When the contract is in

prospect, the company must review all its requirements, and confirm that they are fully understood. It must then draw up a quality plan, showing which of their quality facilities will be required, and what they are going to do to satisfy any demands of the contract, which are not already available. The Ministry must approve the quality plan.

DEF-STAN 05-24 — Inspection System Requirements for Industry

This is appropriate where a proven design already exists, but in order to ensure final conformance, it is necessary to use test and inspection throughout manufacture. Control of design is not therefore required, and the quality manual although encouraged is not mandatory. Other controls are similar to 05-21 although much less intense.

DEF-STAN 05-29 — Basic Inspection Requirements for Industry

This standard is used where it is possible for qualified personnel to check conformance on the final product. It only demands a quality manager, control of inspection equipment, identification of materiel status, and certain records, although the contractor will probably need more than this to ensure his own efficiency.

Further information about these standards is contained in a brochure entitled *The New Quality Requirements for Defence Procurement,* which together with the standards themselves, can be obtained from The Secretariat, Defence Quality Assurance Board, Adelphi, John Adam Street, London.

30.8   The British Standards Institution

The British Standards Institution issues specifications which set national standards for a wide range of industrial and consumer products. These are prepared in close consultation with industry, and other interested bodies. In general they are not mandatory, but the manufacturer who complies with them may well find that:
1   His products are easier to sell.
2   There is less likely to be confusion between his customers and himself about what quality is required

30.9 The role of the quality manager

The quality manager has in effect the job of instituting, organising and controlling all that we have discussed in this book. He will utilise all the information which his quality control systems collect, and he will be always trying to achieve a satisfactory quality more cheaply.

30.10 Questions

What is the object of Ministry of Defence Specifications 05-21 to 05-29, and how is this object achieved? *(25 marks)*

TABLE 1 AQL sampling inspection table

A.O.L.	0·065%			0·10%			0·15%			0·25%			0·40%			0·65%			1·0%			1·5%			2·5%			4·0%			6·5%		
Batch size	n	P	F	n	P	F	n	P	F	n	P	F	n	P	F	n	P	F	n	P	F	n	P	F	n	P	F	n	P	F	n	P	F
2–50	All			All			All			All			32	0	1	20	0	1	13	0	1	8	0	1	5	0	1	3	0	1	8	1	2
51–90	All			All			80	0	1	50	0	1	32	0	1	20	0	1	13	0	1	8	0	1	5	0	1	3	0	1	8	1	2
91–150	All			125	0	1	80	0	1	50	0	1	32	0	1	20	0	1	13	0	1	32	1	2	20	1	2	13	1	2	8	1	2
151–280	200	0	1	125	0	1	80	0	1	50	0	1	32	0	1	20	0	1	50	1	2	32	1	2	20	1	2	13	1	2	13	2	3
281–500	200	0	1	125	0	1	80	0	1	50	0	1	32	0	1	80	1	2	50	1	2	50	2	3	20	1	2	20	2	3	20	3	4
501–1,200	200	0	1	125	0	1	80	0	1	50	0	1	125	1	2	80	1	2	80	2	3	80	3	4	32	2	3	32	3	4	32	5	6
1,201–3,200	200	0	1	125	0	1	80	0	1	200	1	2	125	1	2	125	2	3	125	3	4	125	5	6	50	3	4	50	5	6	50	7	8
3,201–10,000	200	0	1	125	0	1	315	1	2	200	1	2	200	2	3	200	3	4	200	5	6	200	7	8	80	5	6	80	7	8	80	10	11
10,001–35,000	800	1	2	500	1	2	500	2	3	315	2	3	315	3	4	315	5	6	315	7	8	315	10	11	125	7	8	125	10	11	125	14	15
35,001–150,000	800	1	2	500	1	2	800	3	4	500	3	4	500	5	6	500	7	8	500	10	11	500	14	15	200	10	11	200	14	15	200	21	22
150,001–500,000	1,250	2	3	800	2	3	1,250	5	6	800	5	6	800	7	8	800	10	11	800	14	15	800	21	22	315	14	15	315	21	22	200	21	22
Over 500,000	2,000	3	4	1,250	3	4				1,250	7	8	1,250	10	11	1,250	14	15	1,250	21	22	800	21	22	500	21	22	315	21	22	200	21	22

The above is an example of how suitable sampling plans can be selected from BSS: 6001:. The method of use is as follows. Suppose the batch size is 500 and the A.O.L. is to be 1·0 per cent. Take the sample of 50 (Column n) and check it. If the number of defectives does not exceed 1 (column P) the batch is passed; if it is 2 or more (column F) it is failed. n is sample size, P is max. defectives for batch to pass, F is number of defectives (or more) for batch to fail. For further details see section (5.7).

This table has been taken from DEF-131A, by kind permission of the Controller of Her Majesty's Stationery Office.

TABLE 2 Choosing the most economical AQL. (For details about the use of this table, see Section 6.8)

RATIO = $(a + r) \div (i)$

Batch size	0.1	0.2	0.3	0.4	0.5	0.6	0.7	0.8	0.9	1.0	2	3	4	5	6	7	8	9	10	20	30	40	50	60	70	80	90	100	150	200	250	300	400	500	600	700	800	900	1000	1500	1600
2–50	2.5	2.5	2.5	2.5	2.5	2.5	2.5	2.5	2.5	2.5	2.5	2.5	2.5	2.5	2.5	2.5	2.5	2.5	1.5	1.5	1.5	1.0	1.0	1.0	1.0	0.65	0.65	0.65	0.40	0.40	All	All	All	All	All	All	All	All	All	All	All
51–90	2.5	2.5	2.5	2.5	2.5	2.5	2.5	2.5	2.5	2.5	2.5	2.5	2.5	2.5	2.5	2.5	2.5	2.5	1.5	1.0	0.65	0.65	0.65	0.65	0.4	0.4	0.4	0.25	0.25	0.25	0.25	0.25	0.25	All	All	All	All	All	All	All	All
91–150	2.5	2.5	2.5	2.5	2.5	2.5	2.5	2.5	2.5	2.5	2.5	2.5	2.5	2.5	2.5	2.5	2.5	2.5	1.0	1.0	0.65	0.4	0.4	0.4	0.4	0.4	0.4	0.25	0.25	0.25	0.25	0.25	0.15	0.15	0.15	0.15	0.15	0.15	0.10	All	All
151–280	2.5	2.5	2.5	2.5	2.5	2.5	2.5	2.5	2.5	2.5	0.65	0.65	0.65	0.65	0.65	0.65	0.65	0.65	0.65	0.4	0.4	0.25	0.25	0.25	0.15	0.15	0.15	0.15	0.10	0.10	0.10	0.065	0.065	0.065	0.065	0.065	0.065	0.065	0.065	0.065	All
281–500	2.5	2.5	2.5	2.5	2.5	2.5	2.5	2.5	2.5	2.5	0.4	0.4	0.4	0.4	0.4	0.4	0.4	0.4	0.4	0.4	0.25	0.25	0.25	0.25	0.15	0.15	0.15	0.15	0.10	0.10	0.10	0.065	0.065	0.065	0.065	0.065	0.065	0.065	0.065	0.065	All
501–1,200	2.5	2.5	2.5	2.5	2.5	2.5	2.5	2.5	2.5	0.25	0.25	0.25	0.25	0.25	0.25	0.25	0.25	0.25	0.25	0.25	0.25	0.15	0.15	0.15	0.15	0.15	0.15	0.15	0.065	0.065	0.065	0.065	0.065	0.065	0.065	0.065	0.065	0.065	0.065	0.065	All
1,201–3,200	2.5	2.5	0.15	0.15	0.15	0.15	0.15	0.15	0.15	0.15	0.15	0.15	0.15	0.15	0.15	0.15	0.15	0.15	0.15	0.15	0.15	0.15	0.10	0.10	0.10	0.10	0.065	0.065	0.065	0.065	0.065	0.065	0.065	0.065	0.065	0.065	0.065	0.065	0.065	0.065	All
3,201–10,000	2.5	2.5	0.15	0.15	0.15	0.15	0.15	0.15	0.15	0.15	0.15	0.15	0.15	0.15	0.15	0.15	0.15	0.15	0.15	0.10	0.10	0.065	0.065	0.065	0.065	0.065	0.065	0.065	0.065	0.065	0.065	0.065	0.065	0.065	0.065	0.065	0.065	0.065	0.065	0.065	All
10,001–35,000	2.5	2.5	0.10	0.10	0.10	0.10	0.10	0.10	0.10	0.10	0.10	0.10	0.10	0.10	0.10	0.10	0.10	0.10	0.10	0.065	0.065	0.065	0.065	0.065	0.065	0.065	0.065	0.065	0.065	0.065	0.065	0.065	0.065	0.065	0.065	0.065	0.065	0.065	0.065	0.065	All
35,001–150,000	2.5	2.5	0.10	0.10	0.10	0.10	0.10	0.10	0.10	0.10	0.10	0.10	0.10	0.10	0.10	0.10	0.10	0.10	0.065	0.065	0.065	0.065	0.065	0.065	0.065	0.065	0.065	0.065	0.065	0.065	0.065	0.065	0.065	0.065	0.065	0.065	0.065	0.065	0.065	0.065	All
150,001–500,000	0.10	0.10	0.10	0.10	0.10	0.10	0.10	0.10	0.10	0.10	0.10	0.10	0.10	0.10	0.10	0.10	0.10	0.10	0.10	0.065	0.065	0.065	0.065	0.065	0.065	0.065	0.065	0.065	0.065	0.065	0.065	0.065	0.065	0.065	0.065	0.065	0.065	0.065	0.065	0.065	All
Over 500,001	0.10	0.10	0.10	0.10	0.10	0.10	0.10	0.10	0.10	0.10	0.10	0.10	0.10	0.10	0.10	0.10	0.10	0.10	0.10	0.005	0.065	0.065	0.065	0.065	0.065	0.065	0.065	0.065	0.065	0.065	0.065	0.065	0.065	0.065	0.065	0.065	0.065	0.065	0.065	0.065	All

a is cost of one item in batch; r is cost of repairs, etc. if one defective item gets into production lines, and i is cost of inspecting one item. All indicates 100 per cent inspection.

TABLE 3   Constants for the use of control limits on quality control charts

13.2   Controlling variables to specification or drawing limits

Average chart

Draw each control limit a distance equal to $(A''_{0.025} \times$ mean range), *inside* each specification or drawing limit.

Range chart

Draw one control limit, a distance equal to $(D'_{0.001} \times$ mean range), starting from zero range, and measuring upwards.

Values of constants

Sample size	2	3	4	5	6	7	8
$A''_{0.025}$		1.51	1.16	1.02	0.95	0.90	0.87	0.84
$D'_{0.001}$		4.12	2.98	2.57	2.34	2.21	2.11	2.04

For information on the use of these constants, see section 13.2.

14.4   Controlling variables to the best the process is capable of achieving

Average chart

Inner control limits   Draw each control limit a distance equal to $(A'_{0.025} \times$ the mean range), *out* from the grand average.

Outer control limits   Draw each control limit a distance equal to $(A'_{0.001} \times$ the mean range), *out* from the grand average.

Range chart

Inner control limit   Draw one control limit a distance equal to $(D'_{0.025} \times$ mean range), upwards from zero range.

Outer control limit   Draw one control limit a distance equal to $(D'_{0.001} \times$ mean range), upwards from zero range.

Values of constants

Sample size	2	3	4	5	6	7	8
$A'_{0.025}$		1.23	0.67	0.48	0.38	0.32	0.27	0.24
$A'_{0.001}$		1.94	1.05	0.75	0.59	0.50	0.43	0.38
$D'_{0.025}$		2.81	2.17	1.93	1.81	1.72	1.66	1.62
$D'_{0.001}$		4.12	2.98	2.57	2.34	2.21	2.11	2.04

For further information on the use of these constants, see Section 14.4.

15.5 Control limits for number defective

Set the inner limits a distance $2L$, and the outer limits $3L$, both upwards and downwards from the average number of defectives per sample line (c) where

$L = \sqrt{\{c[1 - (c/n)]\}}$

n = sample size

c = average number of defectives per sample

For further information, see Section 15.5.

15.6 Control limits for percentage defective

Set the inner limits a distance $2M$, and the outer limits $3M$, both upwards and downwards from the average percentage of defectives per sample line $(\bar{p})$, where

$M = \sqrt{[\bar{p}(100 - \bar{p})/n]}$

$\bar{p}$ = average percentage of defectives per sample

n = sample size

For further information, see Section 15.6.

ANSWERS TO NUMERICAL QUESTIONS
(Provided by author)

Chapter 2

2b *(ii)* 2% at which the total cost is £1400.
3a *(iv)* 3.54%, £2,828.

Chapter 4

1b *(i)* 0.1829; *(ii)* 0.1667; *(iii)* 195.

Chapter 5

1a *(i)* 0.0544; *(ii)* 0.1333; *(iii)* 0.4544; *(iv)* 0.5878.
2b *(i)* 0.0474, 0.0537; *(ii)* 0.2381, 0.0818; *(iii)* either; *(iv)* Y.
3b Common AQL is at 1%.

Chapter 7

3a Typical rating 86 points, but it will depend on the assumptions made.
3b AQL is 0.65%, also depending on assumptions.

Chapter 11

1b 59.84 mm.
1c *(i)* 1.64%; *(ii)* 8.08%.
2b The data is Normal because the plot on probability paper gives a straight line.
2c Mean = 152.75 ohms; standard deviation = 1.0 ohm.
2d *(i)* 142.5 ohms; *(ii)* 1.24%.

Chapter 13

1 Control limits: average chart = 10.71 and 11.29 ohms; range chart = 1.03 ohms.

Chapter 14

1a Control limits: average chart = 9.034, 9.039, 9.055, 9.060 mm; range chart = 0.040, 0.051 mm.

2b Control limits: average chart = 12.064, 12.069, 12.088, 12.094 mm; range chart = 0.039, 0.051 mm.

2c Conventional limits do not allow for drift.

2d ±0.045 mm.

Chapter 15

1b *(i)* Control limits 0.41, 1.10, 3.90, 4.59%;
(ii) Control limits 2.03, 5.52, 19.48, 22.97

Chapter 16

1a Control limits 0.6, 9.4, 11.5. (The lowest control limit is below zero.)

Chapter 27

1b *(i)* Mean = 120g, standard deviation = 1.15g;
(ii) $t = 3.01$ which is significant.

2b $y = 2.9x - 20.0$.

Chapter 28

1b *(i)* 906 hr; *(ii)* 0.0011 failures per hour; *(iii)* 89.6%.

1c 71.8%.

323